Acing

the SAT Subject Tests in
Math Level 1 &
Math Level 2

by Thomas Hyun

GREENHALL PUBLISHING
THOUSAND OAKS, CA

This edition published by Greenhall Publishing

Greenhall Publishing
Thousand Oaks, CA 91360
http://greenhallpublishing.com

Written by Thomas Hyun
Edited by Erin Hyun

Cover design by Hespenheide Design

Printed by Delta Printing Solutions
Printed and bound in the United States

ISBN-10: 0-9754753-1-2
ISBN-13: 978-0-9754753-1-7

CONTENTS

Getting Started

Welcome to *Acing the SAT Subject Tests in Math Level 1 and Level 2*! As you get ready to tackle either one of these very challenging exams, the next few pages give some background information about the SAT Subject Tests and advice for getting the most out of this book and your individual test preparation.

Test Information

What is the Subject Test?

Subject Tests are hour-long tests that measure your knowledge of specific subjects in math, science, social science, and language. Many colleges require two or three Subject Tests and recommend that Mathematics be among the tests taken. Even for schools that do not require them, Subject Test scores are an increasingly important factor in college admissions. That's because the Subject Tests, much like AP exams, are *achievement* tests that indicate a student has taken hard classes and challenged him/herself academically.

What is the difference between the Math Level 1 and Math Level 2 tests?

The Level 1 covers two years of college prep algebra and one year of college prep geometry. The Level 2 covers these subjects at a higher level (testing some harder algebra and geometry concepts not found on the Level 1) plus some trigonometry/ pre-calculus. Each test is one hour long and contains 50 multiple-choice questions.

Which math test should you take?

First of all, be advised that some universities no longer accept the Math Level 1, or give less weight to applicants who have taken this test. Therefore deciding which test to take may simply depend on which colleges you are applying to. Check with your counselor and the individual schools you are applying to for their requirements.

Even if the colleges you are applying to accept both levels, choosing the more difficult Level 2 test may be to your advantage. Note that while the Level 2 is harder, the curve is slightly more generous (e.g. you can usually miss a few questions on the Level 2 and still get a perfect score of 800).

To help you figure out if you're ready for the Level 2, most of the Level 2 concepts and questions (denoted by the symbol $\boxed{L2}$) have been placed separately at the end of each tutorial and exercise set in this book. For students trying to decide between the two tests, you can complete all of the problems and compare your performance on both types of questions. As long as you are doing all right on the Level 1 questions, it may be worth the time to study and work on the Level 2 material, even if your initial performance on those harder questions isn't great. If you are doing very poorly on both types, it may be sensible to first focus on mastering the Level 1 material.

Calculators

Scientific and graphing calculators are allowed on both the Level 1 and Level 2 tests. A graphing calculator is necessary for some questions, and makes others much easier and quicker to solve. You should have your graphing calculator with you as you work through this book so you are comfortable using it by test day. (And be sure to take extra batteries to the testing center.)

Registering for the test

Plan to take the Subject Tests at the end of your junior year or in the fall of your senior year, after completing the SAT I. (If you haven't taken the SAT I yet, check out our book *Acing the New SAT I Math*!) Contact the colleges you are applying to about deadlines for taking the Subject Test.

Register at least a month in advance to avoid late fees, and to make sure you get a testing location close to home! You can take up to three Subject Tests in one testing day. Check the College Board website (www.collegeboard.com) for upcoming test dates.

Preparing for the Subject Test in Math
How to use this book

Part A of this book, the Math Review, contains twenty chapters that teach you all the concepts you need for the Subject Tests in Math Level 1 and Math Level 2. Each chapter contains a tutorial, exercise set, and solutions set.

The tutorials are broken into a handful of concepts with concise explanations and illustrations. Each concept is followed by an example problem and solution, so you can see how it might be used on the Subject Test. Keep a pencil handy as you read through the tutorial, and work out example problems as you go.

From the tutorial, go on to the exercise set. Correct it using the answer key, and for problems you have missed, consult the answers and explanations section. The detailed solutions show you how to work out each problem step by step.

Part B consists of four practice tests each for Level 1 and Level 2. Students taking the Level 2 should complete all of the Level 1 tests first, making sure you have mastered that material before moving on to the Level 2 tests. Each test is one hour long. Give yourself enough time to finish the test in one sitting.

Scoring

Subject Tests are scored on a scale of 800. After completing a test use the Level 1 or Level 2 scoring guide (page 355 and page 467) to calculate your score. Remember that these scores are only an approximation of your performance: the scale actually works like a curve using the scores of all students nationwide who take a particular Subject Test on a particular day, and thus varies slightly with each test administration. Nonetheless, variations in scoring are usually slight, with an average score being about 500. After working through the tests in this book you should have a good idea of how you're doing.

Study timetable

Ideally you should give yourself two or three months before the test to work through this book from start to finish. Working through a chapter or practice test every day or two, you will have plenty of time left to review and redo questions you've missed or struggled with.

If you're short on time, pick the chapters on topics you are weakest in. In fact, you could start out by taking one of the practice tests, and seeing which kinds of questions you miss more of.

Final Note

Remember, the Subject Test is an achievement test—it's designed to reward learners and doers, and stump even natural math geniuses—so unfortunately there are no shortcuts to a high score.

But by applying some time and effort to take advantage of the arsenal of tools in this book, you will gain the skills and confidence you need to ace the Math Subject Test!

MATH REVIEW

I. Algebra and Trigonometry

CHAPTER 1
Basic Concepts of Algebra

1-1. Real Numbers

Natural Numbers	$\{1,\ 2,\ 3,\ \ldots\}$
Whole Numbers	$\{0,\ 1,\ 2,\ 3,\ \ldots\}$
Integers	$\{\ldots,\ -3,\ -2,\ -1,\ 0,\ 1,\ 2,\ 3,\ \ldots\}$
Prime Numbers	$\{2,\ 3,\ 5,\ 7,\ 11,\ 13,\ 17,\ 19,\ 23,\ 29,\ \ldots\}$
	A prime number is an integer greater than 1 whose only factors are 1 and itself.

Rational Numbers   A rational number is one that can be expressed as a ratio $\dfrac{a}{b}$, where a and b are integers and b is not zero, such as -2, $-\dfrac{4}{3}$, 0, $\dfrac{5}{7}$, 6, and 14.5. The decimal form of a rational number is either a terminating or repeating decimal.

Irrational Numbers   Any real number that is not rational is irrational. $-\sqrt{3}$, $\sqrt{2}$, and π are irrational.

Consecutive Integers $\{\ldots,\ -3,\ -2,\ -1,\ 0,\ 1,\ 2,\ 3,\ \ldots\}$ n, $n+1$, $n+2$ are three consecutive integers, for any integer n.

Consecutive Even Integers $\{\ldots,\ -4,\ -2,\ 0,\ 2,\ 4,\ \ldots\}$ n, $n+2$, $n+4$ are three consecutive even integers if n is an even integer.

Consecutive Odd Integers $\{\ldots,\ -3,\ -1,\ 1,\ 3,\ 5,\ \ldots\}$ n, $n+2$, $n+4$ are three consecutive odd integers if n is an odd integer.

Example 1 □   If the sum of three consecutive integers is six more than twice the largest of the three integers, what is the smallest of the three consecutive integers?

Solution □   Let $x =$ the smallest of the three consecutive integers.

$$\underbrace{x+(x+1)+(x+2)}_{\text{The sum of 3 consecutive integers}} \underset{\text{is}}{=} \underbrace{2(x+2)+6}_{\text{six more than twice the largest integer.}}$$

$$3x+3 = 2x+10$$

$$x = 7$$

1-2. Order of Operations

$$17+[(3-5)^3 \cdot 4 \div 8]-2.5$$

1. **Parentheses**	$=17+[(-2)^3 \cdot 4 \div 8]-2.5$
2. **Exponents**	$=17+[-8 \cdot 4 \div 8]-2.5$
3. **Multiplication**	$=17+[-32 \div 8]-2.5$
4. **Division**	$=17+(-4)-2.5$
5. **Addition**	$=13-2.5$
6. **Subtraction**	$=10.5$

Example 2 □   Evaluate $[(a+b)^2 \div 4] - bc$ if $a = 8$, $b = -2$, and $c = 3$.

Solution □ $[(a+b)^2 \div 4] - bc$

$= [(8 + (-2))^2 \div 4] - (-2)(3)$

$= [(6)^2 \div 4] - (-6)$

$= [36 \div 4] + 6$

$= 9 + 6 = 15$

1-3. Properties of Real Numbers

These properties are true for any real numbers a, b, and c:

Commutative Properties

$a + b = b + a$ $4 + 7 = 7 + 4$

$a \cdot b = b \cdot a$ $4 \cdot 7 = 7 \cdot 4$

Associative Properties

$(a + b) + c = a + (b + c)$ $(4 + 7) + 3 = 4 + (7 + 3)$

$(a \cdot b) \cdot c = a \cdot (b \cdot c)$ $(4 \cdot 7) \cdot 3 = 4 \cdot (7 \cdot 3)$

Distributive Properties

$a(b + c) = ab + ac$ $4(7 + 3) = 4 \cdot 7 + 4 \cdot 3$

$a(b - c) = ab - ac$ $4(7 - 3) = 4 \cdot 7 - 4 \cdot 3$

Example 3 □   Simplify $a(2 - b) - 2(a - b)$.

Solution □ $a(2 - b) - 2(a - b)$

$= 2a - ab - 2a + 2b$ Distributive property

$= 2a - 2a - ab + 2b$ Commutative property

$= -ab + 2b$ Simplify.

1-4. Literal Equations

A **literal equation** is an equation that uses more than one variable.
You can solve a literal equation for a specified variable.

Example 4 □   Given the equation $a(x - 3) = bx + 10$, solve for x.

Solution □ $a(x - 3) = bx + 10$ Given equation

$ax - 3a = bx + 10$ Distributive property

$ax - bx = 3a + 10$ Add $(3a - bx)$ to each side.

$x(a - b) = 3a + 10$ Factor out x.

$x = \dfrac{3a + 10}{(a - b)}$ Divide each side by $(a - b)$.

1-5. Ratios and Proportions

A ratio is a comparison between two numbers. If two values are in a ratio of $a:b$ or $\dfrac{a}{b}$, then the two numbers can be represented by **ax** and **bx**, where x is a positive integer.

A proportion is an equation stating that two ratios are equal.

Example 5 □   If the measures of the four angles of a quadrilateral are in a ratio of $2:3:4:7$, what is the measure of the biggest angle?

Solution   □   The measures of the angles can be represented as $2x$, $3x$, $4x$, and $7x$.

$$2x + 3x + 4x + 7x = 360$$
$$16x = 360$$
$$x = 22.5$$

The measure of the biggest angle is $7(22.5°)$, or $157.5°$.

1-6. Absolute Value

The **absolute value** of x, $|x|$, is the distance between x and the origin on a number line.

If $|x| = 1$, then $x = -1$ or $x = 1$.

$|-1| = 1$ The distance between -1 and the origin is 1.

$|1| = 1$ The distance between 1 and the origin is 1.

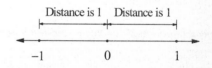

Example 6 □   Solve $3|2x - 7| = 45$.

Solution   □ $3|2x - 7| = 45$

$$\Rightarrow \frac{3|2x-7|}{3} = \frac{45}{3}$$

$$\Rightarrow |2x - 7| = 15$$

$2x - 7 = 15$	or	$2x - 7 = -15$
$2x - 7 + 7 = 15 + 7$		$2x - 7 + 7 = -15 + 7$
$2x = 22$		$2x = -8$
$x = 11$		$x = -4$

The solution set is $\{-4, 11\}$.

1-7. Turning Words into Algebraic Expressions

Verbal Expressions	**Algebraic Expressions**
Four *more than* twice a number	$2n + 4$
Twelve *less than* a number	$x - 12$
The *product* of -3 and a number	$-3n$
The *quotient* of twelve and a number	$\dfrac{12}{x}$

Example 7 □   If the opposite of twice a number is fifteen less than one-fourth of the number, what is the number?

Solution   □ $-2n = \dfrac{1}{4}n - 15 \;\Rightarrow\; -2n - \dfrac{1}{4}n = -15$

$\Rightarrow\; -\dfrac{9}{4}n = -15 \;\Rightarrow\; n = (-\dfrac{4}{9})(-15)$

$\Rightarrow\; n = \dfrac{20}{3}$

1-8. Problem Solving with Equations

When tackling word problems, you need to read the problem carefully to understand it and translate the verbal description into an equation. You can then solve the problem by solving the equation.

a) *A Linear Equation Modeling a Real-life Situation*

$$\boxed{\begin{array}{c}\text{Total}\\\text{cost}\end{array}} = \boxed{\begin{array}{c}\text{Charge}\\\text{for first}\\\text{minute}\end{array}} + \boxed{\begin{array}{c}\text{Rate per}\\\text{additional}\\\text{minute}\end{array}} \cdot \boxed{\begin{array}{c}\text{Number of}\\\text{additional}\\\text{minutes}\end{array}}$$

b) *Motion Problems*

$$\text{Distance} = \text{Rate} \times \text{Time}, \;\; d = r \cdot t, \;\; r = \frac{d}{t}, \;\; t = \frac{d}{r}$$

$$\text{Average speed} = \frac{\text{Total distance traveled}}{\text{Total time}}$$

Example 8 □   a. An overseas phone call costs c cents for the first minute and a cents for each additional minute. If an 8-minute call costs \$6.40 and a 15-minute call costs \$9.20, what are the values of a and c?

b. Mark drove from his home to the library at an average speed of 45 miles per hour, and returned home on the same road at an average speed of 30 miles per hour. If his total driving time was 50 minutes, what is the distance between his home and the library?

Solution   □   a. Let y = the cost of an overseas call,

and x = the total number of minutes.

Then $(x-1)$ = the number of additional minutes.

The equation for the cost of an overseas call is
$y = c + a(x-1)$.

$6.40 = c + a(8-1)$	An 8-minute call costs $6.40.
$9.20 = c + a(15-1)$	A 15-minute call costs $9.20.
$6.4 = c + 7a$	Simplify the first equation.
$9.2 = c + 14a$	Simplify the second equation.
$2.8 = 7a$	Subtract the first equation from the second equation to eliminate the variable c.
$a = 0.4$	Answer
$6.4 = c + 7(0.4)$	Now substitute $a = 0.4$ back into the first equation.
$c = 3.6$	Answer

b. Let t = the time in hours Mark spent driving from his home to the library,

then $\dfrac{5}{6} - t$ = the time in hours spent for the return trip. (50 min = $\dfrac{50}{60}$ hours)

$$d = 45t$$

home ⊟————————⊟ library

$$d = 30(\frac{5}{6} - t)$$

$45t = 30(\dfrac{5}{6} - t)$	The distance going out is the same as the distance returning.
$45t = 25 - 30t$	Simplify.
$75t = 25$	Simplify.
$t = \dfrac{1}{3}$	Divide both sides by 75.
$d = 45t$	The distance between his home and the library is $45t$.
$= 45(\dfrac{1}{3})$	Substitution ($t = \dfrac{1}{3}$)
$= 15$ miles	Answer

1. If $a(b-2) = x+ab$ for all a and b, then $x =$

    (A) $-2a$

    (B) $-2b$

    (C) $2a$

    (D) $2b$

    (E) $b-2$

2. $-\left|3-\left|-5\right|\right| =$

    (A) -8

    (B) -2

    (C) 0

    (D) 2

    (E) 8

3. What is the property illustrated by the following statement?
$-a+(2b+7) = (2b+7)-a$

    (A) Associative property of addition

    (B) Inverse property of addition

    (C) Commutative property of addition

    (D) Distributive property

    (E) Reflexive property

4. If the quotient of a number and three equals five less than twice the number, what is that number?

    (A) -2

    (B) -1

    (C) 1

    (D) 2

    (E) 3

5. If $a(x-1) = x+1$, then $x =$

    (A) $\dfrac{a}{a+1}$

    (B) $\dfrac{a-1}{a}$

    (C) $\dfrac{a}{a-1}$

    (D) $\dfrac{a+1}{a-1}$

    (E) $\dfrac{a-1}{a+1}$

6. Amy and Bobby together earned $90 dollars from selling cookies. If Amy earned $12 less than twice what Bobby earned, how much money did Amy earn?

    (A) $34

    (B) $42

    (C) $48

    (D) $56

    (E) $62

7. Lisa travels on bike for the first 18 miles of a trip at a speed of 24 miles per hour, then jogs the next x miles at a speed of 8 miles per hour. If her average speed for the whole trip is 16 miles per hour, what is the value of x?

    (A) 4.8

    (B) 5.4

    (C) 6.0

    (D) 6.4

    (E) 7.2

8. If $ab - c = 2b + c$, then $b =$

(A) $\dfrac{a}{2}$

(B) $\dfrac{c}{b}$

(C) $\dfrac{c}{a}$

(D) $\dfrac{c}{a+2}$

(E) $\dfrac{2c}{a-2}$

9. If $d = -\dfrac{1}{2}gt^2 + 16$ for $t > 0$, then $t =$

(A) $\sqrt{\dfrac{16-d}{2g}}$

(B) $\sqrt{\dfrac{2(16-d)}{g}}$

(C) $\sqrt{\dfrac{2(d-16)}{g}}$

(D) $\sqrt{\dfrac{2(d+16)}{g}}$

(E) $\sqrt{\dfrac{d-16}{2g}}$

10. A bookstore ordered hardcover books for $12 each and paperback books for $5 each. The ratio of hardcover books to paperback books was $2:7$. If the total bill was $1652, how many paperback books were ordered?

(A) 148

(B) 172

(C) 196

(D) 224

(E) 248

11. The cost of an overseas call is c cents for the first minute and d cents for each additional minute. What is the cost, in cents, of an overseas call that lasts m minutes?

(A) $c + d(m-1)$

(B) $c + m(d-1)$

(C) $c + dm$

(D) $c + dm - 1$

(E) $c(m-1) + d$

12. An investor has d dollars invested in bonds and stocks. He put two-fifths of money in bonds that pay 8% annual interest and the rest in stocks that pay 10% annual interest. If the total income in one year from these investments is $1472, how much money did he invest in bonds?

(A) $4,500

(B) $5,200

(C) $6,400

(D) $9,600

(E) $16,000

13. If a and b are two different integers, such that $a < 0 < b$, which of the following must be true?

I. $\dfrac{a \cdot b}{a - b}$ is positive.

II. $a(a + b)$ is negative.

III. $\dfrac{a^2}{b} \geq 1$

(A) None

(B) I only

(C) II only

(D) I and II only

(E) I and III only

Answer Key

1. A	2. B	3. C	4. E	5. D
6. D	7. C	8. E	9. B	10. C
11. A	12. C	13. B		

Note: Throughout the book, the symbol "$\Rightarrow$" is used to indicate that one step of an equation implies the next step of the equation.

Answers and Explanations

1. A

$$a(b-2) = x + ab$$
$$ab - 2a = x + ab$$
$$ab - ab - 2a = x + ab - ab$$
$$-2a = x$$

2. B

$$-\big|3 - |-5|\big|$$
$$= -|3 - 5|$$
$$= -|-2|$$
$$= -2$$

3. C

$$-a + (2b + 7) = (2b + 7) - a.$$

The commutative property says that the order in which you add does not change the sum.

Choice (C) is correct.

4. E

The quotient of a number and 3	equals	5 less than twice the number
$\dfrac{n}{3}$	$=$	$2n - 5$

$$n = 3(2n - 5) \;\Rightarrow\; n = 6n - 15$$
$$\Rightarrow\; -5n = -15 \;\Rightarrow\; n = 3$$

5. D

$$a(x-1) = x+1$$

$ax - a = x + 1$	Distribute.
$ax - x = a + 1$	Add a to and subtract x from both sides.
$x(a-1) = a + 1$	Factor.
$x = \dfrac{a+1}{a-1}$	Divide by $a-1$.

6. D

Let $x = $ the amount Bobby earned from selling cookies.

Then $2x - 12 = $ the amount Amy earned from selling cookies.

$(2x - 12) + x = 90$	Amy and Bobby together earned $90 dollars.

$$3x - 12 = 90$$
$$3x = 102 \;\Rightarrow\; x = 34$$

The amount Amy earned is
$$2x - 12 = 2(34) - 12 = 56$$

7. C

$$d = r \cdot t \;\Rightarrow\; t = \frac{d}{r}$$

$$t_1 = \frac{18}{24} = \frac{3}{4} \text{ hour is the time spent biking.}$$

$$t_2 = \frac{x}{8} \text{ hour is the time spent jogging.}$$

$$\text{Average speed} = \frac{\text{Total distance}}{\text{Total time}}$$

$$\Rightarrow\; 16 = \frac{18 + x}{\dfrac{3}{4} + \dfrac{x}{8}}$$

$$16\left(\frac{3}{4} + \frac{x}{8}\right) = 18 + x$$

$$12 + 2x = 18 + x$$

$$x = 6$$

8. E

$$ab - c = 2b + c$$
$$ab - c + c = 2b + c + c$$
$$ab = 2b + 2c$$
$$ab - 2b = 2c$$
$$b(a - 2) = 2c$$
$$b = \frac{2c}{a - 2}$$

9. B

$$d = -\frac{1}{2}gt^2 + 16$$
$$d - 16 = -\frac{1}{2}gt^2$$
$$-2(d - 16) = -2(-\frac{1}{2}gt^2)$$
$$2(16 - d) = gt^2$$
$$\frac{2(16 - d)}{g} = t^2$$
$$\sqrt{\frac{2(16 - d)}{g}} = t$$

10. C

Since the ratio of hardcover books to paperback books is $2 : 7$, let $2x =$ the number of hardcover books and $7x =$ the number of paperback books.

$$\$12 \cdot 2x + \$5 \cdot 7x = \$1652$$
$$24x + 35x = 1652$$
$$59x = 1652$$
$$x = 28$$

The number of paperback books ordered
$$= 7x = 7 \cdot 28 = 196$$

11. A

Cost of the first minute		cost of each additional minute		the number of additional minutes

$$\text{Total cost} = \quad c \quad + \quad d \quad \cdot \quad (m - 1)$$

12. C

$$0.08(\frac{2}{5}d) + 0.1(\frac{3}{5}d) = 1,472$$
$$0.032d + 0.06d = 1472$$
$$0.092d = 1472$$
$$d = \frac{1472}{0.092} = 16,000$$

The amount invested in bonds
$$= \frac{2}{5}(16,000) = 6,400$$

13. B

a and b are two different integers such that $a < 0 < b$, so a is a negative number and b is a positive number.
Let's try two different pairs of numbers to test each of the Roman numeral choices.

$$a = -2,\ b = 5 \text{ and } a = -5,\ b = 2.$$

I. If $a = -2$ and $b = 5$,
$$\frac{a \cdot b}{a - b} = \frac{-2 \cdot 5}{-2 - 5} = \frac{-10}{-7} = \frac{10}{7}, \text{ which is a positive.}$$

If $a = -5$ and $b = 2$,
$$\frac{a \cdot b}{a - b} = \frac{-5 \cdot 2}{-5 - 2} = \frac{-10}{-7} = \frac{10}{7}, \text{ which is positive.}$$

Roman numeral I is always true.

II. If $a = -2$ and $b = 5$.
$$a(a + b) = -2(-2 + 5) = -6, \text{ which is negative.}$$

If $a = -5$ and $b = 2$.
$$a(a + b) = -5(-5 + 2) = 15, \text{ which is positive.}$$

Roman numeral II is not always true.

III. If $a = -2$ and $b = 5$.
$$\frac{a^2}{b} = \frac{(-2)^2}{5} = \frac{4}{5}, \text{ which is less than 1.}$$

If $a = -5$ and $b = 2$.
$$\frac{a^2}{b} = \frac{(-5)^2}{2} = \frac{25}{2}, \text{ which is greater than 1.}$$

Roman numeral III is not always true.

CHAPTER 2
Functions and Graphs I

2-1. Relations and Functions

A **relation** is a set of ordered pairs (x, y). The **domain** of a relation is the set of all x-values from the ordered pairs, and the **range** of a relation is the set of all y-values from the ordered pairs.

A **mapping diagram** shows how each element of the domain is paired with each element of the range.

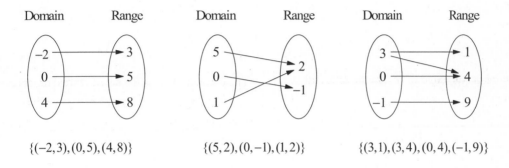

$$\{(-2,3),(0,5),(4,8)\} \qquad \{(5,2),(0,-1),(1,2)\} \qquad \{(3,1),(3,4),(0,4),(-1,9)\}$$

A **function** is a special type of relation in which each element of the domain is paired with exactly one element of the range. The first two relations above are functions, but the third relation is not a function because the 3 in the domain is paired with both 1 and 4 in the range.

Vertical-Line Test

A relation is a function if and only if no vertical line intersects its graph more than once.

Example 1 □   State the domain and range of each relation. Is the relation a function?

a.   b.   c.

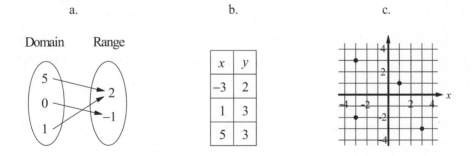

Solution   □   a. The domain is $\{5,0,1\}$. The range is $\{2,-1\}$. This relation is a function.

b. The domain is $\{-3,1,5\}$. The range is $\{2,3\}$. This relation is a function.

c. The domain is $\{-3,1,3\}$. The range is $\{3,1,-2,-3\}$. This relation is not a function, since the -3 in the domain is paired with both 3 and -2 in the range.

The Domain and Range of Six Basic Functions and Their Graphs

(1) $f(x) = x$

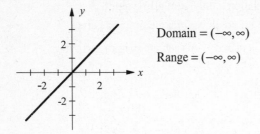

Domain $= (-\infty, \infty)$

Range $= (-\infty, \infty)$

Both the domain and range of f are the set of all real numbers.

(2) $f(x) = x^2$

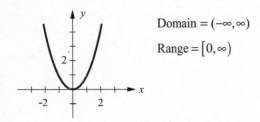

Domain $= (-\infty, \infty)$

Range $= [0, \infty)$

The domain of f is the set of all real numbers, and the range of f is the set of all numbers y such that $y \geq 0$.

(3) $f(x) = \sqrt{x}$

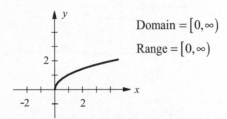

Domain $= [0, \infty)$

Range $= [0, \infty)$

The domain of f is the interval $x \geq 0$, since the expression under a square root has to be nonnegative. The range of the function is all numbers y such that $y \geq 0$, since the expression $\sqrt{x}$ is always nonnegative.

(4) $f(x) = |x|$

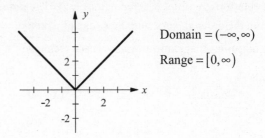

Domain $= (-\infty, \infty)$

Range $= [0, \infty)$

The domain of f is the set of all real numbers, and the range of f is the set of all numbers y such that $y \geq 0$.

(5) $f(x) = \dfrac{1}{x}$

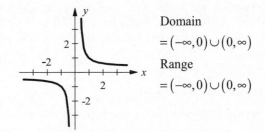

Domain $= (-\infty, 0) \cup (0, \infty)$

Range $= (-\infty, 0) \cup (0, \infty)$

Both the domain and range of $f(x) = \dfrac{1}{x}$ are the set of all real numbers except for $x = 0$ and $y = 0$. Because a number divided by zero is undefined, the denominator can never equal zero and the expression $\dfrac{1}{x}$ can never equal zero.

(6) $f(x) = x^3$

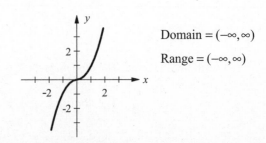

Domain $= (-\infty, \infty)$

Range $= (-\infty, \infty)$

Both the domain and range of f are the set of all real numbers.

2-2. Notation, Value, and Graph of a Function

The symbol $f(x)$ denotes the **value of f at x**.

The value of a function is the y-value that corresponds to the value of x, so $y = f(x)$.

The graph of a function $y = f(x)$ consists of all points (x, y) whose coordinates are solutions of the function.

On a graph, we can read the **value of $f(x)$** as being the height of the graph above or below the x-axis.

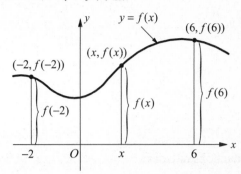

Example 2 □ Let f be the function defined by $f(x) = 3x^2 - x + 1$. Find $f(-3)$ and $f(t-1)$.

Solution □
$$f(-3) = 3(-3)^2 - (-3) + 1 \qquad \text{Replace } x \text{ with } -3.$$
$$= 31$$
$$f(t-1) = 3(t-1)^2 - (t-1) + 1 \qquad \text{Replace } x \text{ with } t-1.$$
$$= 3(t^2 - 2t + 1) - (t-1) + 1$$
$$= 3t^2 - 7t + 5$$

2-3. Definition of Slope

The slope m of the line passing through points (x_1, y_1) and (x_2, y_2) is given by $m = \dfrac{y_2 - y_1}{x_2 - x_1}$,

where $x_1 \neq x_2$.

Example 3 □ If a line passing through the points $(t, 3)$ and $(1, 8)$ has a slope of $\dfrac{5}{3}$, what is the value of t?

Solution □
$$m = \frac{8-3}{1-t} = \frac{5}{3} \implies \frac{5}{1-t} = \frac{5}{3}$$
$$\implies 1 - t = 3$$
$$\implies t = -2$$

2-4. Linear Functions

A function f is a **linear function** if it can be written in the form $f(x) = mx + b$, where m and b are constants.

The graph of a linear function is a nonvertical straight line with slope m and y-intercept b.

Example 4 □   The function f is linear. If $f(0)=3$ and $f(-2)=7$, what is the value of $f(3)$?

Solution   □ $f(x)=mx+b$

$f(0)=m(0)+b=3 \implies b=3$

$\implies f(x)=mx+3$

$f(-2)=m(-2)+3=7$

$\implies -2m=4 \implies m=-2$

$f(x)=-2x+3$

$f(3)=-2(3)+3=-3$ ■

2-5. Equations of Lines

Slope-Intercept Form: $y=mx+b$, where m is the slope and b is the y-intercept.

Equations of lines are generally written in slope-intercept form. When a given equation is written in a different form, you can change it into slope-intercept form to find the slope and the y-intercept.

Point-Slope Form: $y-y_1=m(x-x_1)$, where m is the slope and (x_1,y_1) is a point on the line.

Standard Form: $Ax+By=C$, where A, B, and C are integers.

Vertical Line: $x=a$, where a is the x-intercept. The slope is undefined.

Horizontal Line: $y=b$, where b is the y-intercept. The slope is zero.

The y-coordinate of the point at which a graph crosses the y-axis is called the **y-intercept**.

The x-coordinate of the point at which a graph crosses the x-axis is called the **x-intercept**.

Example 5 □   Find an equation of a line if the x-intercept is 2 and the y-intercept is 5.

Solution   □   If the x-intercept is 2, the line passes through $(2,0)$.

If the y-intercept is 5, the line passes through $(0,5)$.

$m=\dfrac{5-0}{0-2}=-\dfrac{5}{2}$

$y=-\dfrac{5}{2}x+5$ The slope is $-\dfrac{5}{2}$ and the y-intercept is 5.   ■

2-6. Parallel and Perpendicular Lines

Two different lines with equations $y=m_1x+b_1$ and $y=m_2x+b_2$ are **parallel** if $m_1=m_2$ (the slopes are equal). They are **perpendicular** if $m_1 \cdot m_2=-1$ (the slopes are negative reciprocals).

Example 6 □   a. Find an equation of the line which passes through the point $(3,-1)$ and is parallel to $2x-y=10$.

b. Find an equation of the line which passes through the point $(2,5)$ and is perpendicular to $x-2y=-6$.

Solution   □   a. First solve the equation of the given line for y.

$y = 2x - 10$ Slope-intercept form of the given equation

Then the slope of the line parallel to this line is 2.

$y = 2x + b$ Equation of the line parallel to the given line.

$-1 = 2(3) + b$ Substitute $x = 3$ and $y = -1$.

$b = -7$

$y = 2x - 7$ Answer

b. First solve the equation of the given line for y.

$y = \dfrac{1}{2}x + 3$ Slope-intercept form of the given equation

Then the slope of the line perpendicular to this line is -2.

$y = -2x + b$ Equation of the line perpendicular to the given line.

$5 = -2(2) + b$ Substitute $x = 2$ and $y = 5$.

$b = 9$

$y = -2x + 9$ Answer

2-7. Systems of Linear Equations with Two Variables

Solving Systems of Equations Graphically

A set of linear equations with the same two variables is called a **system of linear equations**.
Any ordered pair that is a solution of each equation in the system is called a solution of the system.
A system of linear equations may have **one solution**, **no solution**, or **infinitely many solutions**.

The three types of systems of linear equations are illustrated below graphically.

One solution	**No solution**	**Infinitely many solutions**
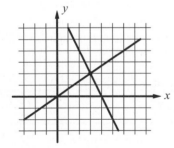	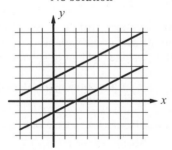	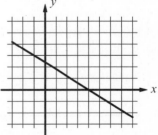
The lines have different slopes and intersect at one point.	The lines have the same slope but different y-intercepts, so they do not intersect.	The graphs are the same line. There are infinitely many solutions.

Solving Systems of Equations Algebraically

Substitution method   1. Solve one equation for either variable.
                                     2. Substitute the resulting equation into the second equation.

Elimination method   1. Multiply one or both equations by a number to obtain equations that have opposite coefficients for one of the variables.
                                     2. Add the equations and solve.

Example 7 □   a. Solve the linear system by the elimination method. $\begin{cases} 4x - 3y = -5 \\ 2x + y = 5 \end{cases}$

b. What is the value of m if the system of equations $\begin{cases} 3x - y = 5 \\ mx = 2y = 16 \end{cases}$

has no solution?

Solution   □   a. $4x - 3y = -5$ First equation

$\underline{6x + 3y = 15}$ Multiply the second equation $(2x + y = 5)$ by 3.

$10x + 0 = 10$ Add the two equations. The opposite coefficients
                              for y result in the y variable being cancelled out.

$x = 1$ Solve for x.

$4(1) - 3y = -5$ Substitute 1 for x back into the first equation.

$y = 3$ Solve for y.

The solution of the system is $(1, 3)$.

b. Solve each equation for y.

$y = 3x - 5$ First equation solved for y.

$y = -\dfrac{m}{2}x + 8$ Second equation solved for y.

If two equations in a system have the same slope but different y-intercepts,
then the system will have no solution.

So, let $3 = -\dfrac{m}{2} \implies m = -6$

Since the two equations have different y-intercepts, the system of equations
will have no solution if the slopes are the same, that is, when $m = -6$. ■

2-8. Systems of Two Equations with Three Variables

On the SAT you may find questions with **two equations and three variables**. On this type of question
you may be asked to solve for one variable or the sum of the variables. Solutions can be found through
the elimination method (obtaining new coefficients, then adding or subtracting the equations).

Example 8 □   If $x - 2y = 3$ and $4x + y + 3z = 15$, what is the value of $x + y + z$?

Solution   □ $-x + 2y \quad = -3$ Multiply the first equation by -1.

$\underline{4x + y + 3z = 15}$ Second equation

$3x + 3y + 3z = 12$ Add the two equations.

$3(x + y + z) = 12$ Factor.

$x + y + z = 4$ Answer ■

2-9. Quadratic Functions

A **quadratic function** is a function that can be written in the form $f(x) = ax^2 + bx + c \ (a \neq 0)$.
The graph of a quadratic function is a parabola.

The line of symmetry for a quadratic function is $x = -\dfrac{b}{2a}$, and the vertex is $(-\dfrac{b}{2a}, f(-\dfrac{b}{2a}))$.

If $a < 0$, f has a **maximum value** at the vertex, that is when $x = -\dfrac{b}{2a}$.

If $a > 0$, f has a **minimum value** at the vertex, that is when $x = -\dfrac{b}{2a}$.

Solutions, Roots, and Zeros of Functions

The **solution** of a function is the value(s) of x for which $f(x) = 0$. Solutions of functions are also called **roots** or **zeros**. On a graph, the solution of the function is the **x-intercept(s).**

Discriminant and Roots of a Quadratic Function

The solutions of the quadratic equation $ax^2 + bx + c = 0$ are given by the **quadratic formula**:

$x = \dfrac{-b \pm \sqrt{b^2 - 4ac}}{2a}$. The expression $b^2 - 4ac$ is called the **discriminant**.

1. If the discriminant $b^2 - 4ac > 0$, then there are two real roots, and the graph crosses the x-axis twice.

2. If $b^2 - 4ac = 0$, then there is one real root, and the graph is tangent to the x-axis.

3. If $b^2 - 4ac < 0$, then there are no real roots, and the graph does not cross the x-axis.

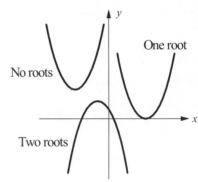

Example 9 □   a. Find the line of symmetry, minimum value, and the vertex of the graph $f(x) = 2x^2 - 4x + 5$.

b. If k is a positive integer and $x^2 + 4x + k = 0$ has two real roots, what is one possible value of k?

Solution   □   a. The line of symmetry is

$$x = -\frac{b}{2a} = -\frac{-4}{2(2)} = \frac{4}{4} = 1$$

The minimum occurs when $x = 1$.

$$f(-\frac{b}{2a}) = f(1) = 2(1)^2 - 4(1) + 5 = 3$$

The minimum value of f is 3.

The vertex is $(1,3)$.

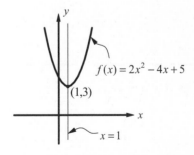

b. If a quadratic function has two real roots, $b^2 - 4ac > 0$.

$$4^2 - 4(1)k > 0 \implies 16 - 4k > 0 \implies 16 > 4k \implies 4 > k$$

Since k is a positive integer, the possible values of k are 1, 2, and 3.

2-10. Transformations of Functions

Original graph: $y = \sqrt{x}$

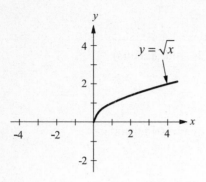

For a function $y = f(x)$ and positive numbers h and k:

Horizontal shifts
h units to the **right**: $\qquad y = f(x - h)$
h units to the **left**: $\qquad y = f(x + h)$

Vertical shifts
k units **downward**: $\qquad y = f(x) - k$
k units **upward**: $\qquad y = f(x) + k$

Reflections
about the **x-axis**: $\qquad y = -f(x)$
about the **y-axis**: $\qquad y = f(-x)$
about the **origin**: $\qquad y = -f(-x)$

Horizontal shifts
2 units to the **right**: $\qquad y = \sqrt{x - 2}$
2 units to the **left**: $\qquad y = \sqrt{x + 2}$

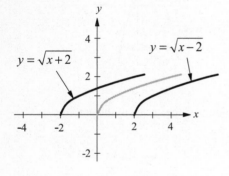

Vertical shifts
3 units **downward**: $y = \sqrt{x} - 3$
3 units **upward**: $\qquad y = \sqrt{x} + 3$

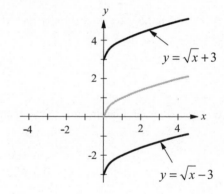

Reflections
about the **x-axis**: $y = -\sqrt{x}$
about the **y-axis**: $y = \sqrt{-x}$

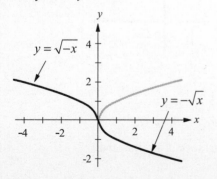

Reflections
about the **origin**: $y = -\sqrt{-x}$

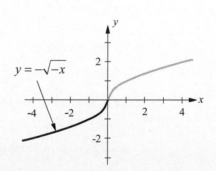

1. If $f(x) = \sqrt{1-2x}$, which of the following values is *not* included in the domain of f ?

    (A) -3

    (B) -2

    (C) -1

    (D) 0

    (E) 1

2. If $f(x) = \dfrac{1}{(x+1)(x-2)}$, which of the following values is *not* included in the domain of f ?

    (A) -2

    (B) -1

    (C) 0

    (D) 1

    (E) 3

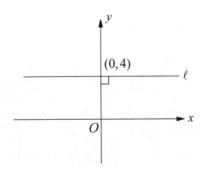

Figure 1

3. In Figure 1, the equation of line ℓ is

    (A) $x - y = 4$

    (B) $x + y = 4$

    (C) $x = 4$

    (D) $y = 4$

    (E) $y = 0$

4. If $f(x) = |2x+3|$ with domain $D = \{-5, -1, 0, 3\}$, which of the following is the range of f ?

    (A) $R = \{-7, 1, 3, 9\}$

    (B) $R = \{-3, 0, 1, 4\}$

    (C) $R = \{1, 3, 7, 9\}$

    (D) $R = \{0, 1, 5, 9\}$

    (E) $R = \{2, 3, 5, 9\}$

5. What is the range of the function defined as
   $f(x) = \dfrac{1}{x} - 3$?

    (A) All real numbers

    (B) All real numbers except -1

    (C) All real numbers except 0

    (D) All real numbers except -3

    (E) All real numbers except 0 and -3

6. Which of the following is the equation of a line that runs through the point $(3,1)$ and is perpendicular to $x + 3y = 5$?

    (A) $y = -3x + 10$

    (B) $y = -\dfrac{1}{3}x + 8$

    (C) $y = 3x - 8$

    (D) $y = \dfrac{1}{3}x$

    (E) $y = 3x + 1$

7. What is the range of the function defined by
$f(x) = -x^2 + 2x + 3$ over the interval $-1 \le x \le 4$?

(A) $-5 \le y \le 4$

(B) $-3 \le y \le 4$

(C) $-3 \le y \le 5$

(D) $0 \le y \le 4$

(E) $0 \le y \le 5$

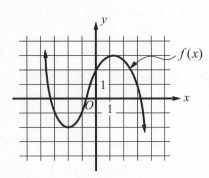

Figure 2

8. In Figure 2, what is the value of $f(-3) \cdot f(0)$?

(A) -2

(B) -1

(C) 0

(D) 2

(E) 3

9. What is the slope of the line $9 - 4y = -3$?

(A) -3

(B) 0

(C) $\dfrac{9}{4}$

(D) 3

(E) Undefined

10. If $2x - y = x + 1$ and $x - y = y - 1$, then $y =$

(A) -1

(B) 0

(C) 1

(D) 2

(E) 3

$$\begin{cases} x - 4y = 4 \\ -2x + ny = 10 \end{cases}$$

11. If the system of equations shown above has no
solution, what is the value of n?

(A) -8

(B) -4

(C) 0

(D) 4

(E) 8

12. If the equation $x^2 - 6x + c = 0$ has one real root,
what is the value of c?

(A) -9

(B) -3

(C) 1

(D) 3

(E) 9

13. If the equation $f(x) = x^2 + bx + 5$ has two real roots, which of the following cannot be the value of b?

    (A) −7

    (B) −5

    (C) 0

    (D) 5

    (E) 8

14. If $f(x) = x^2 + 2x - 5$, which of the following is the equation of $-f(-x)$?

    (A) $-x^2 + 2x + 5$

    (B) $-x^2 + 2x - 5$

    (C) $-x^2 - 2x + 5$

    (D) $x^2 + 2x - 5$

    (E) $x^2 + 2x + 5$

15. If $a + 2b - c = 10$ and $a - b + 2c = 7$, then $b - c =$

    (A) −5

    (B) −3

    (C) 1

    (D) 5

    (E) 8

16. Which of the following could be the graph of a function?

(A) 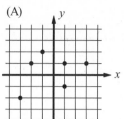   (B)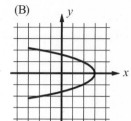

(C) 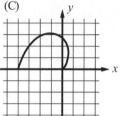   (D)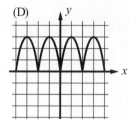

(E)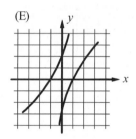

17. The function g is defined as $g(x) = f(-\frac{1}{2}x) + 3$. If $g(4) = 2$, what is the value of $f(-2)$?

    (A) −2

    (B) −1

    (C) 0

    (D) 2

    (E) 4

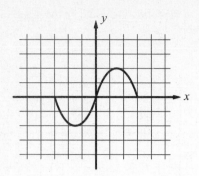

Figure 3

18. If Figure 3 shows the graph of $f(x)$, which of the following graphs represents $f(x+2)-1$?

(A) 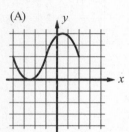   (B)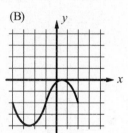

(C) 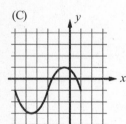   (D)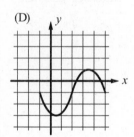

(E)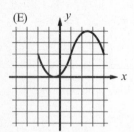

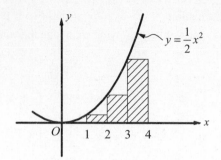

Note: Figure not drawn to scale.

Figure 4

19. Figure 4 shows the graph of $y = \dfrac{1}{2}x^2$ and three inscribed rectangles. What is the sum of the areas of the three rectangles?

(A) $\dfrac{13}{2}$

(B) 7

(C) $\dfrac{15}{2}$

(D) 8

(E) $\dfrac{17}{2}$

Answer Key

1. E	2. B	3. D	4. C	5. D
6. C	7. A	8. A	9. B	10. D
11. E	12. E	13. C	14. A	15. C
16. D	17. B	18. C	19. B	

Answers and Explanations

1. E

$f(x) = \sqrt{1-2x}$

The domain of f is the interval $1 - 2x \geq 0$, since the expression under a square root must be nonnegative.

$1 - 2x \geq 0 \Rightarrow 1 \geq 2x \Rightarrow \dfrac{1}{2} \geq x$

Therefore the domain of f cannot include 1.

2. B

The domain of a rational function is the set of all real numbers except those for which the denominator of the function equals zero.

$f(x) = \dfrac{1}{(x+1)(x-2)}$, so the domain of the given function cannot include $x = -1$ and $x = 2$.

3. D

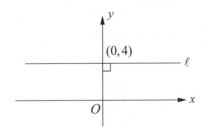

The equation of a horizontal line is $y = b$, where b is the y-intercept.
Therefore $y = 4$ is the equation of the line shown in the graph.

4. C

$f(x) = |2x + 3|$ with domain $D = \{-5, -1, \ 0, \ 3\}$.

$f(-5) = |2(-5) + 3| = 7$

$f(-1) = |2(-1) + 3| = 1$

$f(0) = |2(0) + 3| = 3$

$f(3) = |2(3) + 3| = 9$

The range of f is $R = \{\ 1, \ 3, \ 7, \ 9\}$.

5. D

Graph $f(x) = \dfrac{1}{x} - 3$, using a graphing calculator.

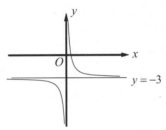

$y = -3$ is the horizontal asymptote of the graph.
The range of $f(x)$ is the set of all real numbers except for -3, since $\dfrac{1}{x} - 3$ can never equal -3.

6. C

$x + 3y = 5$ Equation of the given line

$3y = -x + 5$

$y = -\dfrac{1}{3}x + \dfrac{5}{3}$ Solve the equation for y.

Two lines are perpendicular if their slopes are negative reciprocals. Therefore the slope of the line perpendicular to the given line is 3. $y = 3x + b$ is the equation of the perpendicular line.

Since the line passes through the point $(3, 1)$, find b by substituting $x = 3$ and $y = 1$ into the equation.

$1 = 3(3) + b \Rightarrow b = -8$

Therefore the equation of the perpendicular line is $y = 3x - 8$.

7. A

Method 1

Graph $f(x) = -x^2 + 2x + 3$ in the interval $-1 \le x \le 4$, using a graphing calculator.

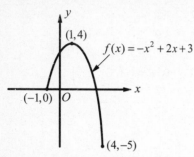

The graph shows -5 is the minimum when $x = 4$, and 4 is the maximum when $x = 1$. So the range of the function is $\{-5 \le y \le 4\}$.

Method 2

Find the value of the function at the end points and at the vertex.

$f(-1) = -(-1)^2 + 2(-1) + 3 = 0$

$f(4) = -(4)^2 + 2(4) + 3 = -5$

A quadratic function has its minimum or maximum value when $x = -\dfrac{b}{2a}$ (at its vertex).

$x = -\dfrac{b}{2a} = -\dfrac{2}{2(-1)} = 1$

$f(1) = -(1)^2 + 2(1) + 3 = 4$

Therefore the range of the function is $\{-5 \le y \le 4\}$.

8. A

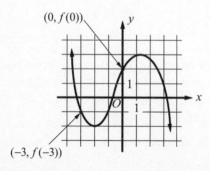

The graph shows $f(-3) = -1$ and $f(0) = 2$.

$f(-3) \cdot f(0) = (-1)(2) = -2$

9. B

$9 - 4y = -3 \implies -4y = -12$

$\implies y = 3$

Since $y = 3$ is a horizontal line, the slope of the line is 0.

10. D

$2x - y = x + 1$	First equation
$2x - y - x = x - x + 1$	Subtract x from both sides.
$x - y = 1$	First equation simplified
$x - y = y - 1$	Second equation
$1 = y - 1$	Substitution
$y = 2$	

11. E

$x - 4y = 4$	First equation
$-4y = -x + 4$	Subtract x from both sides.
$y = \dfrac{1}{4}x - 1$	First equation in slope-intercept form
$-2x + ny = 10$	Second equation
$ny = 2x + 10$	Add $2x$ to both sides.
$y = \dfrac{2}{n}x + \dfrac{10}{n}$	Second equation in slope-int. form

If the system of equations has no solution, the lines have the same slope but different y-intercepts.

Set the slope of the first equation equal to the slope of the second equation.

$\dfrac{1}{4} = \dfrac{2}{n} \implies n = 8$

Check your answer by making sure the second equation has a different y-intercept.

$\dfrac{10}{n} = \dfrac{10}{8}$. The y-intercept is different.

12. E

$x^2 - 6x + c = 0$

If the equation has one real root, $b^2 - 4ac = 0$.

$(-6)^2 - 4(1)(c) = 0 \implies 36 - 4c = 0$

$\implies c = 9$

13. C

$$f(x) = x^2 + bx + 5$$

A quadratic equation has two real roots if $b^2 - 4ac > 0$.

$$b^2 - 4(1)(5) > 0 \implies b^2 - 20 > 0$$

$$\implies (b + \sqrt{20})(b - \sqrt{20}) > 0$$

$$\implies b < -\sqrt{20} \approx -4.47 \text{ or } b > \sqrt{20} \approx 4.47$$

Choice (C) is correct.

14. A

$$f(x) = x^2 + 2x - 5$$

$$f(-x) = (-x)^2 + 2(-x) - 5 = x^2 - 2x - 5$$

$$-f(-x) = -(x^2 - 2x - 5) = -x^2 + 2x + 5$$

15. C

$a + 2b - c = 10$	First equation
$-\lfloor a - b + 2c = 7$	Second equation
$3b - 3c = 3$	Subtract the second equation from the first equation.
$3(b - c) = 3$	Factor.
$b - c = 1$	Divide both sides by 3.

16. D

A relation is a function if and only if no vertical line intersects its graph more than once.

Choice (D) is correct.

17. B

$$g(x) = f(-\frac{1}{2}x) + 3$$

$$g(4) = f(-\frac{1}{2}(4)) + 3 = f(-2) + 3$$

$$g(4) = 2 \implies f(-2) + 3 = 2 \implies f(-2) = -1$$

18. C

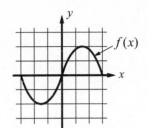

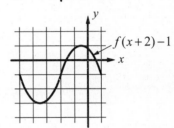

The graph of $f(x+2) - 1$ is the graph of $f(x)$ moved 2 units to the left and 1 unit down.

Choice (C) is correct.

19. B

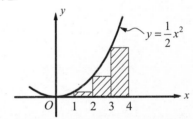

To find the heights of the rectangles, substitute the values of x into the equation of the curve.

$$f(1) = \frac{1}{2}(1)^2 = \frac{1}{2}, \ f(2) = \frac{1}{2}(2)^2 = 2$$

$$f(3) = \frac{1}{2}(3)^2 = \frac{9}{2}$$

Sum of the areas of the inscribed rectangles

$$= 1 \cdot \frac{1}{2} + 1 \cdot 2 + 1 \cdot \frac{9}{2} = 7$$

CHAPTER 3
Polynomials and Factoring

3-1. Laws of Exponents

Laws		**Examples**
Products of Powers	$a^m \cdot a^n = a^{m+n}$	$2^5 \cdot 2^3 = 2^{5+3} = 2^8$
Quotient of Powers	$\dfrac{a^m}{a^n} = a^{m-n}$	$\dfrac{2^7}{2^4} = 2^{7-4} = 2^3$
Power of a Power	$\left(a^m\right)^n = a^{m \cdot n}$	$(2^3)^4 = 2^{3 \cdot 4} = 2^{12}$
Power of a Product	$(a \cdot b)^n = a^n \cdot b^n$	$(2 \cdot 3)^4 = 2^4 \cdot 3^4$
Power of a Quotient	$(\dfrac{a}{b})^n = \dfrac{a^n}{b^n}$	$(\dfrac{2}{3})^5 = \dfrac{2^5}{3^5}$
Negative Exponent	$a^{-n} = \dfrac{1}{a^n} \quad (a \neq 0)$	$2^{-3} = \dfrac{1}{2^3} = \dfrac{1}{8}$
	$(\dfrac{a}{b})^{-n} = (\dfrac{b}{a})^n \quad (ab \neq 0)$	$(\dfrac{2}{3})^{-3} = (\dfrac{3}{2})^3 = \dfrac{3^3}{2^3} = \dfrac{27}{8}$
Zero Exponent	$a^0 = 1 \; (a \neq 0)$	$3^0 = 1, \quad (2ab^2)^0 = 1$

$(-1)^n = 1$ if n is an even integer

$(-1)^n = -1$ if n is an odd integer

Example 1 □ Simplify each expression.   a. $(-2t^3)^2(s^2t)^{-3}$ b. $(\dfrac{x}{2y})^0(\dfrac{x^{-1}}{y^2})^2(x^2y)^{-1}$

Solution □ a. $(-2t^3)^2(s^2t)^{-3} = (-2)^2(t^3)^2(s^2)^{-3}(t)^{-3} = 4 \cdot t^6 \cdot s^{-6} \cdot t^{-3} = 4 \cdot t^{6-3} \cdot s^{-6}$

$$= 4 \cdot t^3 \cdot (\dfrac{1}{s^6}) = \dfrac{4t^3}{s^6}$$

b. $(\dfrac{x}{2y})^0(\dfrac{x^{-1}}{y^2})^2(x^2y)^{-1} = 1 \cdot (\dfrac{x^{-2}}{y^4})(x^{-2}y^{-1}) = \dfrac{x^{-2}x^{-2}y^{-1}}{y^4} = x^{-4}y^{-1-4}$

$$= x^{-4}y^{-5} = \dfrac{1}{x^4y^5}$$

3-2. Polynomials

A **monomial** is an expression that is a number, a variable, or a product of a number and one or more variables. Examples of monomials are -3, $5x$, $2x^2$, and $7xy^2$. A **polynomial** is a monomial or a sum of monomials. The monomials in a polynomial are called the **terms** of the polynomial.

Adding and Subtracting Polynomials

Polynomials are added and subtracted by combining like terms.

Multiplying Polynomials

Products of polynomials are found by using the distributive property and the various laws of exponents. To multiply two **binomials** (a polynomial that has two terms) you can use the **FOIL** method, by which you multiply the first, outside, inside, and last terms.

$$(2x+3)(x-5) = \overbrace{(2x)(x)}^{\substack{\text{Multiply the} \\ \text{first terms}}} + \overbrace{(2x)(-5)}^{\substack{\text{Multiply the} \\ \text{outer terms}}} + \overbrace{3(x)}^{\substack{\text{Multiply the} \\ \text{inner terms}}} + \overbrace{3(-5)}^{\substack{\text{Multiply the} \\ \text{last terms}}}$$

$$= 2x^2 - 10x + 3x - 15$$
$$= 2x^2 - 7x - 15$$

Example 2 □ a. Multiply $(x-2)(3x+1)$.   b. Factor $x^2 - 6x + 8$.

Solution □ a. $(x-2)(3x+1)$ Given equation

$$= \overbrace{(x)(3x)}^{\text{First}} + \overbrace{(x)(1)}^{\text{Outside}} + \overbrace{(-2)(3x)}^{\text{Inside}} + \overbrace{(-2)(1)}^{\text{Last}} \qquad \text{FOIL}$$

$$= 3x^2 + x - 6x - 2 \qquad \text{Simplify.}$$

$$= 3x^2 - 5x - 2 \qquad \text{Combine like terms.}$$

b. The constant term 8 has four possible factors:
  $(1)(8)$, $(2)(4)$, $(-1)(-8)$, $(-2)(-4)$.
  Choose the pair of factors that have a sum of -6: -2 and -4.
  Therefore $x^2 - 6x + 8 = (x-2)(x-4)$.   Answer

3-3. GCF and LCM

To find the **greatest common factor (GCF)** of two or more monomials: From the prime factors common to all of the monomials, take the smallest power of each prime factor, and multiply.

To find the **least common multiple (LCM)** of two or more monomials: From the collection of all the prime factors (whether or not they are common to all the monomials), take the largest power of each prime factor, and multiply.

Example 3 □ Find the GCF and LCM of $24a^2bc^5$, $-36a^3b^2c^4$, and $60a^4b^2c^3$.

Solution □ First factor each monomial completely.

$$24a^2bc^5 \qquad = 2^3 \cdot 3 \cdot a^2bc^5$$
$$36a^3b^2c^4 \qquad = 2^2 \cdot 3^2 a^3b^2c^4$$
$$60a^4b^2c^3 \qquad = 2^2 \cdot 3 \cdot 5 \cdot a^4b^2c^3$$

The smallest power of 2 is 2^2,   The greatest power of 2 is 2^3,

the smallest power of 3 is 3,   the greatest power of 3 is 3^2,

5 is not a common factor,   the greatest power of 5 is 5,

the smallest power of a is a^2,   the greatest power of a is a^4,

the smallest power of b is b, and   the greatest power of b is b^2, and

the smallest power of c is c^3, so   the greatest power of c is c^5, so

$$\text{GCF} = 2^2 \cdot 3a^2bc^3 = 12a^2bc^3. \qquad\qquad \text{LCM} = 2^3 \cdot 3^2 \cdot 5 \cdot a^4b^2c^5 = 360a^4b^2c^5.$$

3-4. Special Products and Factoring Polynomials

Difference of Two Squares: $a^2 - b^2 = (a+b)(a-b)$

Sum of Two Cubes: $a^3 + b^3 = (a+b)(a^2 - ab + b^2)$

Difference of Two Cubes: $a^3 - b^3 = (a-b)(a^2 + ab + b^2)$

Perfect Square Trinomials: $a^2 + 2ab + b^2 = (a+b)^2$

$a^2 - 2ab + b^2 = (a-b)^2$

Cubes of Binomials: $a^3 + 3a^2b + 3ab^2 + b^3 = (a+b)^3$

$a^3 - 3a^2b + 3ab^2 - b^3 = (a-b)^3$

To factor a polynomial completely, first factor out the GCF, if any, then factor the remaining polynomial if possible.

Factoring for several common types of polynomial is shown below.

a) **Factoring out the GCF**

$6x^3 - 15x^2 - 9x$

$= 3x(2x^2 - 5x - 3)$ The GCF of the terms is $3x$.

$= 3x(2x+1)(x-3)$ The remaining terms can be factored into binomials.

b) **Factoring Perfect Squares**

$x^2 - 8x + 16$ The first term (x^2) and the third term $(16 = 4^2)$ are perfect squares,

$= (x)^2 - 2(x)(4) + 4^2$ and the middle term is twice the product of x and 4.

$= (x-4)^2$ Therefore $x^2 - 8x + 16$ is a perfect square trinomial.

c) **Factoring the Difference of Two Squares**

$x^4 - 81 = (x^2)^2 - 9^2$ $x^4 = (x^2)^2$ and $81 = 9^2$, so $(x^2)^2 - 9^2$ is a difference of two squares.

$= (x^2 + 9)(x^2 - 9)$ Factor. $x^2 - 9$ is also a difference of two squares.

$= (x^2 + 9)(x+3)(x-3)$ Factor.

d) **Factoring the Difference of Two Cubes**

$2x^3 - 16$

$= 2(x^3 - 8)$ The GCF of the terms is 2. $x^3 - 8$ is a difference of two cubes $(x^3 - 8 = x^3 - 2^3)$.

$= 2(x-2)(x^2 + 2x + 4)$

e) **Factoring by Grouping**

$3x^3 - 6x^2 + 5x - 10$

$= (3x^3 - 6x^2) + (5x - 10)$ Group terms to find GCFs.

$= 3x^2(x-2) + 5(x-2)$ Factor out the GCF of each binomial.

$= (3x^2 + 5)(x-2)$ Distributive property

Example 4 □ Factor $x - 6\sqrt{x} + 8$.

Solution □ Let $z = \sqrt{x}$. Then $z^2 = x$.

$x - 6\sqrt{x} + 8$

$= z^2 - 6z + 8$ Substitution: $z = \sqrt{x}$

$= (z - 2)(z - 4)$ $(-2)(-4) = 8$ and $-2 + -4 = -6$

$= (\sqrt{x} - 2)(\sqrt{x} - 4)$ Substitution: $z = \sqrt{x}$ ■

3-5. Zero Product Property

For all real numbers a and b, $a \cdot b = 0$ if and only if $a = 0$ or $b = 0$. That is,
a product of factors is equal to zero if and only if one or more of the factors is zero.

Example 5 □ Solve $x^3 - 3x^2 = 4x$.

Solution □ $x^3 - 3x^2 - 4x = 0$ Make one side of the equation 0.

$x(x^2 - 3x - 4) = 0$ Factor out the GCF.

$x(x + 1)(x - 4) = 0$ Factor the polynomial.

$x = 0$ or $x + 1 = 0$ or $x - 4 = 0$ Zero product property

$x = 0$ or $x = -1$ or $x = 4$

The solution set is $\{-1, 0, 4\}$.   Answer   ■

3-6. Sum and Product of Roots

If r_1 and r_2 are the roots of a quadratic equation $ax^2 + bx + c = 0$, then

the sum of roots $= r_1 + r_2 = -\dfrac{b}{a}$, and the product of the roots $= r_1 \cdot r_2 = \dfrac{c}{a}$.

Example 6 □ If a quadratic equation $ax^2 - 3x + c = 0$ has two real roots whose sum

is $\dfrac{1}{2}$ and product is $-\dfrac{2}{3}$, what is the value of $a + c$?

Solution □ The sum of the roots $r_1 + r_2$ is $-\dfrac{b}{a} = \dfrac{1}{2}$, and the product $r_1 \cdot r_2$ is $\dfrac{c}{a} = -\dfrac{2}{3}$.

Rewrite the equations using 6 as a common denominator: $-\dfrac{-3}{a} = \dfrac{3}{6}$ and $\dfrac{c}{a} = -\dfrac{4}{6}$.

From the two equations we can conclude that $a = 6$ and $c = -4$.

Therefore $a + c = 6 + (-4) = 2$.   ■

3-7. Remainder Theorem

If a polynomial $f(x)$ is divided by $x-c$, then the remainder is $f(c)$.

Thus $f(x) = (x-c)q(x) + f(c)$, where $q(x)$ is the quotient.

Example 7 □ Find the remainder of the polynomial $f(x) = x^3 + 3x^2 - 4x - 7$ divided by $x+2$.

Solution □ The remainder theorem says that when $f(x)$ is divided by $x+2$ the remainder is $f(-2)$.

$$f(-2) = (-2)^3 + 3(-2)^2 - 4(-2) - 7 = 5$$

3-8. Factor Theorem

The polynomial $f(x)$ has $x-c$ as a factor if and only if $f(c) = 0$. The factor theorem is corollary of the remainder theorem.

Example 8 □ Are the following binomials factors of the polynomial $f(x) = 2x^3 - 5x^2 - 4x + 3$?

a. $2x - 1$ b. $x + 3$

Solution □ a. First divide the binomial by 2 to obtain $x-c$ format.

$$(2x - 1) \div 2 = x - \frac{1}{2} \;\Rightarrow\; c = \frac{1}{2}.$$

$$f(\tfrac{1}{2}) = 2(\tfrac{1}{2})^3 - 5(\tfrac{1}{2})^2 - 4(\tfrac{1}{2}) + 3 = 0 \qquad \text{Factor theorem}$$

Since $f(\tfrac{1}{2}) = 0$, $2x - 1$ is a factor of the polynomial.

b. If $x + 3 = 0$, then $x = -3$.

$$f(-3) = 2(-3)^3 - 5(-3)^2 - 4(-3) + 3 = -84 \qquad \text{Factor theorem}$$

Since $f(-3) \neq 0$, $x + 3$ is NOT a factor of the polynomial.

3-9. Equality of Polynomials (for All Values of x)

If two linear equations $ax + b$ and $px + q$ are equal, (that is, $ax + b = px + q$ **for all values of x**), then $a = p$ and $b = q$.

If two quadratic equations $ax^2 + bx + c$ and $px^2 + qx + r$ are equal, (that is, $ax^2 + bx + c = px^2 + qx + r$ for all values of x), then $a = p$, $b = q$, and $c = r$.

If two cubic equations $ax^3 + bx^2 + cx + d$ and $px^3 + qx^2 + rx + s$ are equal, (that is, $ax^3 + bx^2 + cx + d = px^3 + qx^2 + rx + s$ for all values of x), then $a = p$, $b = q$, $c = r$, and $d = s$.

Example 9 □   a. If $(x+2)(x-j) = x^2 + kx + 10$ for all values of x, what is the value of $j \cdot k$?

Solution   □   a. $(x+2)(x-j) = x^2 + kx + 10$

$x^2 - jx + 2x - 2j = x^2 + kx + 10$ Multiply the binomial.

$x^2 + (2-j)x - 2j = x^2 + kx + 10$ Simplify the left side of the equation.

$2 - j = k$ and $-2j = 10$ Equality of polynomials

Therefore, $j = -5$ and $k = 7$.

$j \cdot k = -5 \cdot 7 = -35$ Answer   ▪

3-10. Possible Rational Roots of Polynomials

Suppose all the coefficients in the polynomial $f(x) = a_n x^n + a_{n-1} x^{n-1} + \ldots + a_0$ are integers.
Then for p, which is a factor of the constant term a_0, and q, which is a factor of the leading coefficient a_n,

the rational number $\dfrac{p}{q}$ in simplest form is a possible rational root of the polynomial.

Example 10 □   How many possible rational roots does $f(x) = 2x^4 - x^2 + 5x + 6$ have?

Solution   □   Find all factors of the constant term and the leading coefficient.

$p : \pm 1, \ \pm 2, \ \pm 3, \ \pm 6$ Factors of the constant term 6

$q : \pm 1, \ \pm 2,$ Factors of the leading coefficient 2

To list all possible rational roots, choose a numerator from the p list and
a denominator from the q list, writing the rational number in simplest form.

$\dfrac{p}{q} : \pm 1, \ \pm 2, \ \pm 3, \ \pm 6, \ \pm \dfrac{1}{2}, \ \pm \dfrac{3}{2},$

There are 12 possible rational roots.   ▪

3-11. Scientific Notation

In **scientific notation**, a number is expressed in the form $a \times 10^n$, where
$1 \le a < 10$ and n is an integer.

Example 11 □   Write the product $(3.25 \times 10^7) \cdot (7.8 \times 10^{-5})$ in scientific notation.

Solution   □ $(3.25 \times 10^7) \cdot (7.8 \times 10^{-5})$

$= 25.35 \times 10^2$ $3.27 \times 7.8 = 25.35$ and $10^7 \times 10^{-5} = 10^2$

$= 2.535 \times 10 \times 10^2$ $25.35 = 2.5351 \times 10$

$= 2.535 \times 10^3$ ▪▪

1. If $5^x = 10$, then $5^{x-1} =$

   (A) −5

   (B) −2

   (C) 2

   (D) 10

   (E) 50

2. If $12^m = (3k)^m (k)^m$, which of the following could be the value of k?

   (A) $\dfrac{1}{2}$

   (B) 2

   (C) 3

   (D) 4

   (E) 6

3. If $a^n \cdot a^n = a^4 \cdot a^{16}$, what is the value of n?

   (A) 4

   (B) 6

   (C) 8

   (D) 10

   (E) 32

4. If $3^{6-x} = 243$, what is the value of x?

   (A) 1

   (B) 2

   (C) 3

   (D) 4

   (E) 5

5. $ax - 3a - x + 3 =$

   (A) $(a-3)(x-1)$

   (B) $(a-3)(x+1)$

   (C) $(x-3)(a+1)$

   (D) $(x-3)(a-1)$

   (E) $(x+3)(a-1)$

6. If $3x^2 - 8 = 4x$, then $x =$

   (A) −1.5

   (B) 1.72

   (C) 2.43

   (D) 5.00

   (E) 7.72

7. For which of the following equations are there two distinct real solutions?

   I. $x^3 = 8x^2$

   II. $x^2 + 9 = 0$

   III. $x^3 + 3x^2 + 4x = 0$

   (A) I only

   (B) II only

   (C) III only

   (D) I and III only

   (E) II and III only

8. If $(a-b)^3 = -12$, then $(a-b)^2 =$

    (A) −8.00

    (B) −5.24

    (C) 1.86

    (D) 5.24

    (E) 8.00

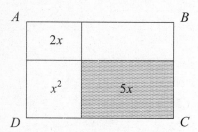

Figure 1

9. Figure 1 shows a rectangular region that has been divided into four smaller rectangular regions, three of which have areas of x^2, $5x$ and $2x$. If the area of rectangle $ABCD$ is 40, what is the area of the shaded region?

    (A) 8

    (B) 10

    (C) 12

    (D) 15

    (E) 18

10. If 4 and −3 are both zeros of the polynomial $p(x)$, then a factor of $p(x)$ is

    (A) $x^2 - 12$

    (B) $x^2 + 12$

    (C) $x^2 + x - 12$

    (D) $x^2 - x + 12$

    (E) $x^2 - x - 12$

11. Which of the following equations has two roots $\dfrac{3+\sqrt{3}}{2}$ and $\dfrac{3-\sqrt{3}}{2}$?

    (A) $2x^2 + 6x + 3 = 0$

    (B) $2x^2 - 6x - 3 = 0$

    (C) $2x^2 - 6x + 3 = 0$

    (D) $x^2 - 3x - 6 = 0$

    (E) $x^2 - 3x - 3 = 0$

12. If $abc \neq 0$ and $a^2 b^5 c^{-3} = \dfrac{a^2 b^3 c}{3ab^{-2}c^4}$, then $a =$

    (A) $\dfrac{1}{9}$

    (B) $\dfrac{1}{3}$

    (C) 3

    (D) $\dfrac{b^4}{3}$

    (E) $\dfrac{3b^4}{c^2}$

13. What is the remainder of $x^7 - 2x^4 + 5x^3 + 7$ divided by $x + 1$?

    (A) −7

    (B) 2

    (C) 5

    (D) 7

    (E) 11

14. If $x-2$ is a factor of $f(x) = x^3 - 3x^2 + 5x + k$, what is the value of k?

    (A) -6

    (B) -3

    (C) -1

    (D) 2

    (E) 4

15. Which of the following is a factor of the polynomial $f(x) = 2x^3 + x^2 + 11x - 6$?

    (A) $x-1$

    (B) $x+1$

    (C) $2x-1$

    (D) $2x+1$

    (E) $3x-2$

16. If $x^{15} = a$ and $x^{11} = b$, which of the following must be equal to x^7?

    (A) $\dfrac{a}{b^2}$

    (B) $\dfrac{b^2}{a}$

    (C) $\dfrac{2b}{a}$

    (D) $2(\sqrt{a} - \sqrt{b})$

    (E) $b^2 - a$

17. If $(x^2 - a)(x + b) = x^3 + 4x^2 - 2x + c$ for all values of x, what is the value of $a + b + c$?

    (A) 5

    (B) 3

    (C) 0

    (D) -1

    (E) -2

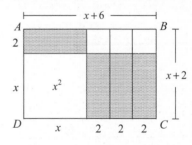

Figure 2

18. In Figure 2, a rectangular region is divided into four squares and four smaller rectangles (shaded regions). If the area of rectangle $ABCD$ is 96, what is the sum of the areas of the shaded regions?

    (A) 32

    (B) 36

    (C) 40

    (D) 48

    (E) 52

19. If $f(x) = 2x^4 + 7x^2 - 2x + 8$, what is the number of possible rational roots?

    (A) 4

    (B) 5

    (C) 6

    (D) 8

    (E) 10

Answer Key

1. C	2. B	3. D	4. A	5. D
6. C	7. A	8. D	9. D	10. E
11. C	12. B	13. B	14. A	15. C
16. B	17. E	18. D	19. E	

Answers and Explanations

1. C

Given $5^x = 10$.

$$5^{x-1} = 5^x \cdot 5^{-1} \qquad\qquad \text{Law of exponents}$$
$$= 10 \cdot \frac{1}{5} \qquad\qquad\qquad 5^x = 10$$
$$= 2$$

2. B

$$12^m = (3k)^m (k)^m \implies 12^m = (3k \cdot k)^m$$
$$\implies 12^m = (3k^2)^m \implies 12 = 3k^2$$
$$\implies 4 = k^2 \implies k = \pm 2$$

3. D

$$a^n \cdot a^n = a^4 \cdot a^{16} \implies a^{n+n} = a^{4+16}$$
$$\implies a^{2n} = a^{20} \implies n = 10$$

4. A

$$3^{6-x} = 243 \implies 3^{6-x} = 3^5$$
$$\implies 6 - x = 5 \implies x = 1$$

5. D

$$ax - 3a - x + 3$$
$$= a(x-3) - (x-3) \qquad\qquad -x + 3 = -(x-3)$$
$$= (x-3)(a-1)$$

6. C

$$3x^2 - 8 = 4x \implies 3x^2 - 4x - 8 = 0$$

This equation is not factorable, so use the quadratic formula.

$$x = \frac{-b \pm \sqrt{b^2 - 4ac}}{2a}$$
$$= \frac{4 \pm \sqrt{(-4)^2 - 4(3)(-8)}}{2(3)} = \frac{4 \pm \sqrt{112}}{6}$$
$$x = \frac{4 + \sqrt{112}}{6} \approx 2.43 \ \text{ or } \ x = \frac{4 - \sqrt{112}}{6} \approx -1.1$$

7. A

Method 1: Solve using factorization, the quadratic
　　　　　 equation, or the discriminant.

I. $x^3 = 8x^2 \implies x^3 - 8x^2 = 0$
　 $\implies x^2(x-8) = 0$
　 $\implies x = 0 \text{ or } x = 8$
This equation has two distinct solutions.

II. $x^2 + 9 = 0$
　 Since $b^2 - 4ac = 0^2 - 4(1)(9) < 0$, there is
　 no solution.

III. $x^3 + 3x^2 + 4x = 0$
　 $x(x^2 + 3x + 4) = 0$
　 $x^2 + 3x + 4 = 0$ has no solution since
　 $b^2 - 4ac = 3^2 - 4(1)(4) < 0$.
　 The only solution is $x = 0$.

Method 2: Use a graphing calculator.

I. Graph $y_1 = x^3 - 8x^2$.

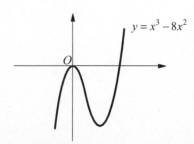

Since there are two x-intercepts, the equation has two distinct solutions.

II. Graph $y_1 = x^2 + 9$.

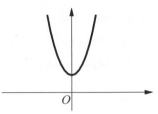

Since there is no x-intercept, the equation has no solution.

III. Graph $y_1 = x^3 + 3x^2 + 4x$.

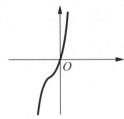

Since there is one x-intercept, the equation has one solution.

Choice (A) is correct.

8. D

$$(a-b)^3 = -12 \implies a-b = (-12)^{\frac{1}{3}} \approx -2.29$$

$$(a-b)^2 = (-2.29)^2 \approx 5.24$$

9. D

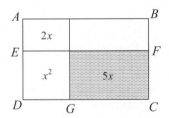

Area of a square $= x^2 \implies DE = DG = x$
Area of a rectangle $= 2x \implies AE = 2$
Area of a rectangle $= 5x \implies GC = 5$

$AD \cdot DC = 40$	The area of rectangle $ABCD$ is 40.
$(x+2)(x+5) = 40$	$AD = x+2$, $DC = x+5$
$x^2 + 7x + 10 = 40$	Multiply the binomials.
$x^2 + 7x - 30 = 0$	Standard form
$(x+10)(x-3) = 0$	Factor
$x = -10$ or $x = 3$	Zero product property

The length must be positive, so discard $x = -10$.
Area of the shaded region
$= FG \cdot GC = 5x = 5(3) = 15$

10. E

If 4 and -3 are both zeros of the polynomial $p(x)$, then $(x-4)(x+3)$ is a factor of $p(x)$.

$$(x-4)(x+3) = x^2 - x - 12$$

11. C

An equation has two roots $\dfrac{3+\sqrt{3}}{2}$ and $\dfrac{3-\sqrt{3}}{2}$.

The sum of the roots $= -\dfrac{b}{a} = \dfrac{3+\sqrt{3}}{2} + \dfrac{3-\sqrt{3}}{2} = 3$

The product of the roots $= \dfrac{c}{a} = \dfrac{3+\sqrt{3}}{2} \cdot \dfrac{3-\sqrt{3}}{2}$

$$= \dfrac{9 - 3\sqrt{3} + 3\sqrt{3} - 3}{4}$$

$$= \dfrac{3}{2}$$

Test each answer choice.

(A) $2x^2 + 6x + 3 = 0$

$-\dfrac{b}{a} = -\dfrac{6}{2} = -3$ \qquad Discard.

(B) $2x^2 - 6x - 3 = 0$

$-\dfrac{b}{a} = -\dfrac{-6}{2} = 3$, $\dfrac{c}{a} = \dfrac{-3}{2}$ \qquad Discard.

(C) $2x^2 - 6x + 3 = 0$

$-\dfrac{b}{a} = -\dfrac{-6}{2} = 3$, $\dfrac{c}{a} = \dfrac{3}{2}$ \qquad Correct.

Then you do not need to test choices (D) and (E), which are also incorrect.

12. B

$$a^2 b^5 c^{-3} = \dfrac{a^2 b^3 c}{3ab^{-2}c^4}$$

$$\implies (a^2 b^5 c^{-3})(3ab^{-2}c^4) = a^2 b^3 c$$

$$\implies 3a^3 b^3 c = a^2 b^3 c \implies \dfrac{3a^3 b^3 c}{a^2} = \dfrac{a^2 b^3 c}{a^2}$$

$$\implies 3ab^3 c = b^3 c \implies a = \dfrac{b^3 c}{3b^3 c} = \dfrac{1}{3}$$

13. B

Use the remainder theorem.

If $f(x) = x^7 - 2x^4 + 5x^3 + 10$ is divided by $x + 1$, the remainder is $f(-1)$.

$$f(-1) = (-1)^7 - 2(-1)^4 + 5(-1)^3 + 10$$
$$= -1 - 2 - 5 + 10 = 2$$

14. A

Use the factor theorem.

If $x - 2$ is a factor of $f(x) = x^3 - 3x^2 + 5x + k$, then $f(2) = 0$.

$$f(2) = 2^3 - 3(2)^2 + 5(2) + k = 0 \implies k = -6$$

15. C

$$f(x) = 2x^3 + x^2 + 11x - 6$$

Use the factor theorem to check each answer choice.

(A) $f(1) = 2(1)^3 + (1)^2 + 11(1) - 6 \neq 0$

Therefore $x - 1$ is not a factor of $f(x)$.

(B) $f(-1) = 2(-1)^3 + (-1)^2 + 11(-1) - 6 \neq 0$

Therefore $x + 1$ is not a factor of $f(x)$.

(C) $f(\frac{1}{2}) = 2(\frac{1}{2})^3 + (\frac{1}{2})^2 + 11(\frac{1}{2}) - 6 = 0$

Therefore $2x - 1$ is a factor of $f(x)$.

16. B

$x^{15} = a$	First equation
$x^{11} = b$	Second equation

$\dfrac{x^{15}}{x^{11}} = \dfrac{a}{x^{11}}$	Divide both sides of the first equation by x^{11}.
$x^4 = \dfrac{a}{b}$	$\dfrac{x^{15}}{x^{11}} = x^4$ and $x^{11} = b$

$\dfrac{x^{11}}{x^4} = \dfrac{b}{x^4}$	Divide both sides of the second equation by x^4.
$x^7 = \dfrac{b}{a/b}$	$\dfrac{x^{11}}{x^4} = x^7$ and $x^4 = \dfrac{a}{b}$

$x^7 = \dfrac{b^2}{a}$	Answer

17. E

$$(x^2 - a)(x + b) = x^3 + 4x^2 - 2x + c$$
$$\implies x^3 + bx^2 - ax - ab = x^3 + 4x^2 - 2x + c$$

According to the equality of polynomials,
$bx^2 = 4x^2$, $-ax = -2x$, and $-ab = c$
$\implies b = 4$, $a = 2$, and $c = -ab = -2 \cdot 4 = -8$.

$$a + b + c = 2 + 4 - 8 = -2$$

18. D

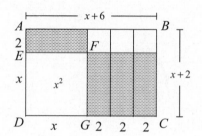

Area of rectangle $ABCD = 96$
$$(x + 6)(x + 2) = 96$$
$$\implies x^2 + 8x + 12 = 96 \implies x^2 + 8x - 84 = 0$$
$$\implies (x + 14)(x - 6) = 0 \implies x = 6 \text{ (The length}$$
cannot be negative so discard $x = -14$.)

In the figure above $EF = FG = x$, and the area of each shaded rectangle is $2x$.

Sum of the areas of the shaded region
$$= 4 \cdot 2x = 8x = 8 \cdot 6 = 48$$

19. E

$$f(x) = 2x^4 + 7x^2 - 2x + 8$$

Let $\dfrac{p}{q}$ be a rational root.

$p : \pm 1, \pm 2, \pm 4, \pm 8$	p must be a factor of the constant term 8.
$q : \pm 1, \pm 2$	q must be a factor of the leading coefficient 2.

Then $\dfrac{p}{q} : \pm 1, \pm 2, \pm 4, \pm 8, \pm \dfrac{1}{2}$.

There are 10 possible rational roots.

CHAPTER 4
Inequalities and Graphs

4-1. Properties of Inequalities

Let a, b, and c be any real numbers.

Transitive Property
If $a < b$ and $b < c$, then $a < c$.

Addition and Subtraction Properties
If $a < b$, then $a + c < b + c$ and $a - c < b - c$.

Multiplication and Division Properties

1. If $a < b$ and c is positive, then $ac < bc$ and $\dfrac{a}{c} < \dfrac{b}{c}$.

2. If $a < b$ and c is negative, then $ac > bc$ and $\dfrac{a}{c} > \dfrac{b}{c}$.

Example 1 □   Solve the inequality and graph its solution set.

Solution   □ $-3x - 14 > x + 6$

$\qquad -x - 3x - 14 > -x + x + 6$ 　　　Add $-x$ to each side.

$\qquad -4x - 14 > 6$

$\qquad -4x - 14 + 14 > 6 + 14$ 　　　Add 14 to each side.

$\qquad -4x > 20$

$\qquad \dfrac{-4x}{-4} < \dfrac{20}{-4}$ 　　　Divide each side by -4, and reverse the inequality sign.

$\qquad x < -5$

Any real number less than -5 is a solution.

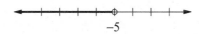

$$-5$$

4-2. Problem Solving Using Inequalities

Verbal Expression	Inequality
x is **at least** 3.	$x \geq 3$
x is **no less than** 3.	$x \geq 3$
x is **greater than or equal to** 3.	$x \geq 3$
x is **at most** 12.	$x \leq 12$
x is **no greater than** 12.	$x \leq 12$
x is **less than or equal to** 12.	$x \leq 12$
x is **between** 3 and 12.	$3 < x < 12$
x is **between** 3 and 12, **inclusive**.	$3 \leq x \leq 12$

Example 2 □   If the sum of three consecutive odd integers is at most 54, what is the greatest possible value of the least of the three integers?

Solution □ $n+(n+2)+(n+4) \le 54$ The sum of three consecutive odd integers is at most 54.

$3n+6 \le 54$

$3n \le 48$

$n \le 16$ Answer   ∎

4-3. Absolute Value Inequalities

Expression	**Equivalent Expression**	**Graph**

$|x|>1$ $x<-1 \text{ or } x>1$

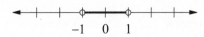

The distance between x and 0 is greater than 1.

$|x|<1$ $-1<x<1$

The distance between x and 0 is less than 1.

Example 3 □   Solve $|5-2x|+7 \ge 24$

Solution □ $|5-2x|+7-7 \ge 24-7$

$|5-2x| \ge 17$

$5-2x \le -17$ or $5-2x \ge 17$

$-2x \le -22$ $-2x \ge 12$

$\dfrac{-2x}{-2} \ge \dfrac{-22}{-2}$ $\dfrac{-2x}{-2} \le \dfrac{12}{-2}$

$x \ge 11$ $x \le -6$

The solution set is $\{x : x \le -6 \text{ or } x \ge 11\}$.   ∎

4-4. Systems of Linear Inequalities

Sketching the Graph of a Linear Inequality

1. Graph the corresponding linear equation. This line separates the coordinate plane into two **half planes.**
   a) Use a dashed line for inequalities with $<$ or $>$.
   b) Use a solid line for inequalities with $\le$ or $\ge$.

2. Test a point in one of the half planes to find whether it is a solution of the inequality.
   Use points such as $(0,0)$, $(1,0)$, $(0,1)$, $(-1,0)$ or $(0,-1)$ as a test point.

3. If the test point is a solution, shade in its half plane. If not, shade in the other half plane.

The graph of a **system of inequalities** consists of points satisfying all of the inequalities in the system. The graph is the region common to all the individual inequalities.

Example 4 □ Graph the systems:

a. $x + 2y > 4$ b. $(y + x)(2y - x) \leq 0$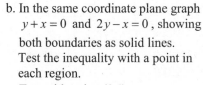
    $y \leq 2x$

Solution □ a. In the same coordinate plane graph $x + 2y = 4$, showing the boundary as a dashed line, and graph $y = 2x$, showing the boundary as a solid line. Test the inequalities with a point in each region.

Test with point $(5,0)$ in Region 1.

$5 + 2(0) > 4$ True

$0 \leq 2(5)$ True

Test with point $(0,5)$ in Region 2.

$0 + 2(5) > 4$ True

$5 \leq 2(0)$ Not true

Test with point $(-5,0)$ in Region 3.

$-5 + 2(0) > 4$ Not true

$0 \leq 2(-5)$ Not true

Test with point $(0,-5)$ in Region 4.

$0 + 2(-5) > 4$ Not true

$-5 \leq 2(0)$ True

Shade in Region 1 since the point in Region 1 satisfies both inequalities.

The graph of the system is shown below.

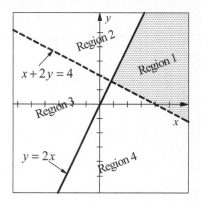

b. In the same coordinate plane graph $y + x = 0$ and $2y - x = 0$, showing both boundaries as solid lines. Test the inequality with a point in each region.

Test with point $(0,1)$.

$(0 + 1)(2 - 0) \leq 0$ Not true

Test with point $(1,0)$.

$(0 + 1)(0 - 1) \leq 0$ True

Test with point $(0,-1)$.

$(-1 + 0)(-2 - 0) \leq 0$ Not true

Test with point $(-1,0)$.

$(0 - 1)(0 + 1) \leq 0$ True

The graph of the system is the shaded region shown below.

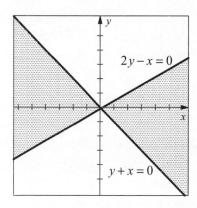

4-5. Systems of Quadratic Inequalities $\boxed{L2}$

The steps used to sketch the graph of a quadratic inequality are similar to those used to sketch the graph of a linear inequality.

Example 5 □   Graph the system: a. $x + y \le 3$ b. $y > 1 - x^2$

$y > x^2 - 2$ $x^2 + y^2 \le 4$

Solution   □   a. In the same coordinate plane graph $x + y = 3$, showing the boundary as a solid line, and graph $y = x^2 - 2$, showing the boundary as a dashed line.

Test the inequalities with the point $(0,0)$, which lies in the region bounded by the two graphs.

$0 + 0 \le 3$ True
$0 > 0 - 2$ True

The graph of the system is the shaded region shown at the right.

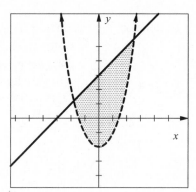

b. In the same coordinate plane graph $y = 1 - x^2$, showing the boundary as a dashed line, and graph $x^2 + y^2 = 4$, showing the boundary as a solid line.

Test the inequalities with point $(0,0)$.

$0 > 1 - 0$ Not true
$0 + 0 \le 4$ True

Test the inequalities with point $(1,1)$.

$1 > 1 - 1$ True
$1 + 1 \le 4$ True

The graph of the system is the shaded region shown at the right.

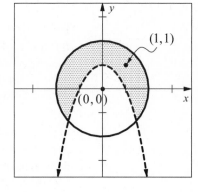

4-6. Polynomial Inequalities $\boxed{L2}$

Steps for Solving a Polynomial Inequality

1. Factor the polynomial and set the polynomial equal to zero. Find the solutions of the linear factors.

2. Locate the solutions on a number line. These numbers will divide the number line into several distinct intervals.

3. Choose a convenient test number from one of the intervals and determine if it satisfies the inequality: that is, if it makes the inequality true.

4. If the test number satisfies the given inequality, that interval is a solution of the inequality. If not, the adjacent intervals are the solutions of the inequality. For a polynomial inequality, solutions are found on alternating intervals on a number line.

Example 6 □   Solve the inequality and graph.

a. $(x+3)(x^2-2x-3) \geq 0$

b. $\dfrac{x^2-4}{x-1} < 0$

Solution   □   a. $(x+3)(x^2-2x-3) \geq 0$

$(x+3)(x-3)(x+1) \geq 0$ Factor the given inequality.

$(x+3)(x-3)(x+1) = 0$ Set the polynomial equal to zero.

$x = -3,\ -1$ and 3 Solutions of the linear factors

The three numbers -3, -1, and 3 divide the real-number line into four intervals which are $(-\infty,-3]$, $[-3,-1]$, $[-1,3]$, and $[3,\infty)$.

Choose zero as a test number and plug it into the given inequality. $(0+3)(0-3)(0+1) > 0 \ \Rightarrow\ -9 > 0$, which is not true. Since zero is on the interval $[-1,3]$, this interval is not a solution to the inequality. Therefore adjacent intervals $[-3,-1]$ and $[3,\infty)$ are solutions to the inequality.

$$\begin{array}{ccc} -3 & -1 & 3 \end{array}$$

b. $\dfrac{x^2-4}{x-1} < 0$

Multiply both sides by $(x-1)^2$. Since $(x-1)^2$ is not negative we don't have to worry about switching the sign.

$\dfrac{(x^2-4)}{(x-1)}(x-1)^2 < 0 \cdot (x-1)^2$

$(x^2-4)(x-1) < 0$

$(x+2)(x-2)(x-1) < 0$ Factor the inequality.

$(x+2)(x-2)(x-1) = 0$ Set the polynomial equal to zero.

$x = -2,\ 1,$ and $2.$ Solutions of the linear factors

The four intervals which are determined by these three numbers are $(-\infty,-2)$, $(-2,1)$, $(1,2)$, and $(2,\infty)$.

Choose zero as a test number and plug it into the original inequality. $\dfrac{0-4}{0-1} < 0 \ \Rightarrow\ 4 < 0$, which is not true. Since zero is on the interval $(-2,1)$, this interval is not a solution to the inequality. Therefore the adjacent intervals $(-\infty,-2)$ and $(1,2)$ are solutions to the inequality.

$$\begin{array}{ccc} -2 & 1 & 2 \end{array}$$

1. If $4x - 7$ is at most 25, what is the maximum value of x?

    (A) 7

    (B) 8

    (C) 9

    (D) 10

    (E) 11

2. If $11 - 2x$ is no less than 8, what is the maximum value of x?

    (A) −2.5

    (B) 1.5

    (C) 4

    (D) 5.5

    (E) 9

3. What are all values of x for which $3 - x^2 \le 1 - x$?

    (A) $-1 \le x \le 2$

    (B) $-2 \le x \le 1$

    (C) $x \le -1$ or $x \ge 2$

    (D) $x \le -2$ or $x \ge 1$

    (E) $x \le 2$

4. What are all values of x for which $|5 - x| < 9$?

    (A) $x > -4$

    (B) $x < -4$ or $x > 14$

    (C) $x < -14$ or $x > 4$

    (D) $-4 < x < 14$

    (E) $-14 < x < 4$

5. Which of the following shaded regions could be the graph of $\begin{cases} y \le x + 3 \\ x + y \le 0 \end{cases}$?

(A)

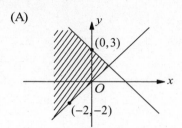

(B)

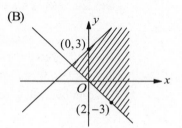

(C)

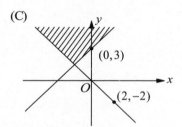

(D)

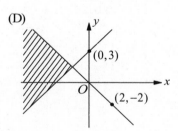

(E)

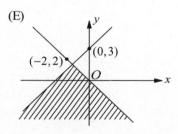

6. Which of the following is equivalent to
   $\{x: \ x \geq 3 \ \ \text{or} \ \ x \leq -9\}$?

   (A) $\{x: \ |x+3| \leq 6\}$

   (B) $\{x: \ |x+3| \geq 6\}$

   (C) $\{x: \ |x-3| \leq 6\}$

   (D) $\{x: \ |x-3| \geq 6\}$

   (E) $\{x: \ |x-3| \leq 3\}$

7. Which of the following is the solution set of
   $\{x: \ 5-x^2 \geq -4x\}$?

   (A) $\{x: \ x \geq 0\}$

   (B) $\{x: \ x \leq 5\}$

   (C) $\{x: \ -4 \leq x \leq 5\}$

   (D) $\{x: \ -1 \leq x \leq 5\}$

   (E) $\{x: \ x \leq -4 \ \text{or} \ x \geq 5\}$

8. If $y = x^2 - 1$ and $-2x + y \leq 7$ what is the
   maximum value of x?

   (A) 4

   (B) 8

   (C) 12

   (D) 15

   (E) 20

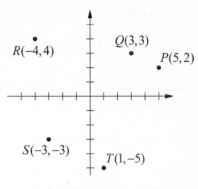

Figure 1

9. For which of the points shown in Figure 1 is
   $\left| \dfrac{1}{2}x + y \right| < 4$?

   (A) P

   (B) Q

   (C) R

   (D) S

   (E) T

10. If $\dfrac{a^3 - b^3}{ab} < 0$, which of the following must be
    true?

    I. $0 < a < b$
    II. $a < b < 0$
    III. $a < 0 < b$

    (A) I only

    (B) II only

    (C) III only

    (D) I and II only

    (E) I, II, and III

11. Which of the following is the graph of
$$\frac{x^2 - 3x - 4}{x + 2} > 0 ? \quad \boxed{L2}$$

(A) ○————————○————————
　　　　−1　　　　　4

(B) ————————○————————●
　　　　　−1　　　　　4

(C) ————○————————○————
　　　−2　−1　　　　4

(D) ————●————○————————●
　　　−2　−1　　　　4

(E) ————○————————————
　　　−2

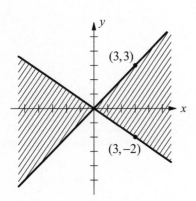

Figure 2

12. Which of the following inequalities is represented by the graph in Figure 2? $\boxed{L2}$

(A) $(2x + 3y)(x - y) \le 0$

(B) $(2x - 3y)(x + y) \le 0$

(C) $(2x + 3y)(x - y) \ge 0$

(D) $(2x - 3y)(x + y) \ge 0$

(E) $(3x + 2y)(x - y) \ge 0$

13. If $y \ge |x|$ and $4xy = 9$, what is the least possible value of y? $\boxed{L2}$

(A) 1.5

(B) 2.25

(C) 9

(D) 18

(E) 36

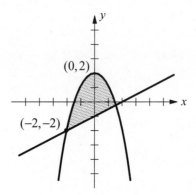

Figure 3

14. Which of the following inequalities is represented by the graph in Figure 3? $\boxed{L2}$

(A) $\begin{cases} y \le -x^2 + 2 \\ 2x + y \ge 1 \end{cases}$

(B) $\begin{cases} y \ge -x^2 + 2 \\ 2x - y \ge 1 \end{cases}$

(C) $\begin{cases} y \ge -x^2 + 2 \\ x - 2y \le 2 \end{cases}$

(D) $\begin{cases} y \le x^2 - 2 \\ x - 2y \ge 1 \end{cases}$

(E) $\begin{cases} y \le -x^2 + 2 \\ x - 2y \le 2 \end{cases}$

Answer Key

1. B   2. B   3. C   4. D   5. E

6. B   7. D   8. A   9. C   10. D

11. C   12. C   13. A   14. E

Answers and Explanations

1. B

$4x - 7 \leq 25$ $\qquad$ $4x - 7$ is at most 25.
$4x \leq 32$
$x \leq 8$
Therefore 8 is the maximum value of x.

2. B

$11 - 2x \geq 8$ $\qquad$ $11 - 2x$ is no less than 8.
$-2x \geq -3$

$\Rightarrow \dfrac{-2x}{-2} \leq \dfrac{-3}{-2} \Rightarrow x \leq \dfrac{3}{2}$

The maximum value of x is 1.5.

3. C

$3 - x^2 \leq 1 - x$
$3 - x^2 - 1 + x \leq 0$ $\qquad$ Subtract $(1-x)$ from both sides.
$-x^2 + x + 2 \leq 0$ $\qquad$ Simplify.
$x^2 - x - 2 \geq 0$ $\qquad$ Multiply each side by -1 and reverse the inequality sign.
$(x+1)(x-2) \geq 0$ $\qquad$ Factor.
$x \leq -1$ or $x \geq 2$ $\qquad$ Answer

4. D

$|5 - x| < 9$
$-9 < 5 - x < 9$
$-14 < -x < 4$

$14 > x > -4$ $\qquad$ Multiply each side by -1 and reverse the inequality sign.

5. E

$\begin{cases} y \leq x + 3 \\ x + y \leq 0 \end{cases}$

Change the equations into slope-intercept form and graph the lines $y = x + 3$ and $y = -x$.

The graphs in answer choice (A) do not represent the equations. Discard (A).

Test an ordered pair that is not on the boundary to find one that satisfies the given inequality.
Try $(0,1)$ which has easy to use numbers.

$\begin{cases} 1 \leq 0 + 3 & \text{True} \\ 0 + 1 \leq 0 & \text{Not true} \end{cases}$

The point $(0,1)$ does satisfy the first inequality, but does not satisfy the second inequality. Therefore point $(0,1)$ should not be included in the shaded region.
Eliminate choices (B), (C), and (D).

Now try $(0,-1)$.

$\begin{cases} -1 \leq 0 + 3 & \text{True} \\ 0 - 1 \leq 0 & \text{True} \end{cases}$

Since $(0,-1)$ satisfies both of the inequalities, the point $(0,-1)$ should lie in the shaded region.

Choice (E) is correct.

6. B

$\{x : x \geq 3 \text{ or } x \leq -9\}$
Solve each inequality in each answer choice.

(A) $|x+3| \leq 6$
$\Rightarrow -6 \leq x + 3 \leq 6$
$\Rightarrow -9 \leq x \leq 3$

(B) $|x+3| \geq 6$
$\Rightarrow x + 3 \geq 6 \text{ or } x + 3 \leq -6$
$\Rightarrow x \geq 3 \text{ or } x \leq -9$

Choice (B) is correct.

7. D

$5 - x^2 \geq -4x \Rightarrow x^2 - 4x - 5 \leq 0$

Solve the equation $x^2 - 4x - 5 = 0$ by factoring.

$x^2 - 4x - 5 = 0 \Rightarrow (x+1)(x-5) = 0$

$\Rightarrow x = -1$ or $x = 5$

The two numbers -1 and 5 divide the real-number line into three intervals which are $(-\infty, -1)$, $(-1, 5)$ and $(5, \infty)$.

Choose zero as a test number and plug it into the given inequality. $3 - 0^2 \geq -4 \cdot 0 \Rightarrow 3 \geq 0$, which is true. Since zero is on the interval $[-1, 5]$, this interval is a solution to the inequality and the adjacent intervals are not solutions to the given inequality.

Choice (D) is correct.

8. A

$y = x^2 - 1$

$-2x + (x^2 - 1) \leq 7$ Substitute $x^2 - 1$ for y.

$x^2 - 2x - 8 \leq 0$ Simplify.

$(x+2)(x-4) \leq 0$ Factor.

$-2 \leq x \leq 4$

The inequality shows the maximum value of x is 4.

9. C

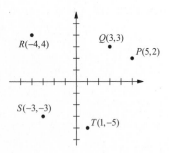

$\left| \dfrac{1}{2}x + y \right| < 4$

(A) $P(5, 2)$ Substitute $x = 5$ and $y = 2$ into the given inequality.

     $\left| \dfrac{1}{2}(5) + 2 \right| < 4$ Not true

(B) $Q(3, 3)$ Substitute $x = 3$ and $y = 3$ into the given inequality.

$\left| \dfrac{1}{2}(3) + 3 \right| < 4$ Not true

(C) $R(-4, 4)$ Substitute $x = -4$ and $y = 4$ into the given inequality.

     $\left| \dfrac{1}{2}(-4) + 4 \right| < 4$ True

Choice (C) is correct.

10. D

$\dfrac{a^3 - b^3}{ab} < 0$

   I. $0 < a < b$

     Pick numbers. Let $a = 2$ and $b = 3$.

     $\dfrac{2^3 - 3^3}{2 \cdot 3} < 0$ True

   II. $a < b < 0$

     Let $a = -3$ and $b = -2$.

     $\dfrac{(-3)^3 - (-2)^3}{(-3)(-2)} < 0$ True

   III. $a < 0 < b$

     Let $a = -2$ and $b = 3$.

     $\dfrac{(-2)^3 - (3)^3}{(-2)(3)} < 0$ Not true

11. C $\boxed{L2}$

$\dfrac{x^2 - 3x - 4}{x + 2} > 0 \Rightarrow \dfrac{(x+1)(x-4)}{x+2} > 0$

We see that the inequality has zeros at $x = -1$ and $x = 4$, and is undefined at $x = -2$. These three numbers divide the real-number line into four intervals: $(-\infty, -2)$, $(-2, -1)$, $(-1, 4)$, and $(4, \infty)$.

Eliminate answer choices (A), (B), and (E).

Choose zero as a test number and plug it into the given inequality. $\dfrac{0^2 - 3 \cdot 0 - 4}{0 + 2} > 0 \Rightarrow -2 > 0$, which is not true. Since zero is on the interval $(-1, 4)$, the interval is not a solution to the inequality. The adjacent intervals $(-2, -1)$ and $(4, \infty)$ are the solutions.

12. C $\boxed{L2}$

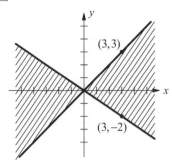

$y = x$ and $y = -\dfrac{2}{3}x$ are the equations of the lines shown in the figure above.
Now change the equations from slope-intercept form into standard form,
$x - y = 0$ and $2x + 3y = 0$.

Eliminate choices (B), (D), and (E) since the equations in these answer choices are not the same as the equations of the lines shown in the figure.
Test an ordered pair that is in the shaded region and not on the boundary to find out which inequality it satisfies.

Try $(1, 0)$.
Substitute $x = 1$ and $y = 0$ into the given inequality.

(A) $(2x + 3y)(x - y) \leq 0$
$(2 \cdot 1 + 3 \cdot 0)(1 - 0) \leq 0$ Not true

(C) $(2x + 3y)(x - y) \geq 0$
$(2 \cdot 1 + 3 \cdot 0)(1 - 0) \geq 0$ True

Choice (C) is correct.

13. A $\boxed{L2}$

Method 1: Graph the inequality and the equation.

$y \geq |x|$ and $4xy = 9$

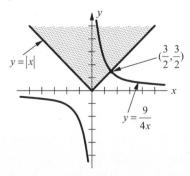

The graph shows the least possible value of y is $\dfrac{3}{2}$.

Method 2: Solve the equations.

$y = |x| \Rightarrow y = x$ if $x \geq 0$ or $y = -x$ if $x < 0$

$4xy = 9 \Rightarrow y = \dfrac{9}{4x}$

$\Rightarrow y = \dfrac{9}{4y}$ (y is substituted for x.)

$\Rightarrow 4y^2 = 9 \Rightarrow y^2 = \dfrac{9}{4} \Rightarrow y = \pm\dfrac{3}{2}$

But y is not negative since $|x|$ is nonnegative.

Therefore $y = \dfrac{3}{2}$.

14. E $\boxed{L2}$

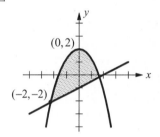

The quadratic equation is $y = -x^2 + 2$ and the equation of the line is $y = \dfrac{1}{2}x - 1$. In standard form the equations are $x^2 + y = 2$ and $x - 2y = 2$.

Eliminate choices (A), (B), and (D), since the equations in these answer choices are not the equations of the curve and line shown in the figure.

Test point $(0, 0)$ which lies in the shaded region.

(C) $\begin{cases} 0 \geq -0^2 + 2 & \text{Not true} \\ 0 - 2 \cdot 0 \leq 2 & \text{True} \end{cases}$

(E) $\begin{cases} 0 \leq -0^2 + 2 & \text{True} \\ 0 - 2 \cdot 0 \leq 2 & \text{True} \end{cases}$

The point $(0, 0)$ satisfies both inequalities in choice (E).

Therefore choice (E) is correct.

CHAPTER 5
Rational Expressions

5-1. Products and Quotients of Rational Expressions

Multiplication Rule for Fractions $\quad \dfrac{a}{b} \cdot \dfrac{c}{d} = \dfrac{ac}{bd}$, if $b \cdot d \neq 0$

Division Rule for Fractions $\quad \dfrac{a}{b} \div \dfrac{c}{d} = \dfrac{a}{b} \cdot \dfrac{d}{c} = \dfrac{ad}{bc}$, if $b \cdot c \cdot d \neq 0$

Example 1 $\square$ Simplify $\dfrac{-14x^2}{10} \cdot \dfrac{5}{21x} \div x^3$.

Solution $\quad\square\quad \dfrac{-14x^2}{10} \cdot \dfrac{5}{21x} \div x^3 = \dfrac{\overset{-2}{\cancel{-14}} \, \overset{1}{\cancel{x^2}}}{\underset{2}{\cancel{10}}} \cdot \dfrac{\overset{1}{\cancel{5}}}{\underset{3}{\cancel{21}} \, x} \cdot \dfrac{1}{\underset{x}{\cancel{x^3}}} = \dfrac{-1}{3x^2}$ $\qquad$ Answer

5-2. Sums and Differences of Rational Expressions

Addition Rule for Fractions $\quad \dfrac{a}{c} + \dfrac{b}{c} = \dfrac{a+b}{c}$, if $c \neq 0$

Subtraction Rule for Fractions $\quad \dfrac{a}{c} - \dfrac{b}{c} = \dfrac{a-b}{c}$, if $c \neq 0$

Example 2 $\square$ Simplify $\dfrac{1}{x-2} + \dfrac{2x}{3x-6}$.

Solution $\quad\square\quad \dfrac{1}{x-2} + \dfrac{2x}{3x-6} = \dfrac{1}{x-2} + \dfrac{2x}{3(x-2)}$ $\qquad$ Factor the denominator.

$\qquad\qquad\qquad\qquad = \dfrac{3 \cdot 1}{3 \cdot (x-2)} + \dfrac{2x}{3(x-2)}$ $\qquad$ The LCD is $3(x-2)$.

$\qquad\qquad\qquad\qquad = \dfrac{3+2x}{3(x-2)}$ $\qquad$ Answer

5-3. Complex Fractions

A **complex fraction** is a fraction whose numerator and/or denominator contains one or more fractions.

Example 3 $\square$ Simplify $\dfrac{1 - \dfrac{2}{3x}}{1 - \dfrac{1}{4x}}$.

Solution $\quad\square\quad$ Method 1: Simplify the numerator and denominator separately, then divide.

$$\dfrac{1 - \dfrac{2}{3x}}{1 - \dfrac{1}{4x}} = \dfrac{1 \cdot \dfrac{3x}{3x} - \dfrac{2}{3x}}{1 \cdot \dfrac{4x}{4x} - \dfrac{1}{4x}} = \dfrac{\dfrac{3x-2}{3x}}{\dfrac{4x-1}{4x}} = \dfrac{3x-2}{3\cancel{x}} \cdot \dfrac{4\cancel{x}}{4x-1} = \dfrac{4(3x-2)}{3(4x-1)}$$

Method 2: Find the LCD of all the fractions that appear in the numerator and denominator. Multiply the numerator and denominator by the LCD.

$$\frac{1-\dfrac{2}{3x}}{1-\dfrac{1}{4x}} = \frac{12x(1-\dfrac{2}{3x})}{12x(1-\dfrac{1}{4x})} = \frac{12x-8}{12x-3} = \frac{4(3x-2)}{3(4x-1)}$$

5-4. Rational Equations

An equation that contains one or more rational expressions is called a **rational equation**.
To solve a rational equation, multiply both sides by the LCD of the fractions.

Example 4 □ Solve $\dfrac{6}{x^2+2x-3}+1=\dfrac{x-3}{x-1}$.

Solution □ $x^2+2x-3=(x+3)(x-1)$. So the LCD is $(x+3)(x-1)$.
Multiply both sides of the equation by the LCD.

$$(x+3)(x-1)\left[\frac{6}{x^2+2x-3}+1\right]=(x+3)(x-1)\left[\frac{x-3}{x-1}\right]$$

$6+(x+3)(x-1)=(x+3)(x-3)$ Distributive property

$6+\cancel{x^2}+2x-3=\cancel{x^2}-9$ Simplify.

$2x+3=-9$

$x=-6$ Answer

5-5. Solving Word Problems Using Rational Equations

Mixture Problems: Amount of acid in the mixture
= Amount of acid in the 1st solution + Amount of acid in the 2nd solution

Work Problems: Work rate × Time = Work done

The part of a job that can be completed in one unit of time is called the work rate.
The fractional parts of a job must have a sum of 1.

Example 5 □ A chemist has 25 liters of solution that is 70% acid. How much water should be added to make a solution that is 20% acid?

Solution □ Let x = number of liters of water to be added.

Amount of acid   Amount of acid   Amount of acid
in the 1st solution   in the water   in the mixture

$$\overbrace{0.7(25)} + \overbrace{0 \cdot x} = \overbrace{0.2(25+x)}$$

$17.5 = 5 + .2x$

$x = 62.5$ Answer

5-6. Long Division and Synthetic Division

When dividing a polynomial function $f(x)$ by $x-c$, long division or synthetic division can be used to find a quotient $q(x)$. Then $f(x)$ can be written as $f(x) = (x-c)q(x) + f(c)$, where $f(c)$ is a remainder.

Before using long division or synthetic division, always arrange the terms so that the degrees of the terms are in descending order. If a polynomial function $f(x)$ does not contain all powers of x, you must include a 0 coefficient for the missing terms.

Example 6 □   a. Use long division to find $q(x)$, if $x^3 - x^2 - 5x + 6 = (x-2)q(x)$.

b. Use synthetic division to find $q(x)$, if $2x^3 - 15x - 7 = (x-3)q(x)$.

Solution   □   a.

$$\begin{array}{r} x^2 + x - 3 \\ x-2 \overline{\smash{\big)}\, x^3 - x^2 - 5x + 6} \end{array}$$

$$x^3 - 2x^2 \qquad\qquad x^2 \text{ multiplied by } (x-2)$$
$$x^2 - 5x \qquad\qquad (x^3 - x^2) - (x^3 - 2x^2) = x^2$$
$$x^2 - 2x \qquad\qquad x \text{ multiplied by } (x-2)$$
$$-3x + 6 \qquad\qquad (x^2 - 5x) - (x^2 - 2x) = -3x$$
$$-3x + 6 \qquad\qquad -3 \text{ multiplied by } (x-2)$$
$$0$$

Therefore $q(x) = x^2 + x - 3$.

b. Write the constant 3, from the divisor $x-3$, on the left. Then write the coefficients of the polynomial to the right.

$$3 \,\lfloor\, 2 \quad 0 \quad -15 \quad -7$$
$$\downarrow \qquad\qquad\qquad\qquad \text{The coefficient of the } x^2 \text{ term is 0.}$$
$$2 \qquad\qquad\qquad\qquad \text{Bring down the first coefficient, 2.}$$

$$3 \,\lfloor\, 2 \quad 0 \quad -15 \quad -7 \qquad \text{Multiply the first coefficient by } 3 \Rightarrow 3 \cdot 2 = 6.$$
$$\downarrow \quad 6 \qquad\qquad\qquad \text{Write the product under the second coefficient}$$
$$2 \quad 6 \qquad\qquad\qquad \text{and add} \Rightarrow 0 + 6 = 6.$$

$$3 \,\lfloor\, 2 \quad 0 \quad -15 \quad -7 \qquad \text{Multiply the sum by } 3 \Rightarrow 3 \cdot 6 = 18.$$
$$\downarrow \quad 6 \quad 18 \qquad\qquad \text{Write the product under the next coefficient}$$
$$2 \quad 6 \quad 3 \qquad\qquad \text{and add} \Rightarrow -15 + 18 = 3.$$

$$3 \,\lfloor\, 2 \quad 0 \quad -15 \quad -7 \qquad \text{Multiply the sum by } 3 \Rightarrow 3 \cdot 3 = 9.$$
$$\downarrow \quad 6 \quad 18 \quad 9 \qquad\quad \text{Write the product under the next coefficient}$$
$$2 \quad 6 \quad 3 \quad 2 \qquad\quad \text{and add} \Rightarrow -7 + 9 = 2. \text{ The remainder is 2.}$$
$$\underset{\text{Coefficients}}{} \atop \text{of quotient}$$

The power of the quotient is one less than that of the dividend.

Therefore $q(x) = 2x^2 + 6x + 3 + \dfrac{2}{x-3}$.

■

5-7. Graphs of Rational Functions

A **rational function** is one that can be written in the form $f(x) = \dfrac{p(x)}{q(x)}$, where

$p(x)$ and $q(x)$ are polynomial functions and $q(x) \neq 0$.

The vertical line $x = a$ is called a **vertical asymptote** of
the graph of f if $f(x)$ approaches infinity (or negative
infinity) as x approaches a from the right or left.
A vertical asymptote occurs at a number where the
denominator is 0, and the numerator is not 0.

The horizontal line $y = b$ is called a **horizontal asymptote**
of the graph of f if $f(x)$ approaches b as x approaches
infinity (or negative infinity).

In the graph at the right, $x = 3$ is a vertical asymptote and
$y = -2$ is a horizontal asymptote.

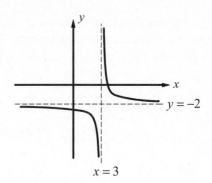

Example 7 □ Determine all the vertical and horizontal asymptotes of the graph of
each function.

         a. $f(x) = \dfrac{2x+1}{x-1}$ b. $f(x) = \dfrac{x^2 - 1}{x+1}$

Solution   □   a. A vertical asymptote occurs at a number where the denominator is 0,
and the numerator is not 0. $x - 1 = 0 \Rightarrow x = 1$
So, the line $x = 1$ is a vertical asymptote.

If the numerator is not a constant, use long division to find the quotient,
which is the horizontal asymptote of the graph.

$$
\begin{array}{r}
2 \quad \leftarrow \text{ quotient} \\
x-1 \,\overline{\smash{\big)}\, 2x+1} \\
\underline{2x-2} \\
3 \quad \leftarrow \text{ remainder}
\end{array}
$$

So, $f(x) = \dfrac{2x+1}{x-1} = 2 + \dfrac{3}{x-1}$ and the line $y = 2$ is a horizontal asymptote.

b. Begin by simplifying the expression.

$f(x) = \dfrac{x^2 - 1}{x-1} = \dfrac{(x+1)(x-1)}{x-1}$

$= x + 1$

At all x-values other than $x = 1$, the
graph of f coincides with the graph
of $g(x) = x + 1$.

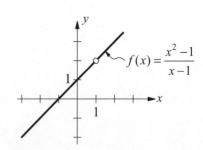

The open dot indicates that the point $(1, 2)$ is excluded from the graph because
$f(x)$ is undefined at $x = 1$. However, since the factor $(x - 1)$ cancels out, there
is no vertical asymptote for the graph.

5-8. Direct, Inverse, and Joint Variation

The variables x and y **vary directly** if for a nonzero constant k, $y = kx$.

The variables x and y **vary inversely** if for a nonzero constant k, $xy = k$ or $y = \dfrac{k}{x}$.

The variables x, y, and z **vary jointly** if for a nonzero constant k, $z = kxy$

The number k is called the **constant of variation**.

Example 8 □   a. If y varies directly as x, and $y = 14$ when $x = 35$, find y when $x = 20$.

b. If z varies directly as y and inversely as the square of x, and $z = 400$ when $y = 25$ and $x = 4$, find y when $z = 280$ and $x = 6$.

Solution □   a. First find k and write an equation of the direct variation.

$$y = kx \;\Rightarrow\; 14 = k(35) \;\Rightarrow\; k = \frac{14}{35} = \frac{2}{5} \;\Rightarrow\; y = \frac{2}{5}x$$

$$y = \frac{2}{5}(20) = 8 \qquad\qquad \text{Answer}$$

b. First find k and write an equation of the joint variation.

$$z = \frac{ky}{x^2} \;\Rightarrow\; 400 = \frac{k \times 25}{4^2} \;\Rightarrow\; k = 256 \;\Rightarrow\; z = \frac{256y}{x^2}$$

When $z = 280$ and $x = 6$, $280 = \dfrac{256y}{6^2}$

$$y = \frac{315}{8} \qquad\qquad \text{Answer}$$

5-9. Partial Fractions Decomposition

Two fractions, such as $\dfrac{3}{x+1}$ and $\dfrac{1}{x-2}$, can be added to obtain $\dfrac{3}{x+1} + \dfrac{1}{x-2} = \dfrac{3(x-2) + 1(x+1)}{(x+1)(x-2)} = \dfrac{4x-5}{x^2 - x - 2}$.

The reverse of this procedure is called the **method of partial fractions**, used for decomposing fractions into the sum of simpler fractions.

Example 9 □   If $\dfrac{x+5}{x^2 - 4x + 3} = \dfrac{A}{x+1} + \dfrac{B}{x-3}$ what are the values of A and B?

Solution □   Multiplying both sides of the equation by the least common denominator $(x+1)(x-3)$ yields the basic equation

$x + 5 = A(x-3) + B(x+1)$.

To solve for A, choose $x = -1$, to eliminate the term $B(x+1)$.

$-1 + 5 = A(-1-3) + B(-1+1) \;\Rightarrow\; 4 = -4A \;\Rightarrow\; A = -1$ Answer

To solve for B, choose $x = 3$, to eliminate the term $A(x-3)$.

$3 + 5 = A(3-3) + B(3+1) \;\Rightarrow\; 8 = 4B \;\Rightarrow\; B = 2$ Answer

1. For $ab \neq 0$, $\dfrac{6ab}{b^3} \cdot (\dfrac{9a}{b^2})^{-1} =$

   (A) $\dfrac{54a^2}{b^4}$

   (B) $\dfrac{2a^2b}{3}$

   (C) $\dfrac{2}{3}$

   (D) $\dfrac{2a^2}{3b}$

   (E) $\dfrac{2}{3b}$

2. For $x \neq 2$, $\dfrac{x}{-x+2} + \dfrac{2}{x-2} =$

   (A) -1

   (B) $\;\;1$

   (C) $\dfrac{1}{x-2}$

   (D) $\dfrac{-1}{x-2}$

   (E) $\dfrac{x+2}{x-2}$

3. If $\dfrac{x}{2} - \dfrac{x-4}{3} = \dfrac{5}{6}$, then $x =$

   (A) -5

   (B) -3

   (C) -1

   (D) $\;\;3$

   (E) $\;\;5$

4. For $x(x+1) \neq 0$, $1 - \dfrac{1}{1+\dfrac{1}{x}} =$

   (A) $\dfrac{-x}{x+1}$

   (B) $\dfrac{x+1}{x}$

   (C) $\dfrac{x}{x+1}$

   (D) $\dfrac{1}{x+1}$

   (E) $\dfrac{-1}{x+1}$

5. If $\dfrac{3}{x} + \dfrac{x}{x-1} = 1$, then $x =$

   (A) $-\dfrac{3}{4}$

   (B) $-\dfrac{1}{4}$

   (C) $\dfrac{1}{2}$

   (D) $\dfrac{3}{4}$

   (E) $\dfrac{3}{2}$

6. If $x^3 - 3x^2y + 3xy^2 - y^3 = (x-y)p(x)$, where $p(x)$ is a polynomial, then $p(x) =$

   (A) $x^2 - y^2$

   (B) $x^2 + y^2$

   (C) $x^2 + xy + y^2$

   (D) $(x+y)^2$

   (E) $(x-y)^2$

7. If $\dfrac{x-1}{x+3} = \dfrac{3x}{2}$, which of the following is the solution set for the equation?

(A) $\{-3, -2\}$

(B) $\{3, -2\}$

(C) $\{-2, -\dfrac{1}{3}\}$

(D) $\{-2, \dfrac{1}{3}\}$

(E) $\{2, -\dfrac{1}{3}\}$

8. If y varies inversely as x, which of the following is the graph of y as a function of x?

(A)
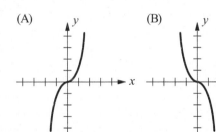

(B)

(C)
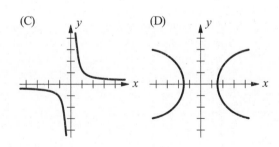

(D)

(E)
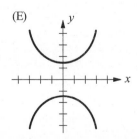

9. W varies inversely as d^2. If $W = 180$ when $d = 3 \times 10^4$, what is the value of W when $d = 1.5 \times 10^3$?

(A) 7.2×10^2

(B) 2×10^5

(C) 3.6×10^5

(D) 1.44×10^6

(E) 2×10^7

10. If $x \neq 2$, $(2x^3 - 4x^2 - x + 3) \div (x - 2) =$

(A) $2x^2 - 8x + 15 - \dfrac{27}{x-2}$

(B) $2x^2 - 1 + \dfrac{1}{x-2}$

(C) $2x^2 + 1 - \dfrac{2}{x-2}$

(D) $2x^2 - x + 6$

(E) $2x^2 + 3x + 1$

11. How many liters of acid should be added to 10 liters of a 25% acid solution, to make a solution that is 40% acid?

(A) 1.2

(B) 1.8

(C) 2.5

(D) 3.6

(E) 4

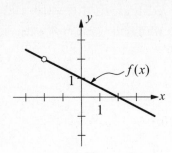

Figure 1

12. Which of the following equations could represent the graph of $f(x)$ shown in Figure 1?

(A) $f(x) = -\dfrac{1}{2}x + 1$

(B) $f(x) = -2x + 1$

(C) $f(x) = \dfrac{-x^2 + 4}{x + 2}$

(D) $f(x) = \dfrac{x^2 - 4}{2x + 4}$

(E) $f(x) = \dfrac{-x^2 + 4}{2x + 4}$

13. Maria can do a job in 3 hours. When Roger helps, they can finish the job in 1 hour and 20 minutes. How long would it take Roger to finish the job working alone?

(A) 1 hour 50 minutes

(B) 2 hour 10 minutes

(C) 2 hour 24 minutes

(D) 2 hour 36 minutes

(E) 2 hour 48 minutes

14. Which of the following lines are asymptote(s) of the graph of $y = \dfrac{x + 1}{x^2 - 2x - 3}$?

I. $x = 3$

II. $x = -1$

III. $y = 0$

(A) I only

(B) I and II only

(C) II and III only

(D) I and III only

(E) I, II, and III

15. If $\dfrac{1}{2x^2 - 5x - 3} = \dfrac{A}{2x + 1} + \dfrac{B}{x - 3}$, what is the value of A?

(A) $-\dfrac{1}{2}$

(B) $-\dfrac{2}{7}$

(C) $\dfrac{1}{7}$

(D) $\dfrac{1}{2}$

(E) $\dfrac{4}{7}$

Answer Key

1. C	2. A	3. B	4. D	5. D
6. E	7. C	8. C	9. A	10. B
11. C	12. E	13. C	14. D	15. B

Answers and Explanations

1. C

$$\frac{6ab}{b^3} \cdot \left(\frac{9a}{b^2}\right)^{-1}$$

$$= \frac{6ab}{b^3} \cdot \left(\frac{b^2}{9a}\right) \qquad \left(\frac{a}{b}\right)^{-1} = \left(\frac{b}{a}\right)$$

$$= \frac{6ab^3}{9ab^3} = \frac{2}{3}$$

2. A

$$\frac{x}{-x+2} + \frac{2}{x-2}$$

$$= \frac{x}{-(x-2)} + \frac{2}{x-2}$$

$$= \frac{-x}{(x-2)} + \frac{2}{x-2}$$

$$= \frac{-x+2}{(x-2)} = \frac{-(x-2)}{(x-2)}$$

$$= -1$$

3. B

$$\frac{x}{2} - \frac{x-4}{3} = \frac{5}{6}$$

$$6 \cdot \frac{x}{2} - 6 \cdot \frac{x-4}{3} = 6 \cdot \frac{5}{6} \qquad \text{Multiply by 6.}$$

$$3x - 2(x-4) = 5$$

$$x + 8 = 5$$

$$x = -3$$

4. D

$$1 - \frac{1}{1+\frac{1}{x}} = 1 - \frac{1}{1 \cdot \frac{x}{x} + \frac{1}{x}}$$

$$= 1 - \frac{1}{\frac{x+1}{x}} = 1 - \frac{x}{x+1}$$

$$= 1 \cdot \frac{x+1}{x+1} - \frac{x}{x+1} = \frac{x+1-x}{x+1}$$

$$= \frac{1}{x+1}$$

5. D

$$\frac{3}{x} + \frac{x}{x-1} = 1$$

Multiply by $x(x-1)$ on both sides.

$$x(x-1)\left(\frac{3}{x}\right) + x(x-1)\left(\frac{x}{x-1}\right) = 1 \cdot x(x-1)$$

$$3(x-1) + x \cdot x = x(x-1)$$

$$3x - 3 + x^2 = x^2 - x$$

$$3x - 3 = -x$$

$$x = \frac{3}{4}$$

6. E

$$x^3 - 3x^2 y + 3xy^2 - y^3 = (x-y)p(x)$$

$$p(x) = \frac{x^3 - 3x^2 y + 3xy^2 - y^3}{(x-y)}$$

$$= \frac{(x-y)^3}{(x-y)} \qquad (x-y)^3 = x^3 - 3x^2 y + 3xy^2 - y^3$$

$$= (x-y)^2$$

7. C

$$\frac{x-1}{x+3} = \frac{3x}{2} \implies 2(x-1) = 3x(x+3)$$

$$\implies 2x - 2 = 3x^2 + 9x$$

$$\implies 3x^2 + 7x + 2 = 0$$

$$\implies (3x+1)(x+2) = 0$$

$$x = -\frac{1}{3} \text{ or } x = -2$$

8. C

If y varies inversely as x, then $xy = k$ or $y = \dfrac{k}{x}$.

Answer choice (C) shows the graph of $y = \dfrac{k}{x}$.

9. A

If W varies inversely as d^2, then

$$W = \frac{k}{d^2}$$

$$180 = \frac{k}{(3 \times 10^4)^2} \cdot \qquad W = 180 \text{ and } d = 3 \times 10^4$$

$$k = 180(3 \times 10^4)^2 \qquad \text{Solve for } k.$$

$$= 1.62 \times 10^{11}$$

$$W = \frac{1.62 \times 10^{11}}{d^2} \qquad \text{Rewrite the equation.}$$

$$W = \frac{1.62 \times 10^{11}}{(1.5 \times 10^4)^2} \qquad d = 1.5 \times 10^4$$

$$= 7.2 \times 10^2$$

10. B

$$(2x^3 - 4x^2 - x + 3) \div (x - 2) =$$

You can use either synthetic division or long division.

```
2 | 2  -4  -1   3
  |      4   0  -2
  ------------------
    2   0  -1 | 1
    coefficient  remainder
    of quotient
```

Therefore

$$(2x^3 - 4x^2 - x + 3) \div (x - 2)$$

$$= 2x^2 - 1 + \frac{1}{x - 2}$$

11. C

Let $x =$ the amount of acid to be added, then $x + 10 =$ the total amount of solution.

$$\underbrace{0.25(10)}_{\substack{\text{amount of acid} \\ \text{in the solution}}} + \underbrace{x}_{\substack{\text{amount of acid added} \\ \text{to the solution}}} = \underbrace{0.4(x + 10)}_{\substack{\text{amount of acid} \\ \text{in the mixture}}}$$

$$2.5 + x = 0.4x + 4$$

$$0.6x = 1.5$$

$$x = 2.5$$

12. E

The graph of $f(x)$ coincides with the graph of $y = -\dfrac{1}{2}x + 1$, at all x-values except $x = -2$.

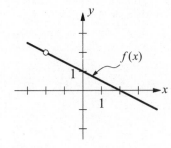

Eliminate choices (A) and (B) which are continuous over the domain. For the rest of the answer choices, which are all undefined at $x = -2$, simplify the rational equation.

(C) $f(x) = \dfrac{-x^2 + 4}{x + 2} = \dfrac{-(x^2 - 4)}{x + 2}$

$$= \frac{-(x + 2)(x - 2)}{x + 2} = -(x - 2) = -x + 2$$

(D) $f(x) = \dfrac{x^2 - 4}{2x + 4} = \dfrac{(x + 2)(x - 2)}{2(x + 2)}$

$$= \frac{x - 2}{2} = \frac{1}{2}x - 1$$

(E) $f(x) = \dfrac{-x^2 + 4}{2x + 4} = \dfrac{-(x^2 - 4)}{2x + 4}$

$$= \frac{-(x + 2)(x - 2)}{2(x + 2)} = \frac{-(x - 2)}{2}$$

$$= -\frac{1}{2}x + 1$$

Choice (E) is correct.

13. C

If Maria can do a job in 3 hours

then her work rate $= \dfrac{1}{3}$.

Let $x =$ the time it takes Roger to finish
the work alone, then

$\dfrac{1}{x} =$ Roger's work rate.

$\overbrace{\dfrac{1}{3}}^{\substack{\text{Maria's} \\ \text{work rate}}} \cdot \overbrace{\left(\dfrac{4}{3}\right)}^{\substack{\text{time}}} + \overbrace{\dfrac{1}{x}}^{\substack{\text{Roger's} \\ \text{work rate}}} \cdot \overbrace{\left(\dfrac{4}{3}\right)}^{\substack{\text{time}}} = \overbrace{1}^{\substack{\text{work done}}}$

(1 hour 20 minutes $= \dfrac{4}{3}$ hours)

$\dfrac{1}{3} \cdot \dfrac{4}{3} + \dfrac{1}{x} \cdot \dfrac{4}{3} = 1 \;\Rightarrow\; \dfrac{4}{9} + \dfrac{4}{3x} = 1$

$\Rightarrow\; \dfrac{4}{3x} = \dfrac{5}{9} \;\Rightarrow\; 15x = 36$

$\Rightarrow\; x = \dfrac{36}{15} = 2.4$ hours

14. D

Simplify the equation.

$y = \dfrac{x+1}{x^2 - 2x - 3} = \dfrac{\cancel{x+1}}{\cancel{(x+1)}(x-3)} = \dfrac{1}{x-3}$

A vertical asymptote occurs at a number for which
the denominator is zero.
Therefore $x = 3$ is the vertical asymptote.

The graph is not continuous at $x = -1$, since the
denominator is zero if $x = -1$. But since the factor
$(x+1)$ cancels out there is a hole, rather than a
vertical asymptote, at $x = -1$.

The graph approaches zero as x approaches infinity,
therefore $y = 0$ is the horizontal asymptote.

You can also use your calculator to graph the
equation.

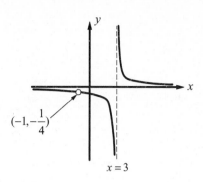

$(-1, -\tfrac{1}{4})$

$x = 3$

Choice (D) is correct.

15. B

Multiply both sides of the equation by the least
common denominator $(2x+1)(x-3)$.

$1 = A(x-3) + B(2x+1)$.

To solve for A, choose $x = -\dfrac{1}{2}$, to eliminate the

term $B(2x+1)$

$1 = A(-\dfrac{1}{2} - 3) + B(2 \cdot -\dfrac{1}{2} + 1)$

$1 = -\dfrac{7}{2}A + 0 \;\Rightarrow\; A = -\dfrac{2}{7}$

CHAPTER 6
Radicals and Complex Numbers

6-1. Definition of Square Root

For any real numbers a and b, if $a^2 = b$, then a is a **square root** of b.

Properties of Square Roots

Product Property $\qquad \sqrt{ab} = \sqrt{a}\sqrt{b}$ where $a \geq 0$ and $b \geq 0$.

Quotient Property $\qquad \sqrt{\dfrac{a}{b}} = \dfrac{\sqrt{a}}{\sqrt{b}}$ where $a \geq 0$ and $b > 0$.

Example 1 $\square$ Simplify each expression. $\qquad$ a. $\sqrt{72}$ $\qquad$ b. $\dfrac{\sqrt{40}}{\sqrt{5}}$

Solution $\qquad \square \quad$ a. $\sqrt{72} = \sqrt{36 \cdot 2} = \sqrt{36} \cdot \sqrt{2} = 6\sqrt{2}$

$\qquad$ b. $\dfrac{\sqrt{40}}{\sqrt{5}} = \sqrt{\dfrac{40}{5}} = \sqrt{8} = \sqrt{4 \cdot 2} = \sqrt{4} \cdot \sqrt{2} = 2\sqrt{2}$

6-2. Definition of n th Root

For any real numbers a and b, and any positive integer n:
If $a^3 = b$, then a is a **cube root** of b and $\sqrt[3]{b} = a$.
If $a^n = b$, then a is an **nth root** of b and $\sqrt[n]{b} = a$.

The symbol $\sqrt[n]{a}$ is called a **radical**. Each part of a radical is given a name, as indicated below.

$$\text{index} \longrightarrow \sqrt[n]{a} \begin{array}{l} \longleftarrow \text{radical sign} \\ \longleftarrow \text{radicand} \end{array}$$

Properties of Radicals

If $\sqrt[n]{a}$ and $\sqrt[n]{b}$ are real numbers, then: $\quad$ 1. $\sqrt[n]{a} \cdot \sqrt[n]{b} = \sqrt[n]{ab}$

$\qquad$ 2. $\dfrac{\sqrt[n]{a}}{\sqrt[n]{b}} = \sqrt[n]{\dfrac{a}{b}}$

Example 2 $\square$ Simplify each expression. $\qquad$ a. $\sqrt[3]{64a^6b^3}$ $\qquad$ b. $\sqrt[4]{81x^8y^{24}}$

Solution ▫ a. $\sqrt[3]{64a^6b^3} = \sqrt[3]{4^3 \, a^6 b^3} = \sqrt[3]{(4a^2b)^3} = 4a^2b$

b. $\sqrt[4]{81x^8y^{24}} = \sqrt[4]{3^4 \, x^8 y^{24}} = \sqrt[4]{(3x^2y^6)^4} = 3x^2y^6$

6-3. Rational Exponents

Definition of $a^{\frac{1}{n}}$:   For any real number a and integer n, where $n > 1$,

$$a^{\frac{1}{n}} = \sqrt[n]{a} \text{ , provided } \sqrt[n]{a} \text{ exists.}$$

Definition of $a^{\frac{m}{n}}$:   For any real number a and integers m and n, where $n > 1$,

$$a^{\frac{m}{n}} = \sqrt[n]{a^m} = (\sqrt[n]{a})^m \text{ , provided } \sqrt[n]{a} \text{ exists.}$$

Example 3 ▫ Simplify each expression.   a. $81^{\frac{1}{3}}$ b. $\dfrac{\sqrt[6]{32}}{\sqrt[3]{2}}$

Solution ▫ a. $81^{\frac{1}{3}} = (3^4)^{\frac{1}{3}} = 3^{\frac{4}{3}} = 3 \cdot 3^{\frac{1}{3}} = 3\sqrt[3]{3}$ Answer

b. $\dfrac{\sqrt[6]{32}}{\sqrt[3]{2}} = \dfrac{32^{\frac{1}{6}}}{2^{\frac{1}{3}}} = \dfrac{(2^5)^{\frac{1}{6}}}{2^{\frac{1}{3}}} = \dfrac{2^{\frac{5}{6}}}{2^{\frac{1}{3}}} = 2^{(\frac{5}{6} - \frac{1}{3})} = 2^{\frac{1}{2}} = \sqrt{2}$ Answer

6-4. Sum of Radicals

Two radicals with the same index and radicand are called **like radicals**. To add or subtract like radicals, add or subtract their coefficients.

Example 4 ▫ Simplify each expression.   a. $\sqrt{8} + \sqrt{18}$ b. $3\sqrt{3}(\sqrt{6} + \sqrt{12})$

Solution ▫ a. $\sqrt{8} + \sqrt{18} = \sqrt{4} \cdot \sqrt{2} + \sqrt{9} \cdot \sqrt{2}$
$= 2\sqrt{2} + 3\sqrt{2}$
$= 5\sqrt{2}$

b. $3\sqrt{3}(\sqrt{6} + \sqrt{12}) = 3\sqrt{3} \cdot \sqrt{6} + 3\sqrt{3} \cdot \sqrt{12}$ Distributive property
$= 3\sqrt{18} + 3\sqrt{36}$
$= 3\sqrt{9} \cdot \sqrt{2} + 3 \cdot 6$
$= 3 \cdot 3 \cdot \sqrt{2} + 18$
$= 9\sqrt{2} + 18$ Answer

6-5. Binomials Containing Radicals and Conjugates

Expressions of the form $\sqrt{a}+\sqrt{b}$ and $\sqrt{a}-\sqrt{b}$ are called **conjugates** of each other. If a and b are integers, the product of the conjugates will be an integer. Conjugates can be used to **rationalize the denominator** containing a binomial radical expression.

Example 5 □   Simplify. a. $(2-\sqrt{3})(3+4\sqrt{3})$ b. $\dfrac{\sqrt{3}-1}{\sqrt{3}+2}$ c. $\dfrac{5}{\sqrt[3]{x}}$

Solution □   a. $(2-\sqrt{3})(3+4\sqrt{3})$

$\qquad = 2\cdot 3+2\cdot 4\sqrt{3}-3\cdot\sqrt{3}-4\sqrt{3}\cdot\sqrt{3}$

$\qquad = 6+8\sqrt{3}-3\sqrt{3}-12$

$\qquad = -6+5\sqrt{3}$ Answer

b. $\dfrac{\sqrt{3}-1}{\sqrt{3}+2}=\dfrac{(\sqrt{3}-1)}{(\sqrt{3}+2)}\cdot\dfrac{(\sqrt{3}-2)}{(\sqrt{3}-2)}$ Multiply numerator and denominator by the conjugate of the denominator.

$\qquad = \dfrac{3-2\sqrt{3}-\sqrt{3}+2}{3-2\sqrt{3}+2\sqrt{3}-4}$

$\qquad = \dfrac{5-3\sqrt{3}}{-1}$ Simplify.

$\qquad = 3\sqrt{3}-5$ Answer

c. $\dfrac{5}{\sqrt[3]{x}}=\dfrac{5}{\sqrt[3]{x}}\cdot\dfrac{\sqrt[3]{x^2}}{\sqrt[3]{x^2}}$ Numerator and denominator are multiplied by $\sqrt[3]{x^2}$, so that the denominator will be a perfect cube.

$\qquad = \dfrac{5\sqrt[3]{x^2}}{\sqrt[3]{x^3}}$

$\qquad = \dfrac{5\sqrt[3]{x^2}}{x}$ Answer

6-6. Equations Containing Radicals

An equation like $\sqrt{2x+5}=3$, which contains a radical with a variable in the radicand, is called a **radical equation**.

Example 6 □   Solve each expression.   a. $2\sqrt[3]{x}+5=11$ b. $x-2\sqrt{x}=3$

Solution □   a. $2\sqrt[3]{x}+5=11$

$\qquad 2\sqrt[3]{x}=6$ Subtract 5 from both sides.

$\qquad \sqrt[3]{x}=3$ Divide both sides by 2.

$\qquad (\sqrt[3]{x})^3=3^3$ Cube both sides.

$\qquad x=27$ Answer

b. $x - 2\sqrt{x} = 3$

$\quad x - 3 = 2\sqrt{x}$ Isolate the radical term.

$\quad x^2 - 6x + 9 = 4x$ Square both sides.

$\quad x^2 - 10x + 9 = 0$ Write in standard form.

$\quad (x - 1)(x - 9) = 0$ Factor.

$\quad x = 1 \ \ \text{or} \ \ x = 9$ Zero-product property

Check each possible solution in the original equation.

$$x - 2\sqrt{x} = 3 \qquad\qquad x - 2\sqrt{x} = 3$$
$$1 - 2\sqrt{1} \overset{?}{=} 3 \qquad\qquad 9 - 2\sqrt{9} \overset{?}{=} 3$$
$$-1 \neq 3 \qquad\qquad\qquad 9 - 6 = 3 \ \checkmark$$

The root 1 does not check.   The root 9 checks.   Therefore the solution set is $\{9\}$.   ■

6-7. The Imaginary Number i

Definition of i : $i = \sqrt{-1}$ and $i^2 = -1$

If n is a positive real number, then $\sqrt{-n} = i\sqrt{n}$.

Example 7 □ Simplify each expression.   a. $\sqrt{-9} - \sqrt{-25}$ b. i^{59}

Solution   □ a. $\sqrt{-9} - \sqrt{-25} = i\sqrt{9} - i\sqrt{25}$
$$\qquad\qquad\qquad\qquad = 3i - 5i$$
$$\qquad\qquad\qquad\qquad = -2i$$

b. $i^{59} = i \cdot i^{58}$ Product of powers
$$\quad = i \cdot (i^2)^{29} \qquad \text{Power of power}$$
$$\quad = i \cdot (-1)^{29} \qquad i^2 = -1$$
$$\quad = -i \qquad\qquad\quad \text{Answer}$$

        ■

6-8. Complex Numbers and Complex Conjugates

A **complex number** is any number that can be written in the form $a + bi$, where a and b are real numbers and i is the **imaginary unit**. The real number a is called the **real part**, and the real number b is called the **imaginary part** of the complex number.

Equality of Complex Numbers

$a + bi = c + di$ if and only if $a = c$ and $b = d$.

Addition and Subtraction of Complex Numbers

Let $a + bi$ and $c + di$ be any two complex numbers.
Then $(a + bi) + (c + di) = (a + c) + (b + d)i$ and $(a + bi) - (c + di) = (a - c) + (b - d)i$

Two complex numbers $a+bi$ and $a-bi$ are called **complex conjugates**. Their product is the real number a^2+b^2. Complex conjugates can be used to simplify the quotient of two imaginary numbers.

Conjugate Root Theorem

If a polynomial function f has $a+bi$ as a root (where a and b are real numbers, and $b \neq 0$), then $a-bi$ is also a root.

Example 8 □   a. Simplify $\dfrac{3-i}{4+3i}$.

             b. Find a cubic function $f(x)$ that has integral coefficients, and 3 and $2-i$ as roots.

Solution   □   a. $\dfrac{3-i}{4+3i} = \dfrac{3-i}{4+3i} \cdot \dfrac{4-3i}{4-3i}$ Multiply the numerator and denominator by the conjugate of the denominator.

$$= \frac{12-9i-4i+3i^2}{16-9i^2}$$

$$= \frac{12-13i+3(-1)}{16-9(-1)} \qquad i^2 = -1$$

$$= \frac{9-13i}{25} \qquad\qquad \text{Answer}$$

b. If $2-i$ is a root of $f(x)$, then $2+i$ is also a root. Therefore, $(x-3)$, $[x-(2-i)]$, and $[x-(2+i)]$ are the factors of $f(x)$.

$$f(x) = (x-3)[x-(2-i)][x-(2+i)]$$
$$= (x-3)[x^2 - x(2+i) - x(2-i) + (2-i)(2+i)] \qquad \text{Multiply the complex parts first.}$$
$$= (x-3)[x^2 - 2x - \cancel{xi} - 2x + \cancel{xi} + (4-i^2)] \qquad \text{Simplify.}$$
$$= (x-3)[x^2 - 4x + 5] \qquad\qquad i^2 = -1$$
$$= x^3 - 4x^2 + 5x - 3x^2 + 12x - 15 \qquad \text{Distribute.}$$
$$= x^3 - 7x^2 + 17x - 15 \qquad\qquad \text{Answer} \qquad ■$$

6-9. Absolute Value of Complex Numbers $\boxed{L2}$

The **absolute value** of the complex number $a+bi$ is defined as $|a+bi| = \sqrt{a^2+b^2}$.

Example 9 □   a. $|3+2i| =$ b. $|-4+3i| =$

Solution   □   a. $|3+2i| = \sqrt{3^2+2^2} = \sqrt{13}$ Answer

             b. $|-4+3i| = \sqrt{(-4)^2+3^2} = \sqrt{25} = 5$ Answer   ■■

1. $\sqrt{20} - \sqrt{45} + \sqrt{80} =$

   (A) $\sqrt{55}$

   (B) $3\sqrt{5}$

   (C) $10 - 3\sqrt{5}$

   (D) $4\sqrt{5}$

   (E) $5\sqrt{3}$

2. $\sqrt{\dfrac{3}{2}} - \sqrt{\dfrac{2}{3}} =$

   (A) $\sqrt{5}$

   (B) $\dfrac{5}{6}$

   (C) $\dfrac{\sqrt{5}}{\sqrt{6}}$

   (D) $\dfrac{\sqrt{5}}{6}$

   (E) $\dfrac{\sqrt{6}}{6}$

3. Which of the following is the reciprocal of
   $1 + \dfrac{1}{\sqrt{2}}$?

   (A) $\sqrt{6}$

   (B) $1 - \sqrt{2}$

   (C) $1 + \sqrt{2}$

   (D) $2 - \sqrt{2}$

   (E) $2 + \sqrt{2}$

4. If $\sqrt{-2y} = 5.6$, then $x =$

   (A) -15.68

   (B) -11.2

   (C) -1.96

   (D) -1.4

   (E) 2.8

5. Which of the following is the solution for the
   equation $\sqrt[4]{-2x+3} = \sqrt{x}$?

   (A) $\{-3\}$

   (B) $\{-3,\ 1\}$

   (C) $\{-1,\ 3\}$

   (D) $\{1\}$

   (E) $\{1,\ 3\}$

6. If $b \neq 0$, $\sqrt[3]{\dfrac{81a}{64b^2}} =$

   (A) $\dfrac{3\sqrt[3]{3ab^2}}{4b^2}$

   (B) $\dfrac{3\sqrt[3]{6ab}}{4b}$

   (C) $\dfrac{3\sqrt[3]{3ab}}{4b}$

   (D) $\dfrac{6\sqrt[3]{3ab}}{4b}$

   (E) $\dfrac{6\sqrt[3]{3ab^2}}{4b^2}$

7. $\sqrt[3]{-16} + \sqrt[3]{250} - \sqrt[3]{54} =$

    (A) $-\sqrt[3]{2}$

    (B) $\sqrt[3]{2}$

    (C) 0

    (D) $2\sqrt[3]{2}$

    (E) $3\sqrt[3]{2}$

8. If $x = 2 - x\sqrt{3}$, then $x =$

    (A) $-\sqrt{3} - 1$

    (B) $-\sqrt{3} + 1$

    (C) $\sqrt{3} - \sqrt{2}$

    (D) $\sqrt{3} + 1$

    (E) $\sqrt{3} - 1$

9. If $i^2 = -1$, then all of the following expressions are equivalent to each other EXCEPT

    (A) $\dfrac{1}{i}$

    (B) $\dfrac{1}{i^3}$

    (C) $\dfrac{1}{i^5}$

    (D) i^7

    (E) $-i$

10. If $x > 1$, $\dfrac{\sqrt{x + \sqrt{x}} \cdot \sqrt{x - \sqrt{x}}}{\sqrt{x - 1}} =$

    (A) $\sqrt{x + 1}$

    (B) $\sqrt{x - 1}$

    (C) $\sqrt{x}$

    (D) $x + 1$

    (E) $x - 1$

11. If $i = \sqrt{-1}$, then $2i\sqrt{2} \cdot \sqrt{-125} =$

    (A) $-10\sqrt{10}$

    (B) $-5\sqrt{10}$

    (C) $5i\sqrt{10}$

    (D) $10i\sqrt{10}$

    (E) $25i\sqrt{5}$

12. If $i^2 = -1$, which of the following is the reciprocal of $\dfrac{1}{2} + \dfrac{\sqrt{3}}{2}i$?

    (A) $-1 - i\sqrt{3}$

    (B) $-1 + i\sqrt{3}$

    (C) $1 - i\sqrt{3}$

    (D) $\dfrac{1 - i\sqrt{3}}{2}$

    (E) $\dfrac{-1 + i\sqrt{3}}{2}$

13. If $(a-2i)^2 = 5+bi$, where a and b are positive real numbers and $i^2 = -1$, what is the value of $a+b$?

   (A) 15

   (B) 12

   (C) 9

   (D) 6

   (E) 3

14. If $f(x) = x - \dfrac{1}{x}$ and $i^2 = -1$, then $f(\dfrac{1}{i}) =$

   (A) $2i$

   (B) $-2i$

   (C) $1-i$

   (D) $1+i$

   (E) -2

15. If $1-2i$ is a solution of the equation $x^2 - 2x + c$, what is the value of c?

   (A) -5

   (B) -3

   (C) 1

   (D) 3

   (E) 5

16. Which of the following is the square root of $-1+2i\sqrt{2}$? $\boxed{L2}$

   (A) $2i\sqrt{2}$

   (B) $1-i\sqrt{2}$

   (C) $1+i\sqrt{2}$

   (D) $-1+2i\sqrt{2}$

   (E) $1-2i\sqrt{2}$

17. What is the value of $|5-10i|$? $\boxed{L2}$

   (A) $-5\sqrt{3}$

   (B) -5

   (C) 5

   (D) $5\sqrt{5}$

   (E) 15

Answer Key

1. B   2. E   3. D   4. A   5. D

6. C   7. C   8. E   9. B   10. C

11. A   12. D   13. A   14. B   15. E

16. C   17. D

Answers and Explanations

1. B

$$\sqrt{20} - \sqrt{45} + \sqrt{80}$$
$$= \sqrt{4}\sqrt{5} - \sqrt{9}\sqrt{5} + \sqrt{16}\sqrt{5}$$
$$= 2\sqrt{5} - 3\sqrt{5} + 4\sqrt{5}$$
$$= 3\sqrt{5}$$

2. E

$$\sqrt{\frac{3}{2}} - \sqrt{\frac{2}{3}} = \frac{\sqrt{3}}{\sqrt{2}} - \frac{\sqrt{2}}{\sqrt{3}}$$
$$= \frac{\sqrt{3} \cdot \sqrt{2}}{\sqrt{2} \cdot \sqrt{2}} - \frac{\sqrt{2} \cdot \sqrt{3}}{\sqrt{3} \cdot \sqrt{3}}$$
$$= \frac{\sqrt{6}}{2} - \frac{\sqrt{6}}{3} = \frac{\sqrt{6}}{6}$$

3. D

The reciprocal of $1 + \dfrac{1}{\sqrt{2}}$ is $\dfrac{1}{1 + \dfrac{1}{\sqrt{2}}}$.

$$\frac{1}{1 + \dfrac{1}{\sqrt{2}}} = \frac{1 \cdot \sqrt{2}}{(1 + \dfrac{1}{\sqrt{2}})\sqrt{2}} = \frac{\sqrt{2}}{\sqrt{2} + 1}$$
$$= \frac{\sqrt{2}(\sqrt{2} - 1)}{(\sqrt{2} + 1)(\sqrt{2} - 1)} = \frac{2 - \sqrt{2}}{2 - 1}$$
$$= 2 - \sqrt{2}$$

4. A

$$\sqrt{-2y} = 5.6$$
$$(\sqrt{-2y})^2 = (5.6)^2$$
$$-2y = 31.36$$
$$y = -15.68$$

5. D

$$\sqrt[4]{-2x + 3} = \sqrt{x}$$
$$(\sqrt[4]{-2x + 3})^4 = (\sqrt{x})^4$$
$$-2x + 3 = x^2$$
$$x^2 + 2x - 3 = 0$$
$$(x + 3)(x - 1) = 0$$
$$x = -3 \text{ or } x = 1$$

Check each possible solution in the original equation.

If $x = -3$, $\sqrt[4]{-2(-3) + 3} \neq \sqrt{-3}$.

The root -3 does not check since square roots of negative numbers are not defined in the set of real numbers.

If $x = 1$, $\sqrt[4]{-2(1) + 3} = \sqrt{1}$.
The root 1 checks.

Therefore the solution set is $\{1\}$.

6. C

$$\sqrt[3]{\frac{81a}{64b^2}}$$
$$= \sqrt[3]{\frac{3^4 a}{2^6 b^2}}$$
$$= \sqrt[3]{\frac{3^3 \cdot 3a \cdot b}{2^6 b^2 \cdot b}} \qquad \text{Multiply top and bottom by } b.$$
$$= \sqrt[3]{\frac{3^3 \cdot 3ab}{2^6 b^3}} \qquad b^2 \cdot b = b^3$$
$$= \frac{3\sqrt[3]{3ab}}{2^2 b} \qquad \sqrt[3]{3^3} = 3, \ \sqrt[3]{2^6} = 2^2, \ \sqrt[3]{b^3} = b$$
$$= \frac{3\sqrt[3]{3ab}}{4b} \qquad \text{Answer}$$

7. C

$$\sqrt[3]{-16} + \sqrt[3]{250} - \sqrt[3]{54}$$
$$= \sqrt[3]{(-2)^3 \cdot 2} + \sqrt[3]{5^3 \cdot 2} - \sqrt[3]{3^3 \cdot 2}$$
$$= \sqrt[3]{(-2)^3} \sqrt[3]{2} + \sqrt[3]{5^3} \cdot \sqrt[3]{2} - \sqrt[3]{3^3} \cdot \sqrt[3]{2}$$
$$= -2 \cdot \sqrt[3]{2} + 5 \cdot \sqrt[3]{2} - 3 \cdot \sqrt[3]{2}$$
$$= 0$$

8. E

$$x = 2 - x\sqrt{3}$$
$$x + x\sqrt{3} = 2$$
$$x(1 + \sqrt{3}) = 2 \qquad \text{Factor.}$$
$$x = \frac{2}{(1+\sqrt{3})} \qquad \text{Divide by } 1+\sqrt{3}.$$
$$x = \frac{2(1-\sqrt{3})}{(1+\sqrt{3})(1-\sqrt{3})} \qquad \text{Rationalize the denominator.}$$
$$x = \frac{2(1-\sqrt{3})}{1-3} \qquad \text{Simplify.}$$
$$x = \sqrt{3} - 1 \qquad \text{Answer}$$

9. B

Simplify each answer choice.

(A) $\dfrac{1}{i} = \dfrac{1 \cdot i}{i \cdot i} = \dfrac{i}{i^2} = \dfrac{i}{-1} = -i$

(B) $\dfrac{1}{i^3} = \dfrac{1 \cdot i}{i^3 \cdot i} = \dfrac{i}{i^4} = \dfrac{i}{1} = i \qquad (i^4 = 1)$

(C) $\dfrac{1}{i^5} = \dfrac{1}{i^4} \cdot \dfrac{1}{i} = \dfrac{1}{i} = -i$

(D) $i^7 = i^4 \cdot i^2 \cdot i = 1 \cdot (-1) \cdot i = -i$

(E) $-i$

Answer choice (B) is different from the others.

10. C

$$\frac{\sqrt{x+\sqrt{x}} \cdot \sqrt{x-\sqrt{x}}}{\sqrt{x-1}}$$
$$= \frac{\sqrt{(x+\sqrt{x})(x-\sqrt{x})}}{\sqrt{x-1}}$$
$$= \frac{\sqrt{(x^2 - x\sqrt{x} + x\sqrt{x} - x)}}{\sqrt{x-1}} \qquad \text{Multiply.}$$
$$= \frac{\sqrt{(x^2 - x)}}{\sqrt{x-1}}$$
$$= \frac{\sqrt{x(x-1)}}{\sqrt{x-1}}$$
$$= \sqrt{\frac{x(x-1)}{x-1}}$$
$$= \sqrt{x}$$

11. A

$$2i\sqrt{2} \cdot \sqrt{-125}$$
$$= 2i\sqrt{2} \cdot i\sqrt{125}$$
$$= 2i\sqrt{2} \cdot i\sqrt{25}\sqrt{5}$$
$$= 2i\sqrt{2} \cdot 5i\sqrt{5}$$
$$= 10i^2\sqrt{10}$$
$$= -10\sqrt{10}$$

12. D

$$\frac{1}{2} + \frac{\sqrt{3}}{2}i = \frac{1 + i\sqrt{3}}{2}$$

The reciprocal is $\dfrac{2}{1+i\sqrt{3}}$.

$$\frac{2}{1+i\sqrt{3}}$$
$$= \frac{2(1-i\sqrt{3})}{(1+i\sqrt{3})(1-i\sqrt{3})}$$
$$= \frac{2(1-i\sqrt{3})}{1 - i\sqrt{3} + i\sqrt{3} - i^2 \cdot 3}$$
$$= \frac{2(1-i\sqrt{3})}{4}$$
$$= \frac{(1-i\sqrt{3})}{2}$$

13. A

$$(a+2i)^2 = 5+bi$$
$$a^2 + 4ai + 4i^2 = 5+bi$$
$$(a^2 - 4) + 4ai = 5+bi$$

According to the equality of complex numbers, $a+bi = c+di$ if and only if $a = c$ and $b = d$.

So, $a^2 - 4 = 5$ and $4a = b$.

$a^2 = 9 \Rightarrow a = \pm 3$, but a is positive, so $a = 3$.

$4a = b \Rightarrow 4(3) = b \Rightarrow b = 12$

$a + b = 3 + 12 = 15$

14. B

$$f(x) = x - \frac{1}{x}$$

$$f(\frac{1}{i}) = \frac{1}{i} - \frac{1}{\frac{1}{i}} = \frac{1}{i} - \frac{i}{1}$$

$$= \frac{1 \cdot i}{i \cdot i} - i = \frac{i}{i^2} - i$$

$$= \frac{i}{-1} - i = -i - i$$

$$= -2i$$

15. E

By the Conjugate Root Theorem, if $x^2 - 2x + c$ has $1 - 2i$ as a root, then $1 + 2i$ is also a root.

Therefore $[x - (1-2i)][x - (1+2i)] = x^2 - 2x + c$.

$[x - (1-2i)][x - (1+2i)]$

$= x^2 - x(1+2i) - x(1-2i) + (1-2i)(1+2i)$

$= x^2 - x - 2xi - x + 2xi + 1 - 4i^2$

$= x^2 - 2x + 5$

$\Rightarrow c = 5$

16. C $\boxed{L2}$

Square each answer choice until you find one that gives you $-1 + 2i\sqrt{2}$.

(A) $(2i\sqrt{2})^2 = 4i^2 \cdot 2 = -8$

(B) $(1 - i\sqrt{2})^2 = 1 - 2i\sqrt{2} + i^2 \cdot 2 = -1 - 2i\sqrt{2}$

(C) $(1 + i\sqrt{2})^2 = 1 + 2i\sqrt{2} + i^2 \cdot 2 = -1 + 2i\sqrt{2}$

Choice (C) is correct.

17. D $\boxed{L2}$

$$|a - bi| = \sqrt{a^2 + b^2}$$

$$|5 - 10i| = \sqrt{5^2 + (-10)^2} = \sqrt{125} = 5\sqrt{5}$$

CHAPTER 7
Functions and Graphs II

7-1. Composition of Functions

Given the two functions f and g, the **composite function**, denoted by $f \circ g$,
is defined as $(f \circ g)(x) = f(g(x))$.

In order for a value of x to be in the domain of $f \circ g$, two conditions must be satisfied:

1) x must be in the domain of g, and
2) $g(x)$ must be in the domain of f.

$f(g(x))$ is evaluated by working from the innermost parentheses to the outside.

$f(g(x))$ and $g(f(x))$ are generally not equal functions.

Example 1 □ If $f(x) = x^2 - 1$ and $g(x) = \sqrt{x+2}$, find the following:
a. $f(g(3))$ b. $g(f(x))$

Solution   □   a. $g(3) = \sqrt{3+2} = \sqrt{5}$

$$f(g(3)) = f(\sqrt{5}) = (\sqrt{5})^2 - 1 = 4 \qquad \text{Answer}$$

b. $g(f(x)) = g(x^2 - 1)$

$$= \sqrt{(x^2 - 1) + 2} = \sqrt{x^2 + 1} \qquad \text{Answer}$$

7-2. Inverse Functions

The functions f and g are **inverse functions** if

$f(g(x)) = x$ for all x-values in the domain of g and

$g(f(x)) = x$ for all x-values in the domain of f.

The inverse of a function f is usually denoted by f^{-1}, which is read " f inverse."

Thus for the definition of inverse functions we can write

$f^{-1}(f(x)) = x$ and $f(f^{-1}(x)) = x$.

The graph of a function f and the graph of its
inverse f^{-1} are symmetric about the line $y = x$.

The graph of f contains the point (a,b)
if and only if the graph of f^{-1} contains the
point (b,a).

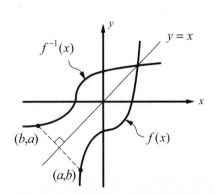

Finding an Inverse Function

1. Replace $f(x)$ with y.
2. Interchange x and y.
3. Solve for y.

Example 2 ◻ Find the inverse of each function.
  a. $(-3, 2)$, $(1, 5)$, $(4, -7)$
  b. $f(x) = -2x + 3$

Solution ◻ a. $(2, -3)$, $(5, 1)$, $(-7, 4)$ The relations (a, b) and (b, a) are inverses
                                                           of each other.

  b. $f(x) = -2x + 3$
    $y = -2x + 3$ Replace $f(x)$ with y.
    $x = -2y + 3$ Interchange x and y.

    $y = \dfrac{-x + 3}{2}$ Solve for y.

  The inverse of $f(x) = -2x + 3$

  is $f^{-1}(x) = \dfrac{-x + 3}{2}$.   Answer

7-3. Graph of $y = |f(x)|$

The graph of $y = |f(x)|$ can be obtained from the graph of $y = f(x)$ by

1) reflecting the portion of the graph that lies below the x-axis about the x-axis, and
2) joining this reflection with the portion of the graph of $y = f(x)$ that lies above the x-axis.

Example 3 ◻ Graph $g(x) = |x^2 - 1|$.

Solution ◻

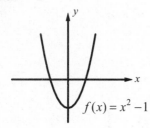

$f(x) = x^2 - 1$

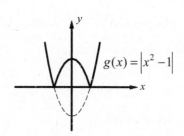

$g(x) = |x^2 - 1|$

7-4. Even and Odd Functions

The function $f(x)$ is **even** if $f(-x) = f(x)$.
The graph of an even function is symmetric about the y-axis.

The function $f(x)$ is **odd** if $f(-x) = -f(x)$.
The graph of an odd function is symmetric about the origin.

Example 4 □ Determine whether each function is even, odd, or neither.

   a. $f(x) = x^3 - 2x$ b. $f(x) = x^4 - 5x^2$ c. $f(x) = x^2 + 4x$

Solution   □ a. $f(-x) = (-x)^3 - 2(-x) = -x^3 + 2x = -(x^3 - 2x) = -f(x)$
   The function is odd because $f(-x) = -f(x)$.
   The graph is symmetric about the origin.

   b. $f(-x) = (-x)^4 - 5(-x)^2 = x^4 - 5x^2 = f(x)$
   The function is even because $f(-x) = f(x)$.
   The graph is symmetric about the y-axis.

   c. $f(-x) = (-x)^2 + 4(-x) = x^2 - 4x \neq f(x)$
   The function is neither even nor odd because $f(-x) \neq f(x)$ and
   $f(-x) \neq -f(x)$.

7-5. Special Functions   L2

The **greatest integer function** is defined as $f(x) = [x]$ = the greatest integer less than
or equal to x.

When the domain of a function is divided into several parts and a different function rule
is applied to each part, the function is called a **piecewise-defined function**.

Example 5 □ a. If $f(x) = [x]$, find $f(-1.5)$, $f(0.5)$, and $f(2.9)$.

   b. Find a complete graph of $f(x) = [x]$.

   c. Find a complete graph of the piecewise function $f(x) = \begin{cases} 3 - x & \text{if } x \leq -1 \\ x^2 + 1 & \text{if } x > -1 \end{cases}$.

Solution   □ a. $f(-1.5) = [-1.5] = -2$ The greatest integer less than or equal to -1.5 is -2.

   $f(0.5) = [0.5] = 0$ The greatest integer less than or equal to 0.5 is 0.

   $f(2.9) = [2.9] = 2$ The greatest integer less than or equal to 2.9 is 2.

   b. To graph the greatest integer function
   $f(x) = [x]$, find several ordered pairs
   for the values $-1 \leq x \leq 1$.

x	-1	-0.5	0	0.5	1	1.5	2
$[x]$	-1	-1	0	0	1	1	2

   For $-1 \leq x < 0$, $[x] = -1$.

   For $0 \leq x < 1$, $[x] = 0$.

   For $1 \leq x < 2$, $[x] = 1$ and so on.

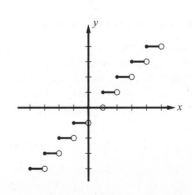

c. The part of the graph of $f(x)$ that lies
to the left of the vertical line $x = -1$ is
the graph of $f(x) = 3 - x$, and the part
of the graph of $f(x)$ that lies to the
right of the vertical line $x = -1$ is
$f(x) = x^2 + 1$.
The solid dot indicates that the point
$(-1, 4)$ is included on the graph and the
open dot indicates that the point $(-1, 2)$
is excluded from the graph.

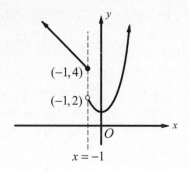

7-6. Graphs of Polynomial Functions $\boxed{L2}$

A **polynomial function of degree n** is defined as an equation of the form
$f(x) = a_n x^n + a_{n-1} x^{n-1} + \ldots + a_1 x + a_0$, where n is a nonnegative integer and
a_n is called the **leading coefficient**.

The graph of a polynomial function of degree n has at most $n - 1$ **turning points.**
A function f is **increasing** on an interval if the value of $f(x)$ increases as x increases in the interval.
A function f is **decreasing** on an interval if the value of $f(x)$ decreases as x increases in the interval.

In the graph shown at the right, the function $f(x)$
increases on the intervals $(-\infty, a)$ and (b, ∞), and
decreases on the interval (a, b).

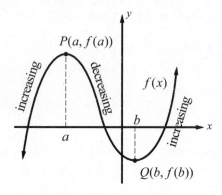

Points such as P and Q are called turning points.
At a turning point the graph changes from increasing
to decreasing or from decreasing to increasing.

The value of $f(a)$ is the **local maximum** of f.
The value of $f(b)$ is the **local minimum** of f.

Fundamental Theorem of Algebra

Every polynomial function with degree greater than zero has at least one root (zero) in
the set of complex numbers. The root(s) may be real numbers or imaginary numbers,
both of which belong to the set of complex numbers.

Graphs of **third degree polynomial functions** $f(x) = ax^3 + bx^2 + cx + d$ look like
one of the four types illustrated below. There is a maximum of two turning points.
There may be one, two, or three **real solutions (zeros)**.

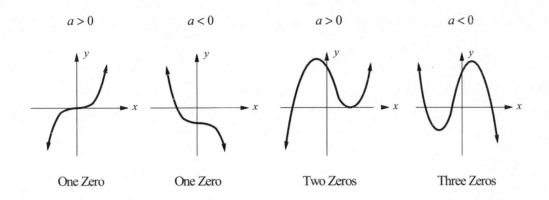

Graphs of **fourth-degree polynomial functions** $f(x) = ax^4 + bx^3 + cx^2 + dx + e$ look like one of the five types illustrated below. There is a maximum of three turning points. There may be anywhere from zero to four **real solutions (zeros)**.

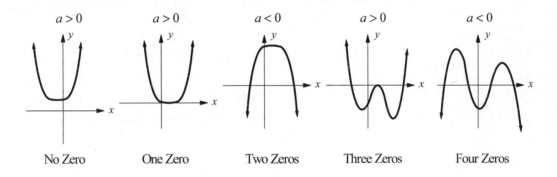

Example 6 □   For each of the graphs below, find the degree of the polynomial function, the number of turning points, and the number of real solutions.

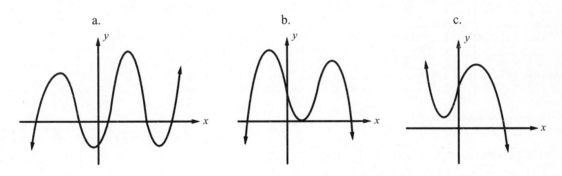

Solution   □   a. The degree of the polynomial is 5. There are 4 turning points. Since the graph intersects the *x*-axis 5 times, the polynomial has 5 real solutions.

b. The degree of the polynomial is 4. There are 3 turning points. Since the graph intersects the *x*-axis 3 times, the polynomial has 3 real solutions.

c. The degree of the polynomial is 3. There are 2 turning points. Since the graph intersects the *x*-axis one time, the polynomial has one real solution.

1. If $f(x) = 2x - 3$ and $g(x) = -x + 5$, then $f(g(x)) =$

(A) $x + 2$

(B) $3x - 8$

(C) $-2x + 7$

(D) $-2x - 7$

(E) $-2x^2 + 13x - 15$

2. If $f(x) = \sqrt[3]{-2x^2 + 5}$ and $g(x) = f(f(x))$, then $g(4) =$

(A) -2.4

(B) -0.8

(C) 2.4

(D) 3

(E) 5.2

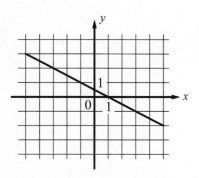

Figure 1

3. Figure 1 shows the graph of $f(x)$. If f^{-1} is the inverse of f, what is $f^{-1}(2)$?

(A) -5

(B) -3

(C) -1

(D) 1

(E) 3

4. If $f(x) = -x^3 + 3$, then $f^{-1}(-5) =$

(A) -128

(B) -22

(C) -2

(D) 2

(E) 5

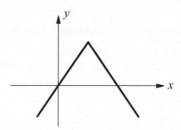

Figure 2

5. Figure 2 shows the graph of $y = f(x)$. Which of the following is the graph of $y = |f(x)|$?

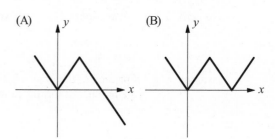

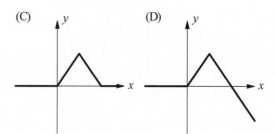

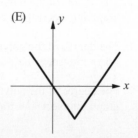

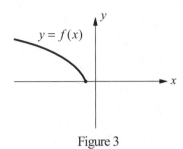

Figure 3

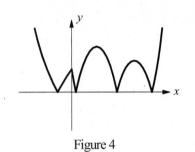

Figure 4

6. Figure 3 shows the graph of $y = f(x)$. Which of the following could be the graph of $y = f^{-1}(x)$?

7. Figure 4 shows the graph of $y = |f(x)|$. Which of the following could be the graph of $y = f(x)$?

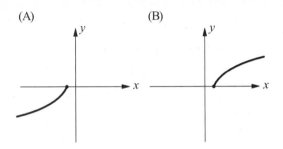

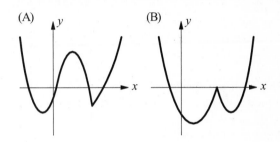

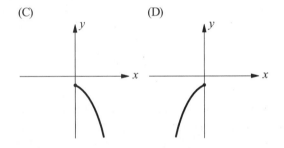

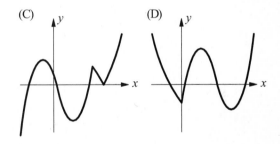

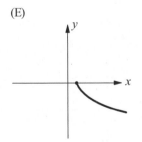

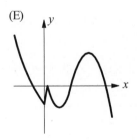

8. A function f is an even function if, for all x-values in the domain, $f(-x) = f(x)$. Which of the following is an even function?

(A) $|x+2|$

(B) $x^3 - 8$

(C) $(x-4)^2$

(D) $x^2 + 2x$

(E) $\dfrac{1}{1-x^2}$

9. If $f(x)$ is an odd function and $(3,7)$ is a point on the graph of f, which of the following is also a point on its graph?

(A) $(-3,-7)$

(B) $(-3,7)$

(C) $(3,-7)$

(D) $(7,3)$

(E) $(-7,-3)$

10. If $f(x) = 2x+3$ and $f(g(x)) = x$, then $g(x) =$

(A) $x+3$

(B) $x-3$

(C) $\dfrac{x+3}{2}$

(D) $\dfrac{x}{2}$

(E) $\dfrac{x-3}{2}$

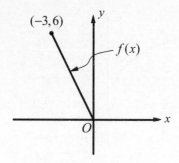

Figure 6

11. If f is a function whose graph is the line segment shown in Figure 6, what is $f^{-1}(3)$?

(A) -1.2

(B) -1.5

(C) -1.8

(D) -2.4

(E) -3.2

12. A piecewise function f is defined as

$$f(x) = \begin{cases} x^2 + 2x & \text{if } x < 0 \\ [x] + 1 & \text{if } 0 \le x < 1 \\ |x-1| & \text{if } x \ge 1 \end{cases} .$$

What is the value of $f(-1) + f(0.5) + f(1.5)$?

$\boxed{L2}$

(A) 0.5

(B) 1

(C) 1.5

(D) 2

(E) 2.5

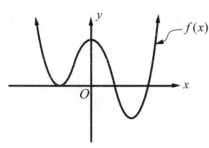

Figure 5

13. The graph of a polynomial function $y = f(x)$ is shown in Figure 5 above. Which of the following is true about the graph of $y = f(x)$? L2

   I. $f(x)$ is an even function.

   II. $f(x)$ has four real zeros.

   III. The leading coefficient is positive.

   (A) None

   (B) I only

   (C) III only

   (D) I and II only

   (E) I and III only

14. What is the range of the function defined by

$$f(x) = \begin{cases} \dfrac{x^2 - x - 2}{x - 2} & \text{if } x < 2 \\ 2 & \text{if } x \ge 2 \end{cases} ?$$ L2

   (A) $y \le 2$

   (B) $2 \le y < 3$

   (C) $y < 3$

   (D) All real numbers except $y = 3$

   (E) All real numbers

15. A function f is increasing if $f(x_1) \le f(x_2)$ whenever $x_1 \le x_2$. Which of the following is an increasing function? L2

   (A) $|x + 1|$

   (B) $1 - x$

   (C) $(x + 1)^2$

   (D) $x^3 - 1$

   (E) $\dfrac{1}{x^2}$

16. A function f is decreasing if $f(x_1) \ge f(x_2)$ whenever $x_1 \le x_2$. Which of the following could be a decreasing function? L2

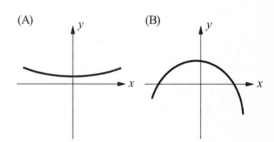

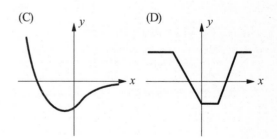

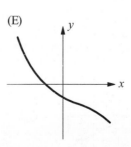

Answer Key

1. C	2. A	3. B	4. D	5. B
6. C	7. D	8. E	9. A	10. E
11. B	12. A	13. C	14. C	15. D
16. E				

Answers and Explanations

1. C

$f(x) = 2x - 3$ and $g(x) = -x + 5$

$f(g(x))$

$= f(-x + 5)$

$= 2(-x + 5) - 3$

$= -2x + 7$

2. A

$f(x) = \sqrt[3]{-2x^2 + 5}$

$g(x) = f(f(x))$

$g(4) = f(f(4))$

$\quad = f(\sqrt[3]{-2(4)^2 + 5}) = f(\sqrt[3]{-32 + 5})$

$\quad = f(\sqrt[3]{-27}) = f(\sqrt[3]{(-3)^3})$

$\quad = f(-3) = \sqrt[3]{-2(-3)^2 + 5}$

$\quad = \sqrt[3]{-18 + 5} = \sqrt[3]{-13}$

$\quad \approx -2.35$

3. B

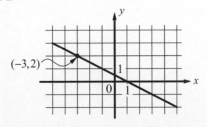

Let $f^{-1}(2) = a$, then $2 = f(a)$.

The graph of $f(x)$ shows that $f(-3) = 2$,

therefore $a = -3$ and $f^{-1}(2) = -3$.

4. D

$f(x) = -x^3 + 3$

To find an inverse function:

1. Replace $f(x)$ with y. $\quad y = -x^3 + 3$
2. Interchange x and y. $\quad x = -y^3 + 3$
3. Solve for y. $\quad y^3 = -x + 3$

$\Rightarrow y = (-x + 3)^{\frac{1}{3}} \Rightarrow f^{-1}(x) = (-x + 3)^{\frac{1}{3}}$

$f^{-1}(-5) = (-(-5) + 3)^{\frac{1}{3}} = (8)^{\frac{1}{3}} = 2$

5. B

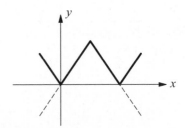

Reflect the portion of the graph of $y = f(x)$
which is below the x-axis over the x-axis.
That is the graph of $y = |f(x)|$.
Choice (B) is correct.

6. C

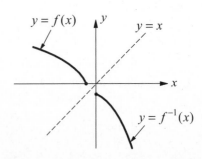

The graph of a function f and the graph of its
inverse f^{-1} are symmetric about the line $y = x$.

7. D

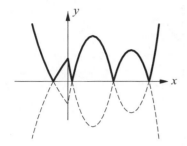

The graph of $y = f(x)$ could have portions lying above the x-axis and portions lying below the x-axis (as illustrated by the dotted line). There are several possibilities for the original graph, but any portion lying below the x-axis would have to be reflected across the x-axis to obtain the graph of $y = |f(x)|$.

Choice (D) is correct.

8. E

A function f is an even function if, for all x-values in the domain, $f(-x) = f(x)$.

Check each answer choice.

(A) $f(x) = |x + 2|$, $f(-x) = |-x + 2|$

$\qquad f(-x) \neq f(x)$

(B) $f(x) = x^3 - 8$, $f(-x) = (-x)^3 - 8 = -x^3 - 8$

$\qquad f(-x) \neq f(x)$

(C) $f(x) = (x - 4)^2$,

$\qquad f(-x) = (-x - 4)^2 = (x + 4)^2$

$\qquad f(-x) \neq f(x)$

(D) $f(x) = x^2 + 2x$,

$\qquad f(-x) = (-x)^2 + 2(-x) = x^2 - 2x$

$\qquad f(-x) \neq f(x)$

(E) $f(x) = \dfrac{1}{1 - x^2}$, $f(-x) = \dfrac{1}{1 - (-x)^2} = \dfrac{1}{1 - x^2}$

$\qquad f(-x) = f(x)$

9. A

A function is odd if $f(-x) = -f(x)$.

Also, since $(3, 7)$ is a point on the graph of f, $f(3) = 7$.

$f(-3) = -f(3)$ $\qquad$ $f(-x) = -f(x)$ by the definition of an odd function.

$f(-3) = -7$ $\qquad$ Substitute 7 for $f(3)$.

Therefore $(-3, -7)$ is a point on the graph of f.

10. E

The functions f and g are inverse functions if $f(g(x)) = x$ or $g(f(x)) = x$.

$f(x) = 2x + 3$ $\quad$ To find an inverse function:

1. Replace $f(x)$ with y. $\qquad y = 2x + 3$
2. Interchange x and y. $\qquad x = 2y + 3$
3. Solve for y. $\qquad x - 3 = 2y$

$\Rightarrow y = \dfrac{x - 3}{2} \Rightarrow g(x) = \dfrac{x - 3}{2}$

11. B

The slope of the line segment is $\dfrac{6 - 0}{-3 - 0} = -2$.

Since the line segment passes through the origin the equation of the line segment is $f(x) = -2x$.

Find an inverse function:
1. Replace $f(x)$ with y. $\qquad y = -2x$
2. Interchange x and y. $\qquad x = -2y$
3. Solve for y. $\qquad y = -\dfrac{1}{2}x$

$\Rightarrow f^{-1}(x) = -\dfrac{1}{2}x \Rightarrow f^{-1}(3) = -\dfrac{1}{2}(3) = -1.5$

12. A $\quad$ $\boxed{L2}$

$f(x) = \begin{cases} x^2 + 2x & \text{if } x < 0 \\ [x] + 1 & \text{if } 0 \leq x < 1 \\ |x - 1| & \text{if } x \geq 1 \end{cases}$

$f(-1) = (-1)^2 + 2(-1) = -1$ $\qquad -1 < 0$

$f(0.5) = [0.5] + 1 = 0 + 1 = 1$ $\qquad 0 \leq 0.5 < 1$

$f(1.5) = |1.5 - 1| = |0.5| = 0.5$ $\qquad 1.5 \geq 1$

$f(-1) + f(0.5) + f(1.5)$
$= -1 + 1 + 0.5 = 0.5$

13. C $\boxed{L2}$

I. An even function is symmetric about the y-axis. $f(x)$ is not.
Roman numeral I is not true.

II. The graph shows three x-intercepts.
Therefore $f(x)$ has three real zeros.
Roman numeral II is not true.

III. $f(x)$ is a fourth degree function, and $f(x) \to \infty$ as $x \to -\infty$ and as $x \to \infty$.
Therefore the leading coefficient is positive.
Roman numeral III is true.

14. C $\boxed{L2}$

$$f(x) = \begin{cases} \dfrac{x^2 - x - 2}{x - 2} & \text{if } x < 2 \\ 2 & \text{if } x \geq 2 \end{cases}$$

Graph the piecewise function.

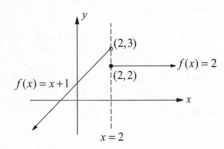

The part of the graph of $f(x)$ that lies to the left of the vertical line $x = 2$ is the graph of

$$f(x) = \frac{x^2 - x - 2}{x - 2} = \frac{(x - 2)(x + 1)}{x - 2} = x + 1.$$

The part of the graph that lies to the right of the vertical line $x = 2$ is $f(x) = 2$.

The open dot indicates that the point $(2, 3)$ is excluded from the graph, and the solid dot indicates that the point $(2, 2)$ is included on the graph.

From the graph we can see that the range of the function is $-\infty < y < 3$.

15. D $\boxed{L2}$

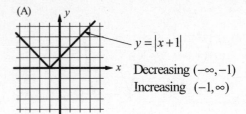

(A) $y = |x + 1|$

Decreasing $(-\infty, -1)$
Increasing $(-1, \infty)$

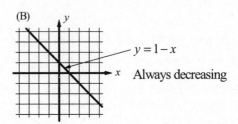

(B) $y = 1 - x$

Always decreasing

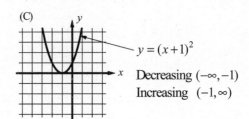

(C) $y = (x + 1)^2$

Decreasing $(-\infty, -1)$
Increasing $(-1, \infty)$

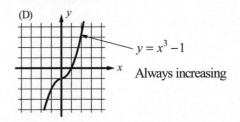

(D) $y = x^3 - 1$

Always increasing

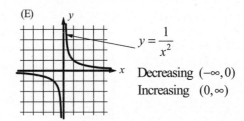

(E) $y = \dfrac{1}{x^2}$

Decreasing $(-\infty, 0)$
Increasing $(0, \infty)$

$y = x^3 - 1$ is an increasing function since the function is always increasing.

Choice (D) is correct.

16. E $\boxed{L2}$

The graph of choice (E) is <u>always</u> decreasing.

Choice (E) is correct.

CHAPTER 8
Analytic Geometry

8-1. Distance Formula

The distance between two points with coordinates (x_1, y_1) and (x_2, y_2) is given by

$d = \sqrt{(x_2 - x_1)^2 + (y_2 - y_1)^2}$.

Example 1 □ Find the value of h if the distance between the points $(3, 10)$ and $(h, 4)$ is 10.

Solution □ $d = \sqrt{(h-3)^2 + (4-10)^2} = 10$ Distance formula

$(h-3)^2 + 36 = 100$ Simplify and square both sides.

$(h-3)^2 = 64$

$h - 3 = \pm 8$ Find the square root.

$h = 11$ or $h = -5$ Answer

8-2. Midpoint Formula

The midpoint of a line segment with endpoints (x_1, y_1) and (x_2, y_2) is the point with

coordinates $M(\dfrac{x_1 + x_2}{2}, \dfrac{y_1 + y_2}{2})$.

Example 2 □ If a line segment has its midpoint at the coordinates $(5, 12)$ and one endpoint at the coordinates $(11, 4)$, what are the coordinates of the other endpoint?

Solution □ Let (x, y) be the coordinates of the other endpoint.

Then $(5, 12) = (\dfrac{11 + x}{2}, \dfrac{4 + y}{2})$. $\Rightarrow$ $5 = \dfrac{11 + x}{2}$ and $12 = \dfrac{4 + y}{2}$

$\Rightarrow$ $x = -1$ and $y = 20$

The coordinates of the other endpoint are $(-1, 20)$.

8-3. Circles

The equation of a circle with center (h, k) and radius r units is $(x - h)^2 + (y - k)^2 = r^2$.

Example 3 □ Find the center and radius of a circle with equation
$x^2 + y^2 + 10x - 6y - 47 = 0$.

Solution □ $(x^2 + 10x + \Box) + (y^2 - 6y + \Box) = 47$ Rearrange the terms.

$(x^2 + 10x + 25) + (y^2 - 6y + 9) = 47 + \boxed{25} + \boxed{9}$ Add $(\dfrac{10}{2})^2$ and $(\dfrac{-6}{2})^2$ to complete

the square for each variable.

$(x + 5)^2 + (y - 3)^2 = 9^2$ Factor to write the equation in the

form $(x - h)^2 + (y - k)^2 = r^2$.

The center of the circle is $(-5, 3)$ and the radius is 9.

8-4. Parabolas

A parabola whose equation is $y = a(x-h)^2 + k$ opens upward if $a > 0$ and downward if $a < 0$. It has a vertex $V(h,k)$ and an axis of symmetry $x = h$.

A parabola whose equation is $x = a(y-k)^2 + h$ opens to the right if $a > 0$ and to the left if $a < 0$. It has a vertex $V(h,k)$ and an axis of symmetry $y = k$.

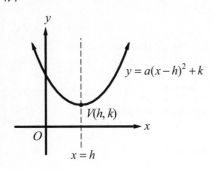

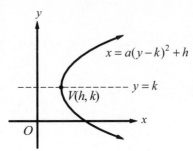

Example 4 □   Find the vertex and axis of symmetry of the parabola $y^2 - 4x - 10y + 5 = 0$.

Solution   □ $4x - 5 = y^2 - 10y$ Rearrange the terms.

$4x - 5 + 25 = y^2 - 10y + 25$ Add $(\frac{-10}{2})^2$, or 25, to both sides.

$4(x+5) = (y-5)^2$ Factor.

$x + 5 = \dfrac{1}{4}(y-5)^2$ or $x = \dfrac{1}{4}(y-5)^2 - 5$ Divide by 4 on both sides.

The vertex is $V(-5,5)$ and
the axis of symmetry is $y = 5$.   Answer

8-5. Ellipses $\boxed{L2}$

The standard form for the equation of an ellipse with center (h,k) and a **horizontal major axis** is

$\dfrac{(x-h)^2}{a^2} + \dfrac{(y-k)^2}{b^2} = 1$, where $a^2 > b^2$.

The standard form for the equation of an ellipse with center (h,k) and a **vertical major axis** is

$\dfrac{(x-h)^2}{b^2} + \dfrac{(y-k)^2}{a^2} = 1$, where $a^2 > b^2$.

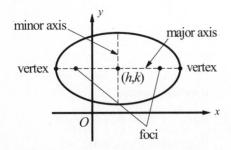

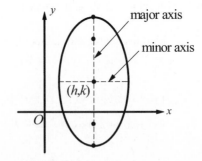

The **length of the major axis** of an ellipse is $2a$. The **length of the minor axis** of an ellipse is $2b$.

The **area of an ellipse** $= \pi ab$.

If the center is $(0,0)$ the equation of an ellipse with a horizontal major axis is

$\dfrac{x^2}{a^2} + \dfrac{y^2}{b^2} = 1$, where $a^2 > b^2$.

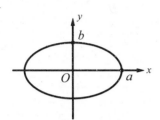

If the center is $(0,0)$ the equation of an ellipse with a vertical major axis is

$\dfrac{x^2}{b^2} + \dfrac{y^2}{a^2} = 1$, where $a^2 > b^2$.

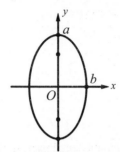

Example 5 ◻   What is the length of the major axis of the ellipse whose equation is
$12x^2 + 4y^2 = 48$?

Solution   ◻ $\dfrac{12x^2}{48} + \dfrac{4y^2}{48} = \dfrac{48}{48}$ Divide both sides by 48.

$\dfrac{x^2}{4} + \dfrac{y^2}{12} = 1$ Standard form for the equation of an ellipse

So, $a = \sqrt{12}$ and $b = 2$.

The length of the major axis is
$2a = 2 \cdot \sqrt{12} = 2 \cdot 2\sqrt{3} = 4\sqrt{3}$.   Answer

8-6. Hyperbolas $\boxed{L2}$

For a hyperbola with center (h,k) that opens to the left and right, the standard form of the equation is $\dfrac{(x-h)^2}{a^2} - \dfrac{(y-k)^2}{b^2} = 1$, where a is the distance from the center to a vertex.

If the center is $(0,0)$ the standard form of the equation is $\dfrac{x^2}{a^2} - \dfrac{y^2}{b^2} = 1$.

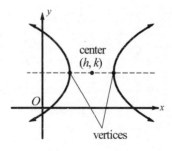

<u>Note</u>: Calculating $y = \pm \dfrac{a}{b}x$ gives you the asymptotes of the hyperbola, but on the SAT you
will not need to find the asymptotes or the value of b of a hyperbola.

For a hyperbola with center (h, k) that opens upward and downward, the standard form of the equation is $\dfrac{(y-k)^2}{a^2} - \dfrac{(x-h)^2}{b^2} = 1$, where a is the distance from center to a vertex.

If the center is $(0, 0)$ the standard form of the equation is $\dfrac{y^2}{a^2} - \dfrac{x^2}{b^2} = 1$.

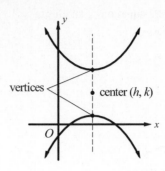

Example 6 □   Find the coordinates of the center of the hyperbola whose equation is $x^2 - 4y^2 + 10x + 24y - 27 = 0$.

Solution   □ $(x^2 + 10x + 25) - 4(y^2 - 6y + 9)$ To complete the square rearrange the terms

$= 27 + 25 - 36$ and add $(\dfrac{10}{2})^2$ and $-4 \cdot (\dfrac{-6}{2})^2$ to both sides.

$(x+5)^2 - 4(y-3)^2 = 16$ Complete the square.

$\dfrac{(x+5)^2}{16} - \dfrac{(y-3)^2}{4} = 1$ Standard form for the equation of a hyperbola

Therefore the center of the hyperbola is $(-5, 3)$.

8-7. Solving Quadratic Systems $\boxed{L2}$

The graph of a system of equations with a line and one or two conic sections will have anywhere from zero to four solutions. Any figure that can be formed by slicing a double cone is called a conic section.

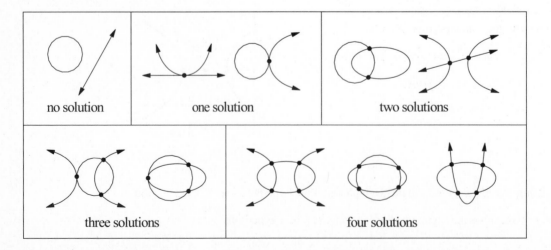

Most conic sections are relations, not functions. Since graphing calculators plot only functions, you must change the equations of conics into the format $y = f(x)$ where $f(x)$ is a function.

Example 7 □ How many solutions exist for the system of equations $\begin{cases} x^2 - y^2 = 16 \\ \dfrac{(x+2)^2}{16} + \dfrac{y^2}{9} = 1 \end{cases}$?

Solution □ Solve the first equation for y.

$$y^2 = x^2 - 16 \;\Rightarrow\; y = \pm\sqrt{x^2 - 16}$$

Enter the equations $y_1 = \sqrt{x^2 - 16}$ and $y_2 = -\sqrt{x^2 - 16}$ into the calculator and graph in the standard viewing window.

Solve the second equation for y.

$$\frac{y^2}{9} = 1 - \frac{(x+2)^2}{16} \;\Rightarrow\; y^2 = 9 - \frac{9(x+2)^2}{16} \;\Rightarrow\; y = \pm\sqrt{9 - \frac{9(x+2)^2}{16}}$$

Enter the equations $y_3 = \sqrt{9 - \dfrac{9(x+2)^2}{16}}$ and $y_4 = -\sqrt{9 - \dfrac{9(x+2)^2}{16}}$ into the calculator and graph in the standard viewing window.

The graph of the equation $x^2 - y^2 = 16$ is the hyperbola whose vertices are $(-4, 0)$ and $(4, 0)$. The graph of the equation $\dfrac{(x+2)^2}{16} + \dfrac{y^2}{9} = 1$ is an ellipse whose center is at $(-2, 0)$. The length of the major axis is 8 and the length of minor axis is 6.

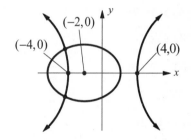

There are two solutions.

1. What is the length of the line segment on the line $y = -x + 4$ whose endpoints have x-coordinates 3 and 9?

   (A) 6

   (B) $5\sqrt{2}$

   (C) $6\sqrt{2}$

   (D) $8\sqrt{2}$

   (E) 14

2. If the point $(-2, 1)$ is the midpoint of the line segment with endpoints $(6, -5)$ and (x, y), then $(x, y) =$

   (A) $(-10, 7)$

   (B) $(-8, 7)$

   (C) $(-2, -4)$

   (D) $(2, -1)$

   (E) $(4, -2)$

3. Three points $P(-2, 0)$, $Q(6, 4)$, and $R(3, 0)$ are connected to form a triangle in an xy-plane. Which of the following is true about the triangle?

   I. $PR = QR$
   II. The area of $\triangle PQR$ is 10.
   III. If M is the midpoint of $\overline{PQ}$, then $\overline{PQ} \perp \overline{MR}$.

   (A) I only

   (B) II only

   (C) I and II only

   (D) I and III only

   (E) I, II, and III

4. If the line $x = -3$ and the circle with center $(1, 2)$ and radius 6 intersect on the xy-plane, what are the y-coordinates of the points of intersection?

   (A) -2.47 and 6.47

   (B) -4.47 and 8.47

   (C) -0.42 and -9.58

   (D) -1 and 7

   (E) -2 and 6

5. Which of the following is the equation of the circle that has center $(4, -3)$ and passes through $(8, 3)$?

   (A) $(x+4)^2 + (y-3)^2 = 52$

   (B) $(x-4)^2 + (y+3)^2 = 52$

   (C) $(x+4)^2 + (y-3)^2 = 100$

   (D) $(x-4)^2 + (y+3)^2 = 16$

   (E) $(x-4)^2 + (y+3)^2 = 81$

6. Which of the following is the center of the circle whose equation is $2x^2 - 8x + 2y^2 + 10y + \dfrac{9}{2} = 0$?

   (A) $(-2, -\dfrac{5}{4})$

   (B) $(-2, \dfrac{5}{2})$

   (C) $(2, -\dfrac{5}{2})$

   (D) $(2, -\dfrac{5}{4})$

   (E) $(2, \dfrac{5}{2})$

7. Which of the following could be the center of a circle tangent to the x-axis and the y-axis?

(A) $(-2,-3)$

(B) $(-3,-3)$

(C) $(0,2)$

(D) $(2,3)$

(E) $(3,4)$

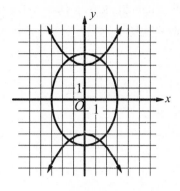

Figure 1

8. If the two circles $(x+2)^2 + (y+2)^2 = 2$ and $x^2 + y^2 = 2$ are tangent to each other, what are the coordinates of the point of tangency?

(A) $(-0.71, 0.71)$

(B) $(-1.41, 1.41)$

(C) $(-1, -1)$

(D) $(-2, -2)$

(E) $(-2.12, -2.12)$

10. Which of the following systems of equations is represented by the graph in Figure 1? $\boxed{L2}$

(A) $\begin{cases} \dfrac{x^2}{4} - \dfrac{y^2}{9} = 1 \\ \dfrac{x^2}{16} + \dfrac{y^2}{9} = 1 \end{cases}$

(B) $\begin{cases} \dfrac{x^2}{4} - \dfrac{y^2}{9} = 1 \\ \dfrac{x^2}{9} + \dfrac{y^2}{16} = 1 \end{cases}$

(C) $\begin{cases} \dfrac{y^2}{9} - \dfrac{x^2}{4} = 1 \\ \dfrac{x^2}{16} + \dfrac{y^2}{9} = 1 \end{cases}$

9. The graph of $x^2 - 2y^2 + 6x - 16y - 27 = 0$ is a hyperbola centered at $\boxed{L2}$

(A) $(-3, 4)$

(B) $(3, -4)$

(C) $(-3, -4)$

(D) $(3, 4)$

(E) $(-6, 8)$

(D) $\begin{cases} \dfrac{y^2}{9} - \dfrac{x^2}{4} = 1 \\ \dfrac{x^2}{3} + \dfrac{y^2}{4} = 1 \end{cases}$

(E) $\begin{cases} \dfrac{y^2}{9} - \dfrac{x^2}{4} = 1 \\ \dfrac{x^2}{9} + \dfrac{y^2}{16} = 1 \end{cases}$

11. What is the length of the major axis of the ellipse whose equation is $4x^2 + 25y^2 = 100$? [L2]

    (A) 2

    (B) 4

    (C) 5

    (D) 10

    (E) 12.5

12. At how many points do the graphs of $x^2 - y^2 = 6$ and $xy = 4$ intersect? [L2]

    (A) None

    (B) One

    (C) Two

    (D) Three

    (E) Four

13. The formula for the area of an ellipse is given by $A = \pi ab$, where a and b are one-half the lengths of the major and minor axes, respectively. What is the area enclosed by the ellipse whose equation is $4x^2 + 9(y-6)^2 = 36$? [L2]

    (A) 4π

    (B) 6π

    (C) 9π

    (D) 24π

    (E) 36π

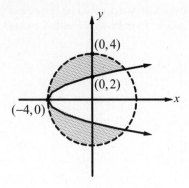

Figure 2

14. Which of the following systems of inequalities is represented by the graph in Figure 2? [L2]

(A) $\begin{cases} x^2 + y^2 > 4 \\ x \le y^2 + 4 \end{cases}$

(B) $\begin{cases} x^2 + y^2 < 4 \\ x \ge y^2 - 4 \end{cases}$

(C) $\begin{cases} x^2 + y^2 > 16 \\ x \le y^2 - 4 \end{cases}$

(D) $\begin{cases} x^2 + y^2 < 16 \\ x \le y^2 - 4 \end{cases}$

(E) $\begin{cases} x^2 + y^2 < 16 \\ x \ge y^2 - 4 \end{cases}$

Answer Key

1. C	2. A	3. E	4. A	5. B
6. C	7. B	8. C	9. C	10. E
11. D	12. C	13. B	14. D	

Answers and Explanations

1. C

$y = -x + 4$

If the x-coordinate is 3, the y-coordinate is
$y = -(3) + 4$, or 1.

If the x-coordinate is 9, the y-coordinate is
$y = -(9) + 4$, or -5.

The length of the line segment between $(3,1)$ and
$(9,-5)$ is

$$d = \sqrt{(9-3)^2 + (-5-1)^2}$$
$$= \sqrt{36+36}$$
$$= 6\sqrt{2}$$

2. A

Use the midpoint formula.

$$(-2,1) = (\frac{6+x}{2}, \frac{-5+y}{2})$$

$$\Rightarrow -2 = \frac{6+x}{2} \text{ and } 1 = \frac{-5+y}{2}$$

$$\Rightarrow x = -10 \text{ and } y = 7$$

$$(x,y) = (-10,7)$$

3. E

$P(-2,0)$, $Q(6,4)$, $R(3,0)$

I. $PR = \sqrt{(3-(-2))^2 + (0-0)^2} = \sqrt{25} = 5$

$QR = \sqrt{(6-3)^2 + (4-0)^2} = \sqrt{25} = 5$

Therefore $PR = QR$, and Roman numeral I is true.

II. Draw the triangle on the xy-plane.

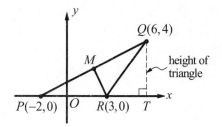

Area of $\triangle PQR = \frac{1}{2} \cdot PR \cdot QT = \frac{1}{2}(5)(4) = 10$

Roman numeral II is true.

III. M is the midpoint of $\overline{PQ}$.

Use the midpoint formula.

$$M = (\frac{-2+6}{2}, \frac{0+4}{2}) = (2,2)$$

Slope of $\overline{PQ} = \frac{4-0}{6-(-2)} = \frac{1}{2}$

Slope of $\overline{MR} = \frac{2-0}{2-3} = -2$

$(\frac{1}{2})(-2) = -1$, therefore the two lines are

perpendicular.

Roman numeral III is true.

4. A

The equation of the circle with center $(1,2)$ and

radius 6 is $(x-1)^2 + (y-2)^2 = 6^2$.

Substitute $x = -3$ into the equation of the circle
since the line intersects the circle.

$$(-3-1)^2 + (y-2)^2 = 6^2$$
$$16 + (y-2)^2 = 36$$
$$(y-2)^2 = 20$$
$$y - 2 = \pm\sqrt{20}$$
$$y = 2 + \sqrt{20} \approx 6.47 \text{ or}$$
$$y = 2 - \sqrt{20} \approx -2.47$$

5. B

The equation of a circle with center $(4,-3)$ is

$(x-4)^2 + (y+3)^2 = r^2$.

Substitute $x = 8$ and $y = 3$ into the equation since the circle passes through $(8,3)$.

$(8-4)^2 + (3+3)^2 = r^2$

$16 + 36 = r^2 \Rightarrow r^2 = 52$

The equation is $(x-4)^2 + (y+3)^2 = 52$.

6. C

$2x^2 - 8x + 2y^2 + 10y + \dfrac{9}{2} = 0$

Complete the square for the x-terms and then the y-terms.

$2(x^2 - 4x + \boxed{4}) + 2(y^2 + 5y + \boxed{\dfrac{25}{4}}) = -\dfrac{9}{2} + 8 + \dfrac{25}{2}$

$\Rightarrow 2(x-2)^2 + 2(y+\dfrac{5}{2})^2 = 16$

The center of the circle is $(2, -\dfrac{5}{2})$.

7. B

Since the circle is tangent to both the x-axis and the y-axis, the center of the circle should lie on the line $y = x$ or $y = -x$.

The point $(-3,-3)$ lies on the line $y = x$.

Choice (B) is correct.

8. C

Sketch the circles on the xy-plane.

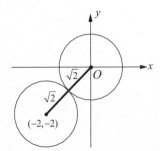

The point of tangency lies in Quadrant III. Eliminate choices (A) and (B).

Now find the center and radius of each circle.

$(x+2)^2 + (y+2)^2 = 2$

$\Rightarrow$ Center $(-2,-2)$, $r = \sqrt{2}$

$x^2 + y^2 = 2$

$\Rightarrow$ Center $(0,0)$, $r = \sqrt{2}$

Since the two circles have the same radius and are tangent to each other, the point of tangency is the midpoint between the two centers of the circles.

Use the midpoint formula.

$M = (\dfrac{-2+0}{2}, \dfrac{-2+0}{2}) = (-1,-1)$

9. C   L2

$x^2 - 2y^2 + 6x - 16y - 27 = 0$

Complete the square for the x-terms and then the y-terms.

$(x^2 + 6x + \boxed{?}) - 2(y^2 + 8y + \boxed{?}) = 27 + \Box - 2\Box$

$(x^2 + 6x + 9) - 2(y^2 + 8y + 16) = 27 + 9 - 2(16)$

$(x+3)^2 - 2(y+4)^2 = 4$

$\dfrac{(x+3)^2}{4} - \dfrac{(y+4)^2}{2} = 1$

The center of the hyperbola is $(-3,-4)$.

10. E   L2

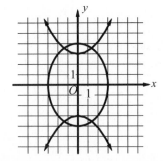

The major axis of the ellipse is vertical, and the length is 8. The length of the minor axis is 6. Therefore $a = 4$ and $b = 3$, and the equation of the ellipse is $\dfrac{x^2}{9} + \dfrac{y^2}{16} = 1$. Eliminate choices (A), (C), and (D).

The graph of the hyperbola opens upward and downward and the distance from the center to the vertex is 4; therefore $a = 4$. We do not know the value of b, but we know the equation of the hyperbola should look like $\dfrac{y^2}{9} - \dfrac{x^2}{\square} = 1$.

Choice (E) is correct.

11. D $\boxed{L2}$

$4x^2 + 25y^2 = 100$

Change the equation into standard form.

$\dfrac{x^2}{25} + \dfrac{y^2}{4} = 1 \;\Rightarrow\; a^2 = 25 \;\Rightarrow\; a = 5$

Length of major axis $= 2a = 2 \cdot 5 = 10$.

12. C $\boxed{L2}$

Solve the equations $x^2 - y^2 = 6$ and $xy = 4$ for y.

$x^2 - y^2 = 6 \;\Rightarrow\; y^2 = x^2 - 6$

$\Rightarrow\; y = \pm\sqrt{x^2 - 6}$

Use a graphing calculator to graph

$y_1 = \sqrt{x^2 - 6}$ and

$y_2 = -\sqrt{x^2 - 6}$.

Now solve and graph the second equation.

$xy = 4 \;\Rightarrow\; y = \dfrac{4}{x}$

Graph $y_3 = \dfrac{4}{x}$.

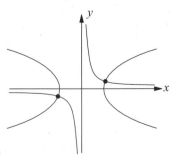

There are two points of intersection.

13. B $\boxed{L2}$

$4x^2 + 9(y-6)^2 = 36 \;\Rightarrow\; \dfrac{x^2}{9} + \dfrac{(y-6)^2}{4} = 1$

$\Rightarrow\; a^2 = 9,\; b^2 = 4$

$\Rightarrow\; a = 3,\; b = 2$

$A = \pi ab = \pi \cdot 3 \cdot 2 = 6\pi$

14. D $\boxed{L2}$

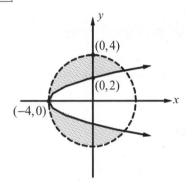

Figure 2

The equation of the circle is $x^2 + y^2 = 16$ and the equation of the parabola is $x = y^2 - 4$.

Eliminate choices (A) and (B), which do not include both equations.

Test the remaining answer choices with the point $(0,3)$, which lies in the shaded region.

(C) $0 + 3^2 > 16$ Not true
     $0 \le 3^2 - 4$ True

(D) $0^2 + 3^2 < 16$ True
     $0 \le 3^2 - 4$ True

(E) $0^2 + 3^2 < 16$ True
     $0 \ge 3^2 - 4$ Not true

Choice (D) is correct.

CHAPTER 9
Exponential and Logarithmic Functions

9-1. Exponential Functions

An equation of the form $y = b^x$, where b is positive and $b \neq 1$, is called an **exponential function** with base b.

General Rules for Exponential Functions

1. If $b > 1$, the value of y increases as the value of x increases.
2. If $b < 1$, the value of y increases as the value of x decreases.
3. The domain is $(-\infty, \infty)$ and the range is $(0, \infty)$.
4. The y-intercept of the graph is 1 and there is no x-intercept.

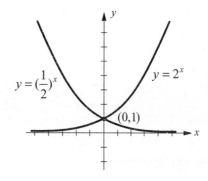

Definition of $b^{\frac{m}{n}}$

If m and n are positive integers then $b^{\frac{m}{n}} = \sqrt[n]{b^m}$.

> Example 1 □ Simplify.   a. $16^{-3/4}$ b. $\dfrac{\sqrt[3]{16}}{\sqrt[3]{4}}$
>
> Solution □ a. $16^{-3/4} = \dfrac{1}{16^{3/4}} = \dfrac{1}{(2^4)^{3/4}} = \dfrac{1}{2^3} = \dfrac{1}{8}$
>
>   b. $\dfrac{\sqrt[3]{16}}{\sqrt[3]{4}} = \dfrac{\sqrt[3]{2^4}}{\sqrt[3]{2^2}} = \dfrac{2^{4/3}}{2^{2/3}} = 2^{(4/3-2/3)} = 2^{2/3} \quad = \sqrt[3]{2^2} \quad = \sqrt[3]{4}$
>
>   ↑   ↑
>   exponential form   simplest radical form

9-2. Logarithmic Functions

Definition of Logarithm

If b and x are positive and $b \neq 1$, $\log_b x = y$ if and only if $x = b^y$. An equation of the form $y = \log_b x$ is called a **logarithmic function**. The domain of a logarithmic function is $(0, \infty)$ and the range is $(-\infty, \infty)$.

The exponential function $y = b^x$ and the logarithmic function $y = \log_b x$ are **inverses** of each other. That is, if $f(x) = b^x$, then $f^{-1}(x) = \log_b x$.

For inverse functions it is true that $f(f^{-1}(x)) = x$ and $f^{-1}(f(x)) = x$.

Therefore for the function $f(x) = b^x$ and its inverse function $f^{-1}(x) = \log_b x$,

$f(f^{-1}(x)) = f(\log_b x) = b^{\log_b x} = x$ and

$f^{-1}(f(x)) = f^{-1}(b^x) = \log_b b^x = x$.

Example 2 □   a. Simplify $\log_3 9\sqrt{3}$.   b. Solve $\log_5 x = -2$.

c. Evaluate $\log_7 7^3$.   d. Evaluate $4^{\log_4 9}$.

Solution   □   a. Let $x = \log_3 9\sqrt{3}$

$3^x = 9\sqrt{3}$ Definition of
logarithm

$3^x = 3^2 \cdot 3^{1/2}$

$3^x = 3^{5/2}$

$x = \dfrac{5}{2}$

$\log_3 9\sqrt{3} = \dfrac{5}{2}$.   Answer

b. $\log_5 x = -2$

$x = 5^{-2}$ Definition of logarithm

$x = \dfrac{1}{25}$ Answer

c. $\log_7 7^3 = 3$ $\log_b b^x = x$

d. $4^{\log_4 9} = 9$ $b^{\log_b x} = x$ ■

9-3. Properties of Logarithms

For all positive numbers M, N, and b, where $b \neq 1$:

1. $\log_b MN = \log_b M + \log_b N$

4. $b^{\log_b N} = N$

2. $\log_b \dfrac{M}{N} = \log_b M - \log_b N$

5. $\log_b b = 1$

3. $\log_b M^p = p \cdot \log_b M$

6. $\log_b 1 = 0$

Example 3 □   Solve $\log_2(x+2) + \log_2(x-2) = 5$.

Solution   □   a. $\log_2(x+2) + \log_2(x-2) = 5$

$\log_2(x+2)(x-2) = 5$ $\log_b MN = \log_b M + \log_b N$

$\log_2(x^2 - 4) = 5$

$x^2 - 4 = 2^5$ Definition of logarithm

$x^2 = 36$

$x = 6$ $x = -6$ cannot be a solution since the
domain of a logarithmic function does
not contain negative numbers.   ■

9-4. Property of Equality for Exponential and Logarithmic Functions

If b is positive and $b \neq 1$, then $b^x = b^y$ if and only if $x = y$.

If b is positive and $b \neq 1$, then $\log_b M = \log_b N$ if and only if $M = N$.

Example 4 □   Solve.   a. $5^{x+1} = 25^{5-x}$ b. $\log_3(x-7) - \log_3 5 = 2\log_3 4$

Solution   □   a. $5^{x+1} = 25^{5-x}$

$5^{x+1} = (5^2)^{5-x}$ $25 = 5^2$

$5^{x+1} = 5^{10-2x}$ Law of exponents

$x + 1 = 10 - 2x$ Property of equality for exponential functions

$x = 3$ Answer

b. $\log_3(x-7) - \log_3 5 = 2\log_3 4$

$$\log_3 \frac{(x-7)}{5} = 2\log_3 4 \qquad \log_b \frac{M}{N} = \log_b M - \log_b N$$

$$\log_3 \frac{(x-7)}{5} = \log_3 4^2 \qquad \log_b M^p = p \cdot \log_b M$$

$$\frac{(x-7)}{5} = 4^2 \qquad \text{Property of equality for logarithmic functions}$$

$$x - 7 = 80$$

$$x = 87 \qquad \text{Answer}$$

9-5. Common and Natural Logarithms

Common Logarithms

The function $y = \log_{10} x$ is called the **common logarithmic function**. It is usually written without the subscript 10, so $\log_{10} x$ is written as **$\log x$**.

Natural Logarithms $\boxed{L2}$

The function $y = \log_e x$ is called the **natural logarithmic function**. It is usually written without the subscript e, and is written as **$\ln x$**. The number e is an irrational number whose value is approximately 2.718.

The only logarithmic functions programmed in a graphing calculator are the common logarithmic function $y = \log x$ and the natural logarithmic function $y = \ln x$.

A formula called the **change of base formula** can be used to graph or evaluate logarithmic functions with bases other than 10 and e.

Change of Base Formula

$$\log_b x = \frac{\log_a x}{\log_a b}$$

Example 5 ☐   a. Find the value of $\log_7 52$.   b. Solve $5^x = 38$.

Solution   ☐   a. $\log_7 52 = \dfrac{\log 52}{\log 7}$ Change of base formula

$$\approx \frac{1.716}{.845} \qquad \text{Use calculator.}$$

$$\approx 2.03 \qquad \text{Answer}$$

b. $5^x = 38$

$\ln 5^x = \ln 38$ Take the natural log of each side.

$x\ln 5 = \ln 38$ Property of logarithms

$x = \dfrac{\ln 38}{\ln 5}$ Divide both sides by $\ln 5$, then use a calculator.

$x \approx 2.26$ Answer

9-6. Formulas for Compound Interest and Population Growth

The equation $A = P(1+r)^t$ yields the **final amount** of money or final population, A, given that
$P =$ the **initial amount** of money invested or the initial population,
$t =$ the **number of years elapsed** since the money was invested or population growth began, and
$r =$ the **annual interest rate**, or population growth rate.

The equation for compound interest is modified when interest is not compounded annually:

$A = P(1+\dfrac{r}{4})^{4t}$ if the interest is compounded **quarterly**,

$A = P(1+\dfrac{r}{12})^{12t}$ if the interest is compounded **monthly**,

$A = P(1+\dfrac{r}{365})^{365t}$ if the interest is compounded **daily**,

$A = Pe^{rt}$ if the interest is compounded **continuously**.

Example 6 □   a. A town has a population of 27,500 people at the end of 2005. If the population is increasing at the rate of 8% per year, what will the population of the town be at the end of 2015?

b. How long will it take for an investment to double in value at 6% interest compounded continuously?

Solution   □   a. $A = P(1+r)^t$, where the population grows at r percent per year.

$A = 27500(1+0.08)^{10}$ Make substitutions: $P = 27500$, $r = 0.08$, and $t = 10$.

$= 27500(1.08)^{10}$
$= 59{,}370$ Answer

b. $A = Pe^{rt}$, if interest is compounded continuously.

$A = Pe^{0.06t}$ $r = 0.06$

$2P = Pe^{0.06t}$ Since the investment doubles in value, $A = 2P$.

$2 = e^{0.06t}$ Divide both sides by P and simplify.

$\ln 2 = \ln e^{0.06t}$ Take the natural log of each side.

$\ln 2 = 0.06t \cdot \ln e$ Property of logarithm

$\ln 2 = 0.06t$ $\ln e = 1$

$t = \dfrac{\ln 2}{0.06}$ Divide both sides by 0.06.

≈ 11.55 Answer

9-7. Exponential Growth and Decay $\boxed{L2}$

Exponential Growth Formula

$f(t) = a \cdot e^{kt}$ where

$k > 0$,

a = the initial population count, and

t = the number of years (or any other unit of time) elapsed since a given starting point.

Exponential Decay Formula

$f(t) = a \cdot e^{kt}$ where

$k < 0$,

a = the initial amount of a substance, and

t = the number of years (or any other unit of time) elapsed since a given starting point.

When dealing with the time n required to double or half the amount of a substance, the model for exponential growth and decay can be written as $f(t) = a(2)^{\frac{t}{n}}$ and $f(t) = a(\frac{1}{2})^{\frac{t}{n}}$, respectively.

Example 7 □   a. A certain population of bacteria increases in size according to the exponential function $f(t) = ae^{0.116t}$, where a is the initial amount and t is the number of days elapsed. If the bacteria population is now 1000, what is the number of bacteria in 21 days?

b. The half-life of radium is 1620 years and the amount of radium remaining after t years can be calculated by the exponential function $f(t) = ae^{-0.00043t}$, where a is the initial amount and t is the number of years elapsed. If you start with 50 grams of radium, how much will be left after 500 years?

Solution   □   a. $f(t) = ae^{0.116t}$ Exponential growth formula

$f(t) = 1000e^{(0.116)(21)}$ Make substitutions: $a = 1000$ and $t = 21$.

$\approx 11,427$ Answer

b. $f(t) = ae^{-0.00043t}$ Exponential decay formula

$f(t) = 50e^{(-0.00043)(500)}$ Make substitutions: $a = 50$ and $t = 500$.

≈ 40.3 Answer

1. If $f(x) = a \cdot 2^x$ and $f(3) = 4$, then $a =$

   (A) $\dfrac{1}{3}$

   (B) $\dfrac{1}{2}$

   (C) 2

   (D) 3

   (E) 6

2. If $f(x) = \sqrt[4]{x^3}$, then $f(4) =$

   (A) 1.75

   (B) 2

   (C) 2.83

   (D) 6.35

   (E) 8

3. If $25^{(x-1)} = 5\sqrt{5}$, then $x =$

   (A) 0.125

   (B) 0.5

   (C) 0.875

   (D) 1.25

   (E) 1.75

4. $\log_3 14 =$

   (A) 1.1

   (B) 1.4

   (C) 1.9

   (D) 2.4

   (E) 2.9

5. If $f(n) = \dfrac{n}{3^n}$, what is the least integer n such that $f(n) < 0.001$?

   (A) 7

   (B) 8

   (C) 9

   (D) 10

   (E) 11

6. $\log_3 \dfrac{1}{243} =$

   (A) −5

   (B) −4

   (C) −3

   (D) 3

   (E) 5

7. Mike invests \$22,000 at 5.6% interest compounded annually. What is the value of the investment after 8 years?

   (A) \$23,376

   (B) \$26,024

   (C) \$28,556

   (D) \$34,020

   (E) \$36,623

8. The population growth of a bacteria culture can be found by an exponential function $f(t) = a \cdot 16^{0.32t}$, where a is the initial amount and t is the elapsed time in hours. Approximately how many hours would it take for 500 bacteria to grow to 12,000 bacteria?

(A) 2.1

(B) 2.7

(C) 3.6

(D) 4.5

(E) 5.5

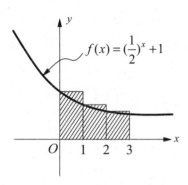

$f(x) = (\frac{1}{2})^x + 1$

Figure 1

Note: Figure not drawn to scale.

9. Figure 1 shows the graph of $f(x) = (\frac{1}{2})^x + 1$.

What is the sum of the areas of the three circumscribed rectangles shown?

(A) 4.75

(B) 5.25

(C) 5.75

(D) 6.5

(E) 7.25

10. If $f(x) = \log_5 x$, then $f^{-1}(2x) =$ $\boxed{L2}$

(A) $(\sqrt[4]{5})^x$

(B) $(\sqrt{5})^x$

(C) 5^x

(D) 10^x

(E) 25^x

11. If $e^x = 10^y$, what is the value of $\dfrac{x}{y}$? $\boxed{L2}$

(A) 0.27

(B) 0.43

(C) 1.67

(D) 2.30

(E) 3.68

12. If $f(x) = 10^x$ and the inverse function of f is denoted by f^{-1}, then what is $f^{-1}(ab)$ where $a > 0$ and $b > 0$? $\boxed{L2}$

(A) 10^{ab}

(B) $\log_{10}(a+b)$

(C) $\log_{10} a + \log_{10} b$

(D) $\dfrac{1}{\log_{10}(ab)}$

(E) $\log_{10} a \cdot \log_{10} b$

13. If $f(x) = \log_2 x$, then $f^{-1}(\frac{x}{2}) =$ L2

    (A) $(\sqrt[4]{2})^x$

    (B) $(\sqrt{2})^x$

    (C) 2^x

    (D) 4^x

    (E) x^2

14. Which of the following is the solution of the equation $2\log_5 x = \log_5(x+2)$?   L2

    (A) -1

    (B) 2

    (C) 3

    (D) 7

    (E) 9

15. If $\log_3 a + \log_3 6 = \log_3 18$, then $a =$ L2

    (A) 3

    (B) 6

    (C) 9

    (D) 12

    (E) 15

16. If $f(x) = a \cdot b^x$, then $\log f(6) - \log f(2) =$ L2

    (A) b^4

    (B) ab^4

    (C) $3\log ab$

    (D) $4\log b$

    (E) $\log(ab^6 - ab^2)$

17. If $f(x) = \ln 2x$ and the inverse function of f is denoted by f^{-1}, then what is $f^{-1}(a-b)$ where $a > b > 0$?   L2

    (A) $\dfrac{e^a - e^b}{2}$

    (B) $\dfrac{e^a}{2e^b}$

    (C) $2(e^a - e^b)$

    (D) $\dfrac{e^a \cdot e^b}{2}$

    (E) $(a-b)e^x$

Answer Key

1. B	2. C	3. E	4. D	5. C
6. A	7. D	8. C	9. A	10. E
11. D	12. C	13. B	14. B	15. A
16. D	17. B			

Answers and Explanations

1. B

$$f(x) = a \cdot 2^x \text{ and } f(3) = 4$$
$$f(3) = a \cdot 2^3 = 4$$
$$\Rightarrow 8a = 4 \Rightarrow a = \frac{1}{2}$$

2. C

$$f(x) = \sqrt[4]{x^3}$$
$$f(4) = \sqrt[4]{4^3}$$
$$= \sqrt[4]{64} \approx 2.83 \qquad \text{Use a calculator.}$$

3. E

$$25^{(x-1)} = 5\sqrt{5}$$
$$(5^2)^{(x-1)} = 5 \cdot 5^{\frac{1}{2}}$$
$$5^{2x-2} = 5^{\frac{3}{2}}$$
$$2x - 2 = \frac{3}{2}$$
$$x = \frac{7}{4}$$

4. D

$$\log_3 14 = \frac{\log 14}{\log 3} \qquad \text{Apply change of base formula and use a calculator.}$$
$$\approx 2.4$$

5. C

$$f(n) = \frac{n}{3^n}$$

Using your calculator, try each answer choice.

(A) $f(7) = \dfrac{7}{3^7} \approx 0.0032 > 0.001$

(B) $f(8) = \dfrac{8}{3^8} \approx 0.0012 > 0.001$

(C) $f(9) = \dfrac{9}{3^9} \approx 0.000457 < 0.001$

Therefore 9 is the least integer which makes $f(n) < 0.001$.

6. A

$$\log_3 \frac{1}{243} = \log_3 \frac{1}{3^5}$$
$$= \log_3 3^{-5}$$
$$= -5 \log_3 3 \qquad \log M^p = p \log M$$
$$= -5 \qquad \log_3 3 = 1$$

7. D

Use the compound interest formula.

$$A = P(1+r)^t$$
$$A = 22,000(1 + 0.056)^8$$
$$= 34,019.98$$

8. C

$$f(t) = a \cdot 16^{0.32t}$$
$$12,000 = 500 \cdot 16^{0.32t} \qquad a = 500$$
$$\qquad\qquad\qquad\qquad\qquad \text{Final amount} = 12,000$$
$$24 = 16^{0.32t} \qquad \text{Divide by 500.}$$
$$\log 24 = \log 16^{0.32t} \qquad \text{Take the log of both sides.}$$
$$\log 24 = 0.32t \cdot \log 16 \qquad \log M^p = p \log M$$
$$\frac{\log 24}{\log 16} = 0.32t \qquad \text{Divide by } \log 16.$$
$$1.1462 = 0.32t \qquad \text{Simplify.}$$
$$t \approx 3.58 \qquad \text{Answer}$$

9. A

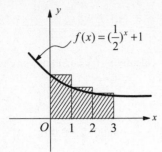

$$f(x) = (\frac{1}{2})^x + 1$$

$$f(0) = (\frac{1}{2})^0 + 1 = 1 + 1 = 2$$

$$f(1) = (\frac{1}{2})^1 + 1 = \frac{1}{2} + 1 = \frac{3}{2}$$

$$f(2) = (\frac{1}{2})^2 + 1 = \frac{1}{4} + 1 = \frac{5}{4}$$

Sum of the areas of the rectangles
$$= 1 \cdot f(0) + 1 \cdot f(1) + 1 \cdot f(2)$$
$$= 2 + \frac{3}{2} + \frac{5}{4}$$
$$= 4.75$$

10. E $\boxed{L2}$

$f(x) = \log_5 x$
To find an inverse function:

1. Replace $f(x)$ with y. $y = \log_5 x$
2. Interchange x and y. $x = \log_5 y$
3. Solve for y. $y = 5^x$

$$\Rightarrow f^{-1}(x) = 5^x$$
$$f^{-1}(2x) = 5^{2x} = (5^2)^x = 25^x$$

11. D $\boxed{L2}$

$e^x = 10^y$
$\ln e^x = \ln 10^y$ Take the natural log of both sides.
$x \ln e = y \ln 10$ $\ln M^p = p \ln M$
$x = y \ln 10$ $\ln e = 1$

$$\frac{x}{y} = \ln 10 \approx 2.3$$

12. C $\boxed{L2}$

$$f(x) = 10^x$$

To find an inverse function:

1. Replace $f(x)$ with y. $y = 10^x$
2. Interchange x and y. $x = 10^y$
3. Solve for y. $\log x = \log 10^y$

$\Rightarrow \log x = y \log 10$
$\Rightarrow y = \log x$ $\log 10 = 1$
$\Rightarrow f^{-1}(x) = \log x$

$$f^{-1}(ab) = \log(ab) = \log a + \log b$$

13. B $\boxed{L2}$

$f(x) = \log_2 x$
To find an inverse function:

1. Replace $f(x)$ with y. $y = \log_2 x$
2. Interchange x and y. $x = \log_2 y$
3. Solve for y.   By the definition of a logarithm, $y = 2^x$.

$$y = 2^x \Rightarrow f^{-1}(x) = 2^x$$
$$f^{-1}(\frac{x}{2}) = 2^{\frac{x}{2}} = (2^{\frac{1}{2}})^x = (\sqrt{2})^x$$

14. B $\boxed{L2}$

$2 \log_5 x = \log_5 (x+2)$
$\log_5 x^2 = \log_5 (x+2)$ $p \log M = \log M^p$
$x^2 = x + 2$ Property of equality
$x^2 - x - 2 = 0$
$(x+1)(x-2) = 0$
$x = -1$ or $x = 2$

If $x = -1$, $\log_5 x$ is undefined. So $x = 2$ is the only solution.

15. A $\boxed{L2}$

$\log_3 a + \log_3 6 = \log_3 18$

$\log_3 a \cdot 6 = \log_3 18$ $\log M + \log N = \log MN$

$6a = 18$ Property of equality

$a = 3$

16. D $\boxed{L2}$

$f(x) = a \cdot b^x$

$\log f(6) - \log f(2)$

$= \log a \cdot b^6 - \log a \cdot b^2$ $f(6) = a \cdot b^6,\ f(2) = a \cdot b^2$

$= \log \dfrac{ab^6}{ab^2}$ $\log M - \log N = \log \dfrac{M}{N}$

$= \log b^4$ Simplify.

$= 4 \log b$ $\log M^p = p \log M$

17. B $\boxed{L2}$

$f(x) = \ln 2x$

To find an inverse function:

1. Replace $f(x)$ with y. $y = \ln 2x$

2. Interchange x and y. $x = \ln 2y$

3. Solve for y.   By the definition of
                              a logarithm, $2y = e^x$.

$2y = e^x \implies y = \dfrac{1}{2}e^x \implies f^{-1}(x) = \dfrac{1}{2}e^x$

$f^{-1}(a-b) = \dfrac{1}{2}e^{(a-b)} = \dfrac{1}{2}e^a \cdot e^{-b} = \dfrac{1}{2} \cdot \dfrac{e^a}{e^b}$

CHAPTER 10
Trigonometric Functions

10-1. Angles and their Measures

An **angle** is a figure formed by two rays with a common endpoint, the vertex.

On a coordinate plane, an angle may be generated by the rotation of two rays that share a vertex at the origin. One ray, called the **initial side** of the angle, is fixed and the other ray, called the **terminal side** of the angle, is rotated about the origin.

An angle is in **standard position** if the vertex is located at $(0,0)$ and the initial side lies along the positive x-axis.

Counterclockwise rotations produce **positive angles** and clockwise rotations produce **negative angles**.

When two angles have the same initial side and the same terminal side, they are called **coterminal angles**. Coterminal angles can be found by adding or subtracting a multiple of $360°$. In the third figure below, the angles of $150°$ and $-210°$ are coterminal angles.

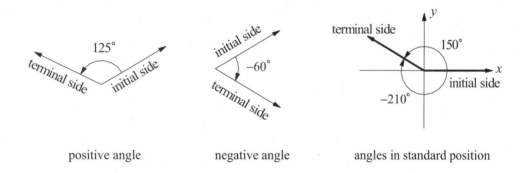

| positive angle | negative angle | angles in standard position |

The Radian Measure of an Angle $\boxed{L2}$

In a circle, one **radian** is the measure of the central angle that intercepts an arc equal in length to the radius of the circle.

Since the circumference of a circle is $2\pi r$ and a complete revolution has degree measure $360°$, 2π radians $= 360°$, or π radians $= 180°$.

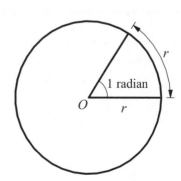

The conversion formula π **radians** $= 180°$ can be used to convert from one system of measurement to the other:

$$1 \text{ radian} = \frac{180°}{\pi} \approx 57.3° \quad \text{and} \quad 1° = \frac{\pi}{180} \text{ radians}$$

Example 1 □   a. Express $75°$ in radians.   b. Express $\dfrac{\pi}{4}$ radians in degrees.

Solution   □   a. $75° = 75 \cdot \dfrac{\pi}{180}$ radians $= \dfrac{5\pi}{12}$ radians   Answer

b. $\dfrac{\pi}{4}$ radians $= \dfrac{\pi}{4} \cdot \dfrac{180°}{\pi} = 45°$ Answer

10-2. Trigonometric Functions of Acute Angles

The trigonometric functions of any angle $0° < \theta < 90°$ are defined as follows:

$\sin\theta = \dfrac{\text{opposite side}}{\text{hypotenuse}} = \dfrac{y}{r}$ $\csc\theta = \dfrac{1}{\sin\theta} = \dfrac{r}{y}$ $(y \neq 0)$

$\cos\theta = \dfrac{\text{adjacent side}}{\text{hypotenuse}} = \dfrac{x}{r}$ $\sec\theta = \dfrac{1}{\cos\theta} = \dfrac{r}{x}$ $(x \neq 0)$

$\tan\theta = \dfrac{\text{opposite side}}{\text{adjacent side}} = \dfrac{y}{x}$ $\cot\theta = \dfrac{1}{\tan\theta} = \dfrac{x}{y}$ $(y \neq 0)$

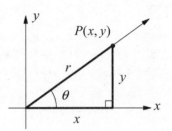

Example 2 □   In the figure at the right, what is the value of x?

Solution   □ $\sin\theta = \dfrac{\text{opposite}}{\text{hypotenuse}}$

$\sin 38° = \dfrac{15}{x}$ $\Rightarrow$

$\sin 38° \cdot x = 15$

$x = \dfrac{15}{\sin 38°} = \dfrac{15}{0.616}$

$= 24.36$

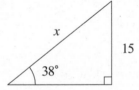

10-3. Trigonometric Functions and the Unit Circle

The **unit circle** is a circle with center $(0,0)$ and radius 1, whose equation is $x^2 + y^2 = 1$.

Let $P(x, y)$ be a point on the unit circle on the terminal side of θ. Then the six trigonometric functions for any angle θ are defined as follows:

$\sin\theta = \dfrac{y}{r} = \dfrac{y}{1} = y$ $\csc\theta = \dfrac{1}{y}$ $(y \neq 0)$

$\cos\theta = \dfrac{x}{r} = \dfrac{x}{1} = x$ $\sec\theta = \dfrac{1}{x}$ $(x \neq 0)$

$\tan\theta = \dfrac{y}{x}$ $(x \neq 0)$ $\cot\theta = \dfrac{x}{y}$ $(y \neq 0)$

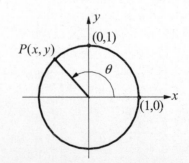

$\cos\theta$ is the x-coordinate of the point $P(x, y)$ and $\sin\theta$ is the y-coordinate of the point $P(x, y)$, each associated with angle θ. Therefore $\cos\theta$ is positive in quadrants I and IV, and $\sin\theta$ is positive in quadrants I and II.

The **reference angle** associated with θ is the acute angle formed by the x-axis and the terminal side of the angle θ. A reference angle can be used to evaluate trigonometric functions for angles greater than $90°$.

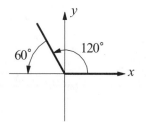 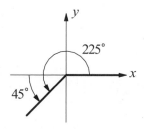 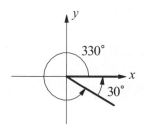

The reference angle for $120°$ is $60°$.

The reference angle for $225°$ is $45°$.

The reference angle for $330°$ is $30°$.

Example 3 □ a. Find the reference angle associated with $-120°$.
 b. Find the reference angle associated with $310°$.

Solution □ a. The reference angle associated with $-120°$ is $60°$, since the terminal side of $\theta = -120°$ makes a $60°$ angle with the x-axis.

 b. The reference angle associated with $310°$ is $50°$, since the terminal side of $\theta = 310°$ makes a $50°$ angle with the x-axis.

10-4. Familiar Angles

Angles in standard position whose measures are multiples of $\dfrac{\pi}{6}$ radians or multiples of $\dfrac{\pi}{4}$ radians are called **familiar angles**. The sine and cosine values for angles with radian measures $0, \dfrac{\pi}{6}, \dfrac{\pi}{4}, \dfrac{\pi}{3},$ and $\dfrac{\pi}{2}$ are summarized in the following table.

θ	0	$\dfrac{\pi}{6}$ or $30°$	$\dfrac{\pi}{4}$ or $45°$	$\dfrac{\pi}{3}$ or $60°$	$\dfrac{\pi}{2}$ or $90°$
$\sin\theta$	$\dfrac{\sqrt{0}}{2} = 0$	$\dfrac{\sqrt{1}}{2} = \dfrac{1}{2}$	$\dfrac{\sqrt{2}}{2}$	$\dfrac{\sqrt{3}}{2}$	$\dfrac{\sqrt{4}}{2} = 1$
$\cos\theta$	$\dfrac{\sqrt{4}}{2} = 1$	$\dfrac{\sqrt{3}}{2}$	$\dfrac{\sqrt{2}}{2}$	$\dfrac{\sqrt{1}}{2} = \dfrac{1}{2}$	$\dfrac{\sqrt{0}}{2} = 0$

Example 4 □   Angles with a reference angle of 30° are 150°, 210°, and 330°.

$$(30° = \frac{\pi}{6}, \ 150° = \frac{5\pi}{6}, \ 210° = \frac{7\pi}{6}, \ 330° = \frac{11\pi}{6})$$

Use the 30°-60°-90° triangle ratio to find the trigonometric values
of these angles and put the appropriate sign to the number found.
(See Chapter 17 for an explanation of special triangle ratios.)

$\sin 150° = \dfrac{1}{2}$

$\cos 150° = -\dfrac{\sqrt{3}}{2}$

$\tan 150° = -\dfrac{\sqrt{3}}{3}$

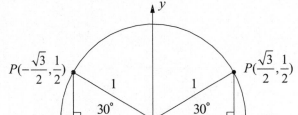

$\sin 30° = \dfrac{1}{2}$

$\cos 30° = \dfrac{\sqrt{3}}{2}$

$\tan 30° = \dfrac{\sqrt{3}}{3}$

$\sin 210° = -\dfrac{1}{2}$

$\cos 210° = -\dfrac{\sqrt{3}}{2}$

$\tan 210° = \dfrac{\sqrt{3}}{3}$

$\sin 330° = -\dfrac{1}{2}$

$\cos 330° = \dfrac{\sqrt{3}}{2}$

$\tan 330° = -\dfrac{\sqrt{3}}{3}$

Angles with a reference angle of 60° are 120°, 240°, and 300°.

$$(60° = \frac{\pi}{3}, \ 120° = \frac{2\pi}{3}, \ 240° = \frac{4\pi}{3}, \ 300° = \frac{5\pi}{3})$$

Use the 30°-60°-90° triangle ratio to find the trigonometric values of these
angles and put the appropriate sign to the number found.

$\sin 120° = \dfrac{\sqrt{3}}{2}$

$\cos 120° = -\dfrac{1}{2}$

$\tan 120° = -\sqrt{3}$

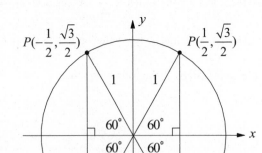

$\sin 60° = \dfrac{\sqrt{3}}{2}$

$\cos 60° = \dfrac{1}{2}$

$\tan 30° = \sqrt{3}$

$\sin 240° = -\dfrac{\sqrt{3}}{2}$

$\cos 240° = -\dfrac{1}{2}$

$\tan 240° = \sqrt{3}$

$\sin 300° = -\dfrac{\sqrt{3}}{2}$

$\cos 300° = \dfrac{1}{2}$

$\tan 300° = -\sqrt{3}$

Angles with a reference angle of $45°$ are $135°$, $225°$, and $315°$.

($45° = \dfrac{\pi}{4}$, $135° = \dfrac{3\pi}{4}$, $225° = \dfrac{5\pi}{4}$, $315° = \dfrac{7\pi}{4}$)

Use the $45°$-$45°$-$90°$ triangle ratio to find the trigonometric values of these angles and put the appropriate sign to the number found.

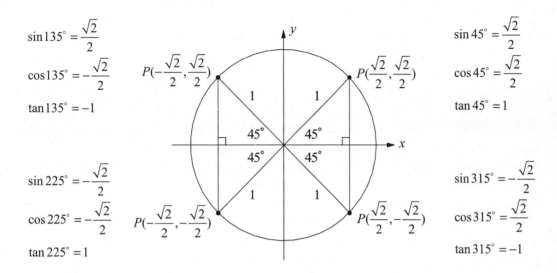

$\sin 135° = \dfrac{\sqrt{2}}{2}$

$\cos 135° = -\dfrac{\sqrt{2}}{2}$

$\tan 135° = -1$

$\sin 225° = -\dfrac{\sqrt{2}}{2}$

$\cos 225° = -\dfrac{\sqrt{2}}{2}$

$\tan 225° = 1$

$\sin 45° = \dfrac{\sqrt{2}}{2}$

$\cos 45° = \dfrac{\sqrt{2}}{2}$

$\tan 45° = 1$

$\sin 315° = -\dfrac{\sqrt{2}}{2}$

$\cos 315° = \dfrac{\sqrt{2}}{2}$

$\tan 315° = -1$

For the angles $0°$, $90°$, $180°$, and $270°$, $\cos\theta = x$ and $\sin\theta = y$

$\Rightarrow P(x, y) = P(\cos\theta, \sin\theta)$.

($90° = \dfrac{\pi}{2}$, $180° = \pi$, $270° = \dfrac{3\pi}{2}$, $360° = 2\pi$)

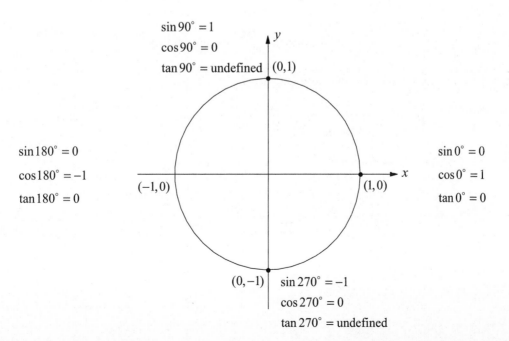

$\sin 90° = 1$

$\cos 90° = 0$

$\tan 90° =$ undefined

$\sin 180° = 0$

$\cos 180° = -1$

$\tan 180° = 0$

$\sin 0° = 0$

$\cos 0° = 1$

$\tan 0° = 0$

$\sin 270° = -1$

$\cos 270° = 0$

$\tan 270° =$ undefined

10-5. Basic Trigonometric Identities

Identities from the Definitions of Trigonometric Functions

$$\tan\theta = \frac{\sin\theta}{\cos\theta} \qquad \sec\theta = \frac{1}{\cos\theta} \qquad \csc\theta = \frac{1}{\sin\theta} \qquad \cot\theta = \frac{1}{\tan\theta}$$

Pythagorean Identities

$$\sin^2\theta + \cos^2\theta = 1 \qquad \tan^2\theta + 1 = \sec^2\theta \qquad \cot^2\theta + 1 = \csc^2\theta$$

Opposite Angle Formulas

$$\sin(-\theta) = -\sin\theta \qquad \cos(-\theta) = \cos\theta \qquad \tan(-\theta) = -\tan\theta$$

Cofunction Identities

$$\sin\theta = \cos(90° - \theta) \qquad \cos\theta = \sin(90° - \theta) \qquad \tan\theta = \cot(90° - \theta)$$

Example 5 □ $(\sin\theta + \cos\theta)^2 + (\sin\theta - \cos\theta)^2 =$

Solution   □ $(\sin\theta + \cos\theta)^2 + (\sin\theta - \cos\theta)^2$

$= (\sin^2\theta + 2\sin\theta\cos\theta + \cos^2\theta)$

$+ (\sin^2\theta - 2\sin\theta\cos\theta + \cos^2\theta)$ Multiply.

$= 2\sin^2\theta + 2\cos^2\theta$ Simplify.

$= 2(\sin^2\theta + \cos^2\theta)$ Factor.

$= 2$ $\sin^2\theta + \cos^2\theta = 1$

10-6. Graphs of $\sin x$, $\cos x$ and $\tan x$ $\boxed{L2}$

For the functions $y = a\sin bx$ and $y = a\cos bx$, the **period** is $\dfrac{2\pi}{|b|}$ and the **amplitude** is $|a|$.

For the graph of $y = \sin x$, the period $= 2\pi$ and the amplitude $= 1$.

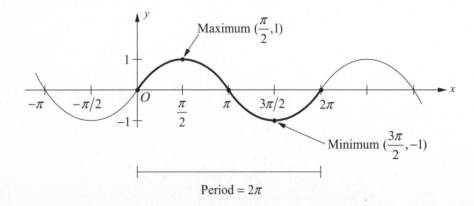

For the graph of $y = \cos x$, the period $= 2\pi$ and the amplitude $= 1$.

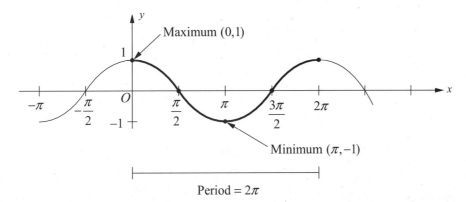

For the functions $y = \tan bx$ the **period** is $\dfrac{\pi}{|b|}$. Since the tangent function has no maximum or minimum value, it has no amplitude.

For the graph of $y = \tan x$, the period $= \pi$.

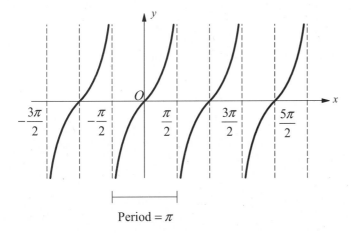

Example 6 □ Graph $y = 2\cos x$.

Solution   □ The period of the function $y = 2\cos x$ is 2π and the amplitude is 2.

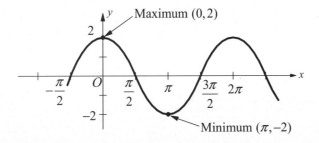

10-7. Law of Sines ⬚L2

In any triangle ABC,

$$\frac{\sin A}{a} = \frac{\sin B}{b} = \frac{\sin C}{c}$$

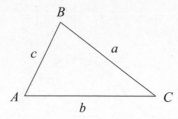

Example 7 □ What is the perimeter of $\triangle ABC$ shown below?

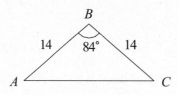

Solution □ $m\angle A = m\angle C$ since $AB = BC$.

$$m\angle A = m\angle C = \frac{180 - 84}{2} = 48$$

$$\frac{\sin 48^\circ}{14} = \frac{\sin 84^\circ}{AC} \;\Rightarrow\; AC = 18.74$$

Perimeter of $\triangle ABC = 14 + 14 + 18.74 = 46.74$ Answer

10-8. Law of Cosines ⬚L2

In any triangle ABC,

$$c^2 = a^2 + b^2 - 2ab \cos C$$
$$b^2 = a^2 + c^2 - 2ac \cos B$$
$$a^2 = b^2 + c^2 - 2bc \cos A$$

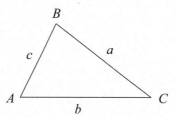

Example 8 □ What is the value of x in $\triangle ABC$ shown below?

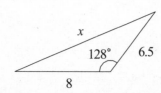

Solution □ $x^2 = 8^2 + (6.5)^2 - 2(8)(6.5) \cos 128^\circ$ Law of cosines

$\quad = 64 + 42.25 - (104)(-.616)$

$\quad = 170.3$

$x = 13.05$ Answer

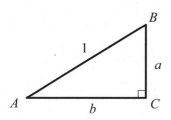

Figure 1

1. In right triangle ABC in Figure 1, $\sin \angle ABC =$

(A) $\dfrac{1}{a}$

(B) a

(C) $\dfrac{1}{b}$

(D) b

(E) $\dfrac{b}{a}$

2. If $0° < \theta < 90°$ and $\cos\theta = \dfrac{2}{3}$, then $\sin\theta =$

(A) 0.58

(B) 0.64

(C) 0.75

(D) 0.81

(E) 0.89

3. If $\cos\theta = -\dfrac{5}{13}$ and $0 < \theta < 180°$, $\tan\theta =$

(A) -2.4

(B) $-\dfrac{5}{12}$

(C) $\dfrac{5}{12}$

(D) 2.4

(E) $-\dfrac{12}{13}$

4. If $0° < \theta < 90°$, then $\dfrac{1 - \cos^2\theta}{\sin\theta\cos\theta} =$

(A) $\cot\theta$

(B) $\tan\theta$

(C) $\sec\theta$

(D) $\csc\theta$

(E) $1 + \cos\theta$

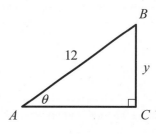

Figure 2

5. In Figure 2, if $\theta = 40°$, what is the value of y?

(A) 6.48

(B) 7.71

(C) 8.36

(D) 9.46

(E) 10.29

6. For all θ, $\cos\theta - \cos(-\theta) + \sin\theta - \sin(-\theta) =$

(A) 0

(B) $2\cos\theta$

(C) $2\sin\theta$

(D) $-2\sin\theta$

(E) $2(\cos\theta - \sin\theta)$

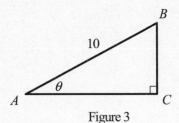

Figure 3

7. In figure 3, if $\theta = 38°$, what is the area of the right triangle ABC to the nearest whole number?

(A) 16

(B) 18

(C) 20

(D) 24

(E) 48

8. If $\sin x = 3\cos x$, where x is in radians, what is the value of x? L2

(A) 0.54

(B) 0.62

(C) 0.74

(D) 1.06

(E) 1.25

9. Which of the following could be the period of the trigonometric function $y = \tan 2x$? L2

(A) $\dfrac{\pi}{2}$

(B) π

(C) 2π

(D) 3π

(E) 4π

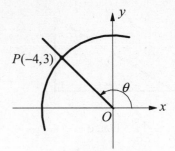

Figure 4

10. In the rectangular coordinate system in Figure 4, point P is on a circle whose center is at the origin. What is the value of $\cos\theta$? L2

(A) −0.8

(B) −0.75

(C) −0.6

(D) 0.6

(E) 0.8

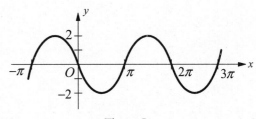

Figure 5

11. Which of the following could be an equation of the graph shown in Figure 5? L2

(A) $y = 2\sin x$

(B) $y = \sin 2x$

(C) $y = -2\sin 2x$

(D) $y = -\sin 2x$

(E) $y = -2\sin x$

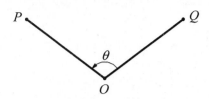

Figure 6

12. In Figure 6, $PO = OQ = 9.6 \times 10^{-9}$ cm . If the measure of angle θ is $105°$, what is the distance between P and Q? $\boxed{L2}$

(A) 1.52×10^{-8} cm

(B) 1.68×10^{-8} cm

(C) 1.76×10^{-8} cm

(D) 1.85×10^{-8} cm

(E) 1.96×10^{-8} cm

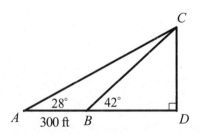

Figure 7

Note: Figure not drawn to scale.

13. Figure 7 shows that the angle of elevation from A to C is $28°$, and from B to C is $42°$. If the distance from A to B is 300ft, what is the distance from B to D? $\boxed{L2}$

(A) 373

(B) 430

(C) 485

(D) 506

(E) 588

14. From the top of a 100-ft building, the angle of elevation to the top of a tower across a field is $30°$. From the base of the building, the angle of elevation to the top of the tower is $54°$. How tall is the tower to the nearest foot? $\boxed{L2}$

(A) 112

(B) 125

(C) 136

(D) 158

(E) 172

15. In triangle ABC, $m\angle A = 32$, $m\angle B = 100$, and $BC = 8$. What is the length of $\overline{AC}$? $\boxed{L2}$

(A) 10.9

(B) 11.8

(C) 13.2

(D) 14.9

(E) 16.1

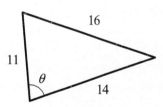

Figure 8

Note: Figure not drawn to scale.

16. In Figure 8, what is the measure of angle θ? $\boxed{L2}$

(A) $56°$

(B) $64°$

(C) $79°$

(D) $84°$

(E) $89°$

Answer Key

1. D   2. C   3. A   4. B   5. B

6. C   7. D   8. E   9. A   10. A

11. E   12. A   13. B   14. E   15. D

16. C

Answers and Explanations

1. D

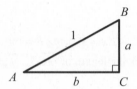

$$\sin \angle ABC = \frac{b}{1} = b$$

2. C

$$\sin^2 \theta + \cos^2 \theta = 1 \qquad \text{Pythagorean identity}$$
$$\sin^2 \theta + (\frac{2}{3})^2 = 1 \qquad \text{Given } \cos \theta = \frac{2}{3}$$
$$\sin^2 \theta = 1 - (\frac{2}{3})^2 = \frac{5}{9}$$
$$\sin \theta = \sqrt{\frac{5}{9}} \approx 0.745 \qquad \text{Answer}$$

3. A

If $0° < \theta < 180°$ and $\cos \theta = -\frac{5}{13}$, the terminal side of the angle lies in Quadrant II. So $x = -5$ and $r = 13$.

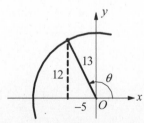

Now use the Pythagorean theorem to find y.

$$13^2 = (-5)^2 + y^2 \implies y = \pm 12$$

In Quadrant II y is positive, so $y = 12$.

$$\tan \theta = \frac{y}{x} = \frac{12}{-5} = -2.4$$

4. B

$$\frac{1 - \cos^2 \theta}{\sin \theta \cos \theta}$$
$$= \frac{\sin^2 \theta}{\sin \theta \cos \theta} \qquad \sin^2 \theta = 1 - \cos^2 \theta$$
$$= \frac{\sin \theta}{\cos \theta}$$
$$= \tan \theta$$

5. B

$$\sin \theta = \frac{y}{12}$$
$$\sin 40° = \frac{y}{12} \qquad \theta = 40°$$
$$y = 12 \cdot \sin 40° \approx 7.71$$

6. C

Use the opposite angle formulas $\sin(-\theta) = -\sin \theta$ and $\cos(-\theta) = \cos \theta$.

$$\cos \theta - \cos(-\theta) + \sin \theta - \sin(-\theta)$$
$$= \cos \theta - \cos \theta + \sin \theta - (-\sin \theta)$$
$$= 2 \sin \theta$$

7. D

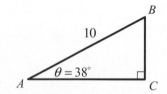

In the figure above, $AC = 10 \cos 38° \approx 7.88$ and $BC = 10 \sin 38° \approx 6.16$.

Area of $\triangle ABC$

$= \dfrac{1}{2} \cdot AC \cdot BC$

$= \dfrac{1}{2}(7.88)(6.16)$

$= 24.27$

8. E   L2

$\sin x = 3\cos x$

$\dfrac{\sin x}{\cos x} = 3$ Divide both sides by $\cos x$.

$\tan x = 3$ $\tan x = \dfrac{\sin x}{\cos x}$

$x = \tan^{-1} 3 \approx 1.249$ Use a calculator.

9. A   L2

The period of a tangent function $y = a\tan bx$ is

$\dfrac{\pi}{|b|}$. Therefore the period of the tangent function

$y = \tan 2x$ is $\dfrac{\pi}{2}$.

10. A   L2

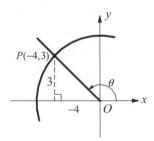

In the rectangular coordinate system shown above, $x = -4$ and $y = 3$.

$r = \sqrt{x^2 + y^2} = \sqrt{(-4)^2 + 3^2} = \sqrt{25} = 5$

$\cos\theta = \dfrac{x}{r} = \dfrac{-4}{5} = -0.8$

11. E   L2

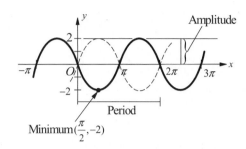

Minimum$(\dfrac{\pi}{2}, -2)$

Sine and cosine functions have a period of $\dfrac{2\pi}{|b|}$

and an amplitude of $|a|$. Since the graph shows a period of 2π and an amplitude of 2, answer choices (A) and (E) are possible.

Substitute the minimum point $(\dfrac{\pi}{2}, -2)$ into the possible equations.

$y = 2\sin x \;\Rightarrow\; -2 = 2\sin\dfrac{\pi}{2} \;\Rightarrow\; -2 \neq 2$

Choice (A) is incorrect.

$y = -2\sin x \;\Rightarrow\; -2 = -2\sin\dfrac{\pi}{2} \;\Rightarrow\; -2 = -2$

Choice (E) is correct.

12. A   L2

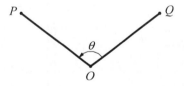

Use the law of cosines.

$PQ^2 = PO^2 + QO^2 - 2 \cdot PO \cdot QO \cdot \cos\theta$

$PQ^2 = (9.6\times10^{-9})^2 + (9.6\times10^{-9})^2$

$\qquad\qquad - 2(9.6\times10^{-9})(9.6\times10^{-9})\cos 105°$

$\qquad \approx 2.32\times10^{-16}$

$PQ \approx 1.523\times10^{-8}$

13. B $\boxed{L2}$

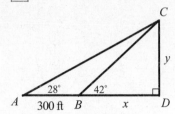

Let x = the distance from B to D, and $y = CD$.

$\tan 28° = \dfrac{y}{300+x} \Rightarrow 0.53 = \dfrac{y}{300+x}$

$\Rightarrow 0.53(300+x) = y$

From $\triangle BCD$ $\tan 42° = \dfrac{y}{x} \Rightarrow 0.9 = \dfrac{y}{x}$

$\Rightarrow 0.9x = y$

Make substitutions.

$0.53(300+x) = 0.9x \Rightarrow 159 + 0.53x = 0.9x$

$\Rightarrow 159 = 0.37x$

$\Rightarrow x \approx 429.7$

14. E $\boxed{L2}$

Make a sketch.

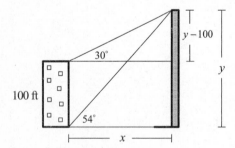

Let x = distance between building and tower, and y = height of the tower.

$\tan 30° = \dfrac{y-100}{x} \Rightarrow 0.577 = \dfrac{y-100}{x}$

$\Rightarrow 0.577x = y - 100 \Rightarrow 0.577x + 100 = y$

$\tan 54° = \dfrac{y}{x} \Rightarrow 1.376 = \dfrac{y}{x} \Rightarrow 1.376x = y$

Make substitutions.

$0.577x + 100 = 1.376x \Rightarrow 100 = 0.799x$

$\Rightarrow x \approx 125.2$

$y = 1.376x = 1.376(125.2) \approx 172.3$

15. D $\boxed{L2}$

In triangle ABC, $m\angle A = 32$, $BC = 8$ and $m\angle B = 100$.

Make a sketch.

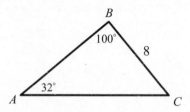

Use the law of sines.

$\dfrac{\sin 32°}{8} = \dfrac{\sin 100°}{AC}$

$\Rightarrow AC = \dfrac{8 \cdot \sin 100°}{\sin 32°} \approx 14.87$

16. C $\boxed{L2}$

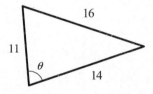

Use the law of cosines.

$16^2 = 11^2 + 14^2 - 2(14)(11)\cos\theta$

$\cos\theta = \dfrac{11^2 + 14^2 - 16^2}{2(14)(11)} \approx 0.198$

$\theta = \cos^{-1}(0.198) = 79°$

CHAPTER 11
Trigonometric Identities and Applications

L2 Chapter 11 is for Level 2 only.

11-1 Trigonometric Identities

Sum and Difference Formulas

$\sin(A+B) = \sin A \cos B + \cos A \sin B$ $\sin(A-B) = \sin A \cos B - \cos A \sin B$

$\cos(A+B) = \cos A \cos B - \sin A \sin B$ $\cos(A-B) = \cos A \cos B + \sin A \sin B$

$\tan(A+B) = \dfrac{\tan A + \tan B}{1 - \tan A \tan B}$ $\tan(A-B) = \dfrac{\tan A - \tan B}{1 + \tan A \tan B}$

Double-Angle Formulas

$\sin 2\theta = 2 \sin \theta \cos \theta$

$\cos 2\theta = \cos^2 \theta - \sin^2 \theta = 2\cos^2 \theta - 1 = 1 - 2\sin^2 \theta$

$\tan 2\theta = \dfrac{2 \tan \theta}{1 - \tan^2 \theta}$

Example 1 □ a. Simplify $\cos(\theta + \dfrac{3\pi}{2})$.

b. If $0° \le \theta \le 90°$ and $\sin \theta = \dfrac{1}{3}$, then $\sin 2\theta =$

Solution □ a. $\cos(\theta + \dfrac{3\pi}{2}) = \cos \theta \cos \dfrac{3\pi}{2} - \sin \theta \sin \dfrac{3\pi}{2}$ Sum and difference formula

$= \cos \theta (0) - \sin \theta (-1)$ $\cos \dfrac{3\pi}{2} = 0$ and $\sin \dfrac{3\pi}{2} = -1$

$= \sin \theta$ Answer

b. $\sin \theta = \dfrac{1}{3}$

Draw a right triangle whose acute angle is θ, side opposite of angle θ is 1, and hypotenuse is 3.

By the Pythagorean theorem, the adjacent side $= \sqrt{3^2 - 1^2} = \sqrt{8} = 2\sqrt{2}$,

then $\cos \theta = \dfrac{2\sqrt{2}}{3}$.

$\sin 2\theta = 2 \sin \theta \cos \theta$ Double-angle formula

$= 2 \cdot \dfrac{1}{3} \cdot \dfrac{2\sqrt{2}}{3}$ Substitution

$= \dfrac{4\sqrt{2}}{9}$ Answer

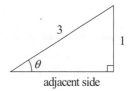

adjacent side

11-2 Trigonometric Equations

A **trigonometric equation** is any statement involving the conditional equality of two trigonometric expressions. (Most trigonometric equations are true for *some* but not *all* values of the variable.) The values that satisfy the equation are called **solutions** of the equation.

Example 2 □ Solve each trigonometric equation over the interval $0 \leq x < 2\pi$.

a. $\sin x = \sqrt{3} \cos x$ b. $\cos 2x = -\sin x$

Solution □ a. $\sin x = \sqrt{3} \cos x$

$$\frac{\sin x}{\cos x} = \sqrt{3}$$ Divide both sides by $\cos x$.

$$\tan x = \sqrt{3}$$ $\tan x = \dfrac{\sin x}{\cos x}$

$$x = 60° \text{ or } 240°$$ Answer

b. $\cos 2x = -\sin x$

$$1 - 2\sin^2 \theta = -\sin x$$ Double-angle formula

$$2\sin^2 x - \sin x - 1 = 0$$ Write in standard form.

$$(2\sin x + 1)(\sin x - 1) = 0$$ Factor.

$$2\sin x + 1 = 0 \quad \text{or} \quad \sin x - 1 = 0$$ Zero product property

$$\sin x = -\frac{1}{2} \qquad\qquad \sin x = 1$$

$$x = 210° \text{ or } 330° \qquad x = 90°$$ Answer

11-3 Inverse Trigonometric Functions

The **inverse sine function**, denoted by $y = \sin^{-1} x$ or $y = \arcsin x$, is the function with a domain of $[-1,1]$ and a range of $[-\frac{\pi}{2}, \frac{\pi}{2}]$ that satisfies the relation $\sin y = x$.

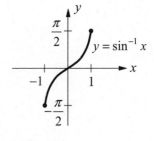

$\sin(\sin^{-1} x) = x$ for all x-values in the interval $[-1,1]$

$\sin^{-1}(\sin x) = x$ for all x-values in the interval $[-\frac{\pi}{2}, \frac{\pi}{2}]$

The **inverse cosine function**, denoted by $y = \cos^{-1} x$ or $y = \arccos x$, is the function with a domain of $[-1,1]$ and a range of $[0, \pi]$ that satisfies the relation $\cos y = x$.

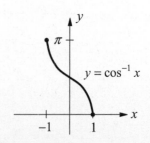

$\cos(\cos^{-1} x) = x$ for all x-values in the interval $[-1,1]$

$\cos^{-1}(\cos x) = x$ for all x-values in the interval $[0, \pi]$

The **inverse tangent function**, denoted by $y = \tan^{-1} x$ or $y = \arctan x$, is the function with a domain of $(-\infty, \infty)$ and a range of $(-\frac{\pi}{2}, \frac{\pi}{2})$ that satisfies the relation $\tan y = x$.

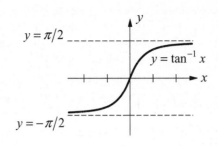

$\tan(\tan^{-1} x) = x$ for every real number x

$\tan^{-1}(\tan x) = x$ for all x-values in the interval $(-\frac{\pi}{2}, \frac{\pi}{2})$

Example 3 □   Evaluate each of the following:

a. $\arcsin(-1)$ b. $\cos^{-1}(\cos\frac{2}{3})$ c. $\cos[\arctan(1.5)]$

Solution   □   a. $\arcsin(-1)$ is that number in the interval $[-\frac{\pi}{2}, \frac{\pi}{2}]$ whose sine is -1.

Since $\sin(-\frac{\pi}{2}) = -1$, we have

$\arcsin(-1) = -\frac{\pi}{2}$ Answer

b. Since $\cos^{-1}(\cos x) = x$,

$\cos^{-1}(\cos\frac{2}{3}) = \frac{2}{3}$ Answer

c. Use a calculator set in radian mode.
   $\cos[\arctan(1.5)]$
   $= \cos(.9828)$ $\arctan(1.5) = .9828$
   $= .5547$ Answer   ■

11-4 Vectors

A **vector** is a directed line segment. The symbol $\overrightarrow{PQ}$ (read "vector PQ") denotes the vector extending from point $P(x_1, y_1)$, the **initial point**, to point $Q(x_2, y_2)$, the **terminal point**. $\overrightarrow{PQ} = \langle x_2 - x_1, y_2 - y_1 \rangle$.

Boldface letters such as **u** and **v** are often used to denote vectors, and the vector $\overrightarrow{PQ}$ can also be written as $\mathbf{u} = \langle a, b \rangle = \langle x_2 - x_1, y_2 - y_1 \rangle$.

The length or **magnitude** of the vector $\mathbf{u} = \langle a, b \rangle$ is denoted by $|\mathbf{u}|$, and $|\mathbf{u}| = \sqrt{a^2 + b^2}$.

If two vectors **u** and **v** have the same length and the same direction, we say that they are equal and we write $\mathbf{u} = \mathbf{v}$.

For each real number k and each vector $\mathbf{u} = \langle a, b \rangle$, the product $k\mathbf{u}$ is defined as $k\mathbf{u} = k\langle a, b \rangle = \langle ka, kb \rangle$.

In the figure at the right, $\mathbf{u} = \mathbf{v}$, since the two vectors $\mathbf{u}$ and $\mathbf{v}$ have the same magnitude and the same direction. Vectors $\mathbf{u}$ and $\mathbf{w}$ have the same magnitude, but their directions are opposite each other. Therefore $\mathbf{u} = -\mathbf{w}$, or $\mathbf{u} + \mathbf{w} = 0$.

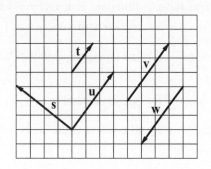

The magnitude of $\mathbf{u}$ is $|\mathbf{u}| = \sqrt{3^2 + 4^2} = \sqrt{25} = 5$.

The directions of vectors $\mathbf{u}$ and $\mathbf{t}$ are the same, but the magnitudes are not, thus $\mathbf{u} \neq \mathbf{t}$.
The magnitude of vectors $\mathbf{u}$ and $\mathbf{s}$ are the same, but the directions are not, thus $\mathbf{u} \neq \mathbf{s}$.

Vector Addition and Subtraction, an Algebraic Approach

Let $\mathbf{u} = \langle a, b \rangle$ and $\mathbf{v} = \langle c, d \rangle$ be two vectors. Then
$$\mathbf{u} + \mathbf{v} = \langle a, b \rangle + \langle c, d \rangle = \langle a+c, b+d \rangle$$
$$\mathbf{u} - \mathbf{v} = \langle a, b \rangle - \langle c, d \rangle = \langle a-c, b-d \rangle$$

Vector Addition and Subtraction, a Geometric Approach
Given two vectors $\mathbf{u}$ and $\mathbf{v}$, you can find their **sum** or **resultant** by using either of the following two methods. Since the definition for vector equality involves magnitude and direction, but not location, you are free to move a given vector to another location.

The Triangle Method

Place the initial point of $\mathbf{v}$ at the terminal point of $\mathbf{u}$. Then $\mathbf{u} + \mathbf{v}$ is equal to the vector extending from the initial point of $\mathbf{u}$ to the terminal point of $\mathbf{v}$.

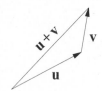

The Parallelogram Method

Position $\mathbf{u}$ and $\mathbf{v}$ so that their initial points coincide. Then the vector $\mathbf{u} + \mathbf{v}$ is the directed diagonal of the parallelogram determined by $\mathbf{u}$ and $\mathbf{v}$.

Example 4 □   a. Given the four points $A = (3,5)$, $B = (-4,1)$, $C = (-2,7)$, and $D = (6,6)$, compute $\overrightarrow{CD} - \overrightarrow{AB}$.

Let $\mathbf{u} = \langle 4, 7 \rangle$ and $\mathbf{v} = \langle -2, 5 \rangle$ for parts b-d. Compute each of the following.

b. $\mathbf{u} + \mathbf{v}$ c. $2\mathbf{u} - \mathbf{v}$ d. $|\mathbf{u} + \mathbf{v}|$

Solution   □   a. $\overrightarrow{AB} = \langle -4-3,\ 1-5 \rangle = \langle -7,\ -4 \rangle$

$\overrightarrow{CD} = \langle 6+2,\ 6-7 \rangle = \langle 8,\ -1 \rangle$

$\overrightarrow{CD} - \overrightarrow{AB} = \langle 8,\ -1 \rangle - \langle -7,\ -4 \rangle = \langle 15,\ 3 \rangle$ Answer

b. $\mathbf{u} + \mathbf{v} = \langle 4,\ 7 \rangle + \langle -2,\ 5 \rangle$

$= \langle 4-2,\ 7+5 \rangle$

$= \langle 2,\ 12 \rangle$ Answer

c. $2\mathbf{u} - \mathbf{v} = 2 \langle 4,\ 7 \rangle - \langle -2,\ 5 \rangle$

$= \langle 8,\ 14 \rangle - \langle -2,\ 5 \rangle$

$= \langle 10,\ 9 \rangle$ Answer

d. $|\mathbf{u} + \mathbf{v}| = |\langle 2,\ 12 \rangle|$

$= \sqrt{2^2 + 12^2}$

$= \sqrt{148}$ or $2\sqrt{37}$ Answer

11-5 Polar Coordinates

A **polar coordinate system** consists of a point O called the **pole**, and a ray called the **polar axis**, whose endpoint is the fixed point O.

The **polar coordinates** of a point P are an ordered pair (r, θ), where r is the distance from the origin O to the point P, and θ is the measure of the angle formed by the polar axis and the segment $\overline{OP}$.

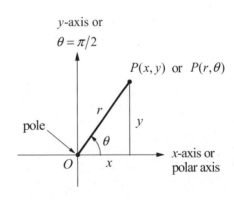

Comparing Rectangular and Polar Coordinate Systems

Rectangular Coordinates		Polar Coordinates
Origin	⇔	Pole
Positive x-axis	⇔	Polar axis or $\theta = 0$
$P(x, y)$	⇔	$P(r, \theta)$
Positive y-axis	⇔	$\theta = \pi/2$

Coordinate-System Conversion Formulas

$x = r\cos\theta$ $y = r\sin\theta$

$r^2 = x^2 + y^2$ $\tan\theta = \dfrac{y}{x}\ (x \neq 0)$

Example 5 □   a. Convert $(3,\frac{\pi}{3})$ to rectangular coordinates.

b. Convert $(-1,-1)$ to polar coordinates.

c. Sketch a complete graph of $r = 3$.

Solution   □   a. $x = r\cos\theta$ $\qquad\qquad\qquad$ $y = r\sin\theta$

$\qquad = 3\cos\dfrac{\pi}{3}$ $\qquad\qquad\qquad = 3\sin\dfrac{\pi}{3}$

$\qquad = 3\cdot\dfrac{1}{2} = \dfrac{3}{2}$ $\qquad\qquad\qquad = 3\cdot\dfrac{\sqrt{3}}{2} = \dfrac{3\sqrt{3}}{2}$

The rectangular coordinates are $(\dfrac{3}{2},\dfrac{3\sqrt{3}}{2})$.

b. The point $(-1,-1)$ is in quadrant III.

$r^2 = x^2 + y^2$

$r = \sqrt{x^2 + y^2} = \sqrt{(-1)^2 + (-1)^2} = \sqrt{2}$

$\tan\theta = \dfrac{y}{x} = \dfrac{-1}{-1} = 1 \Rightarrow \theta = \tan^{-1}(1) \Rightarrow \theta = \dfrac{\pi}{4}$

Since the point is in the third quadrant, $\theta = \pi + \dfrac{\pi}{4} = \dfrac{5\pi}{4}$.

The polar coordinates are $(\sqrt{2},\dfrac{5\pi}{4})$.

c. $r = 3$

$r^2 = 9$ $\qquad\qquad$ Square both sides.

$x^2 + y^2 = 9$ $\qquad\quad$ $r^2 = x^2 + y^2$

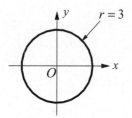

The graph of the equation is a circle
whose center is $(0,0)$ and radius is 3.

1. If $\cos\theta = 0.34$, then $\cos(\pi - \theta) =$

    (A) 0

    (B) 0.34

    (C) −0.34

    (D) 0.66

    (E) −0.66

2. If $\sin 2x = 0.72$, then $3\sin x \cos x =$

    (A) 0.84

    (B) 0.96

    (C) 1.08

    (D) 1.44

    (E) 2.16

3. If $\cos x = 0.4$, what is the value of $\cos 2x$?

    (A) 0.68

    (B) 0.8

    (C) −0.46

    (D) −0.68

    (E) −0.8

4. Which of the following is equivalent to $\sin(\theta + \frac{3\pi}{2})$?

    (A) $\cos\theta$

    (B) $-\cos\theta$

    (C) $\sin\theta$

    (D) $-\sin\theta$

    (E) $2\sin\theta$

5. If $0 \le x \le \frac{\pi}{2}$ and $\cos x = 0.6$, then $\tan\frac{x}{2} =$

    (A) 0.18

    (B) 0.3

    (C) 0.4

    (D) 0.5

    (E) 0.75

6. If $0 < x < \frac{\pi}{2}$ and $4\cos^2 x = 3$, what is the radian measure of x?

    (A) $\dfrac{\pi}{9}$

    (B) $\dfrac{\pi}{8}$

    (C) $\dfrac{\pi}{6}$

    (D) $\dfrac{\pi}{4}$

    (E) $\dfrac{\pi}{3}$

7. If $0° < \theta < 90°$ and $3\sin^2\theta + 2\sin\theta - 1 = 0$, what is the angle measure of θ?

    (A) 19.5°

    (B) 27°

    (C) 33.5°

    (D) 42.6°

    (E) 56.2°

8. Where defined, $\dfrac{\sin^2 x - 1}{\cos x} =$

(A) $\sin x - 1$

(B) $\sin x$

(C) $\cos x - 1$

(D) $\cos x$

(E) $-\cos x$

9. If $0° < \theta < 90°$ and $\cos \theta = u$, then $\sin \theta =$

(A) $\dfrac{1}{u^2 - 1}$

(B) $\dfrac{u}{u^2 - 1}$

(C) $\dfrac{u^2 - 1}{u}$

(D) $\sqrt{1 - u^2}$

(E) $\sqrt{1 + u^2}$

10. If $\arctan(\tan x) = 1$ and $0 \le x < \dfrac{\pi}{2}$, then x could equal

(A) 1

(B) $\dfrac{\pi}{8}$

(C) $\dfrac{\pi}{6}$

(D) $\dfrac{\pi}{4}$

(E) $\dfrac{\pi}{3}$

11. If the magnitudes of vectors $\mathbf{u}$ and $\mathbf{v}$ are 7 and 15, respectively, then the magnitude of vector $|\mathbf{u} + \mathbf{v}|$ could NOT be

(A) 7

(B) 8

(C) 14

(D) 19

(E) 22

12. Which of the following is the solution set of $\cos 2x = -\dfrac{1}{2}$ over the interval $0° < x < 360°$?

(A) $\left\{30°, 150°\right\}$

(B) $\left\{30°, 150°, 210°, 330°\right\}$

(C) $\left\{60°, 120°\right\}$

(D) $\left\{60°, 120°, 240°, 300°\right\}$

(E) $\left\{60°, 150°, 210°, 300°\right\}$

13. If a point has rectangular coordinates $(6, 6\sqrt{3})$, which of the following are its polar coordinates?

(A) $(9, \dfrac{\pi}{4})$

(B) $(10, \dfrac{\pi}{6})$

(C) $(12, \dfrac{\pi}{3})$

(D) $(12\sqrt{3}, \dfrac{\pi}{3})$

(E) $(12\sqrt{3}, \dfrac{2\pi}{3})$

14. What is the value of $\sin(\arccos 0.75)$?

(A) 0.49

(B) 0.66

(C) 0.75

(D) 0.82

(E) 0.89

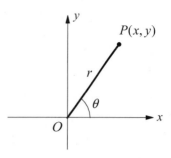

Figure 2

17. In Figure 2, if $r\sin\theta + r\cos\theta = 1$, then $y =$

(A) $x - 1$

(B) $x + 1$

(C) $-x + 1$

(D) $-x - 1$

(E) $-\dfrac{1}{x} + 1$

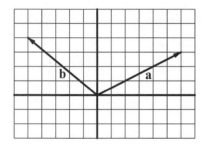

Figure 1

15. The grid in Figure 1 consists of unit squares. The initial point of the two vectors **a** and **b** lies at the origin. If **c** is a vector such that $\mathbf{c} = \mathbf{a} + \mathbf{b}$, what is the magnitude of **c**?

(A) 4.8

(B) 5.2

(C) 5.8

(D) 6.4

(E) 7.1

18. In a $\triangle ABC$ if $A + B = 90°$, which of the following cannot be true?

(A) $\cos A = \sin B$

(B) $\sin A = \cos B$

(C) $\cot(A + B) = 0$

(D) $\csc(A + B) = 1$

(E) $\cos(A + B) = \sin(A + B)$

16. $\operatorname{arcsec}\sqrt{2} + \operatorname{arccsc}\sqrt{2} =$

(A) $0°$

(B) $45°$

(C) $90°$

(D) $135°$

(E) $180°$

19. Which of the following is equivalent to $\cos(x - 30°) + \sin(x - 60°)$?

(A) $\sin x$

(B) $\cos x$

(C) $\sqrt{3}\cos x$

(D) $\cos x + \sin x$

(E) $\cos x - \sin x$

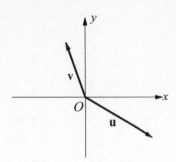

Figure 3

20. Figure 3 shows two vectors **u** and **v**. Which of the following shows **u** + **v** ?

(A)   (B)

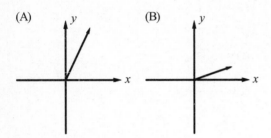

(C)   (D)

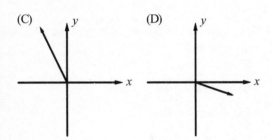

(E)

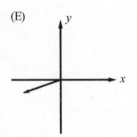

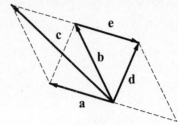

Figure 4

21. Figure 4 shows vectors **a**, **b**, **c**, **d**, and **e**. Which of the following statements is incorrect?

(A) **a** = −**e**

(B) **a** + **b** = **c**

(C) **a** + **d** = **b**

(D) **b** + **e** = **d**

(E) **c** + **d** = **b**

22. For all u in the interval $[-1, 1]$, $\sin(2\sin^{-1}u) =$

(A) $2u\sqrt{1+u^2}$

(B) $2u\sqrt{1-u^2}$

(C) 2

(D) $2u^2 - 1$

(E) $2u^2 + 1$

23. If $\arcsin(\dfrac{x}{2}) = u$, then $\cos u =$

(A) $2x$

(B) $\sqrt{4-x^2}$

(C) $\sqrt{4+x^2}$

(D) $\dfrac{\sqrt{4-x^2}}{2}$

(E) $1 - \dfrac{x^2}{4}$

Answer Key

1. C	2. C	3. D	4. B	5. D
6. C	7. A	8. E	9. D	10. A
11. A	12. D	13. C	14. B	15. E
16. C	17. C	18. E	19. A	20. B
21. E	22. B	23. D		

Answers and Explanations

1. C

$$\cos(\pi - \theta)$$
$$= \cos \pi \cos \theta + \sin \pi \sin \theta \qquad \text{Difference formula}$$
$$= -1 \cdot \cos \theta + 0 \cdot \sin \theta \qquad \cos \pi = -1, \ \sin \pi = 0$$
$$= -\cos \theta$$
$$= -0.34 \qquad \text{Given } \cos \theta = 0.34$$

2. C

$$\sin 2x = 0.72$$
$$\sin 2x = 2 \sin x \cos x \qquad \text{Double-angle formula}$$
$$0.72 = 2 \sin x \cos x \qquad \text{Substitution}$$
$$\sin x \cos x = 0.36 \qquad \text{Divide both sides by 2.}$$
$$3 \sin x \cos$$
$$= 3(0.36) = 1.08 \qquad \text{Answer}$$

3. D

$$\cos x = 0.4$$
$$\cos 2x = 2 \cos^2 x - 1 \qquad \text{Double-angle formula}$$
$$= 2(0.4)^2 - 1$$
$$= -0.68$$

4. B

$$\sin(\theta + \frac{3\pi}{2})$$
$$= \sin \theta \cos \frac{3\pi}{2} + \cos \theta \sin \frac{3\pi}{2} \quad \text{Sum formula}$$

$$= \sin \theta \cdot 0 + \cos \theta \cdot (-1) \qquad \cos \frac{3\pi}{2} = 0, \ \sin \frac{3\pi}{2} = -1$$
$$= -\cos \theta \qquad\qquad\qquad\quad \text{Answer}$$

5. D

Given $0 \le x \le \frac{\pi}{2}$ and $\cos x = 0.6$.
Use a calculator.

$$\cos x = 0.6 \ \Rightarrow \ x = \cos^{-1}(0.6) \approx 53°$$
$$\tan(\frac{x}{2}) = \tan(\frac{53°}{2})$$
$$= \tan(26.5°)$$
$$= .5$$

6. C

$$4 \cos^2 x = 3 \ \Rightarrow \ \cos^2 x = \frac{3}{4}$$
$$\Rightarrow \ \cos x = \pm\sqrt{\frac{3}{4}} = \pm\frac{\sqrt{3}}{2}$$

Since $0 < x < \frac{\pi}{2}$, $\cos x$ is positive.

Therefore $\cos x = \frac{\sqrt{3}}{2}$

$$x = \cos^{-1}(\frac{\sqrt{3}}{2}) = \frac{\pi}{6}$$

7. A

$$3 \sin^2 \theta + 2 \sin \theta - 1 = 0$$
$$\Rightarrow \ (3 \sin \theta - 1)(\sin \theta + 1) = 0$$
$$\Rightarrow \ 3 \sin \theta - 1 = 0 \ \text{or} \ \sin \theta + 1 = 0$$
$$\Rightarrow \ \sin \theta = \frac{1}{3} \ \text{or} \ \sin \theta = -1$$

If $\sin \theta = \frac{1}{3}$, $\theta = \sin^{-1}(\frac{1}{3}) \approx 19.47°$.

If $\sin \theta = -1$, $\theta = \sin^{-1}(-1) = 270°$.

Since $0° < \theta < 90°$, $\theta = 19.47°$.

8. E

$$\frac{\sin^2 x - 1}{\cos x}$$

$$= \frac{-(1 - \sin^2 x)}{\cos x}$$

$$= \frac{-(\cos^2 x)}{\cos x} \qquad \cos^2 x = 1 - \sin^2 x$$

$$= -\cos x$$

9. D

$\cos \theta = u$

Draw a right triangle whose hypotenuse is 1 and side adjacent to θ has length u.

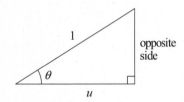

By the Pythagorean theorem,

the opposite side $= \sqrt{1 - u^2}$.

$$\sin \theta = \frac{\sqrt{1 - u^2}}{1} = \sqrt{1 - u^2}$$

10. A

$\arctan(\tan x) = 1$ or

$\tan^{-1}(\tan x) = 1$

$\Rightarrow \quad x = 1$

11. A

If the magnitudes of vectors **u** and **v** are 7 and 15, respectively, then the maximum magnitude of $|\mathbf{u} + \mathbf{v}|$ is $15 + 7$, or 22, and the minimum magnitude of $|\mathbf{u} + \mathbf{v}|$ is $15 - 7$, or 8.

So $8 \le |\mathbf{u} + \mathbf{v}| \le 22$.

Therefore 7 is not possible.

12. D

$$\cos 2x = -\frac{1}{2}$$

$$2\cos^2 x - 1 = -\frac{1}{2} \qquad \text{Double-angle formula}$$

$$2\cos^2 x = \frac{1}{2}$$

$$\cos^2 x = \frac{1}{4}$$

$$\cos x = \pm\sqrt{\frac{1}{4}} = \pm\frac{1}{2}$$

If $\cos x = \frac{1}{2}$, $x = 60°$ or $300°$.

If $\cos x = -\frac{1}{2}$, $x = 120°$ or $240°$.

Therefore the solution set is

$\left\{60°, 120°, 240°, 300°\right\}$.

13. C

$(6, 6\sqrt{3}) \Rightarrow x = 6$ and $y = 6\sqrt{3}$

Use the coordinate-system conversion formula.

$$\tan \theta = \frac{y}{x} = \frac{6\sqrt{3}}{6} = \sqrt{3}$$

$$\theta = \tan^{-1}(\sqrt{3}) = 60°$$

$$r^2 = x^2 + y^2 = 6^2 + (6\sqrt{3})^2 = 144$$

$$\Rightarrow r = 12$$

Therefore the polar coordinate is $(12, 60°)$

or $(12, \frac{\pi}{3})$.

14. B

Use a calculator.

$\sin(\cos^{-1}(.75)) = .6614$

15. E

$$\mathbf{a} = <6,3> \text{ and } \mathbf{b} = <-5,4>$$
$$\mathbf{c} = \mathbf{a} + \mathbf{b}$$
$$= <6,3> + <-5,4>$$
$$= <6-5,3+4>$$
$$= <1,7>$$

The magnitude of vector $\mathbf{c}$ is
$$\mathbf{c} = \sqrt{1^2 + 7^2} = \sqrt{50} \approx 7.07.$$

16. C

Let $\theta = \text{arc sec}\sqrt{2}$, then $\sec\theta = \sqrt{2}$.

$$\sec\theta = \sqrt{2} \Rightarrow \frac{1}{\cos\theta} = \sqrt{2}$$

$$\Rightarrow \cos\theta = \frac{1}{\sqrt{2}} \Rightarrow \theta = 45°$$

Let $\alpha = \text{arccsc}\sqrt{2}$, then $\csc\alpha = \sqrt{2}$.

$$\csc\alpha = \sqrt{2} \Rightarrow \frac{1}{\sin\alpha} = \sqrt{2}$$

$$\Rightarrow \sin\alpha = \frac{1}{\sqrt{2}} \Rightarrow \alpha = 45°$$

$$\text{arcsec}\sqrt{2} + \text{arccsc}\sqrt{2}$$
$$= \theta + \alpha = 45° + 45° = 90°$$

17. C

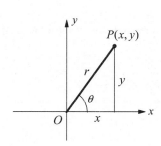

In the figure, $x = r\cos\theta$ and $y = r\sin\theta$.
$$r\sin\theta + r\cos\theta = 1 \Rightarrow y + x = 1$$
$$\Rightarrow y = -x + 1$$

18. E

Given $A + B = 90°$.

Draw a right triangle, where $\angle A$ and $\angle B$ are acute angles.

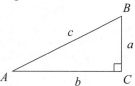

(A) $\cos A = \dfrac{b}{c}$ and $\sin B = \dfrac{b}{c}$.

Therefore $\cos A = \sin B$.

(B) $\sin A = \dfrac{a}{c}$ and $\cos B = \dfrac{a}{c}$.

Therefore $\sin A = \cos B$.

(C) $\cot(A+B) = \cot 90° = 0$.

(D) $\csc(A+B) = \csc 90° = 1$.

(E) $\cos(A+B) = \cos 90° = 0$, and
$\sin(A+B) = \sin 90° = 1$.
Therefore $\cos(A+B) \neq \sin(A+B)$.

19. A

Use sum and difference formulas.

$$\cos(x-30°) + \sin(x-60°)$$
$$= \cos x \cos 30° + \sin x \sin 30°$$
$$\quad + \sin x \cos 60° - \cos x \sin 60°$$
$$= \cos x \cdot \frac{\sqrt{3}}{2} + \sin x \cdot \frac{1}{2} + \sin x \cdot \frac{1}{2} - \cos x \cdot \frac{\sqrt{3}}{2}$$
$$= \sin x$$

20. B

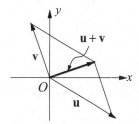

The resultant of the vectors $\mathbf{u}$ and $\mathbf{v}$ is the directed diagonal of the parallelogram determined by $\mathbf{u}$ and $\mathbf{v}$.

Choice (B) is correct.

21. E

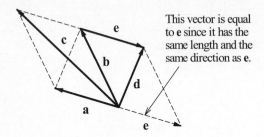

This vector is equal to **e** since it has the same length and the same direction as **e**.

(A) **a** = −**e**

Vectors **a** and **e** have the same magnitude (length) but opposite directions. Therefore **a** = −**e** .

(B) **a** + **b** = **c**
c is the directed diagonal of the parallelogram determined by **a** and **b**. Therefore **a** + **b** = **c** .

(C) **a** + **d** = **b**
b is the directed diagonal of the parallelogram determined by **a** and **d**. Therefore **a** + **d** = **b** .

(D) **b** + **e** = **d**
d is the directed diagonal of the parallelogram determined by **b** and **e**. Therefore **b** + **e** = **d** .

(E) **c** + **d** = **b**
This is not true since **b** is not the directed diagonal of the parallelogram determined by **c** and **d**.

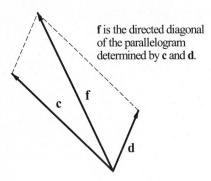

f is the directed diagonal of the parallelogram determined by **c** and **d**.

22. B

Let $\theta = \sin^{-1} u$, then $\sin \theta = \sin(\sin^{-1} u) = u$

Draw a right triangle whose acute angle is θ, hypotenuse is 1, and side opposite of θ has length u.

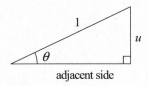

By the Pythagorean theorem,

adjacent side = $\sqrt{1 - u^2}$.

$\sin(2\sin^{-1} u)$

$= \sin(2\theta)$ $\theta = \sin^{-1} u$

$= 2\sin\theta\cos\theta$ Double-angle formula

$= 2u\sqrt{1 - u^2}$ $\sin\theta = u$, $\cos\theta = \sqrt{1 - u^2}$

23. D

$\arcsin(\dfrac{x}{2}) = u$

Take the sine of both sides of the given equation.

$\sin[\arcsin(\dfrac{x}{2})] = \sin u \ \Rightarrow \ \dfrac{x}{2} = \sin u$.

Draw a right triangle whose acute angle is u, hypotenuse is 2, and side opposite of u has length x.

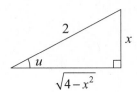

By the Pythagorean theorem the adjacent side is $\sqrt{4 - x^2}$.

Therefore $\cos u = \dfrac{\sqrt{4 - x^2}}{2}$.

CHAPTER 12
Sequences and Series

12-1. Sequences and Series

A **sequence of numbers** is a set of numbers with a specific order.

A sequence is **finite** if it has a limited number of terms and **infinite** if it does not.

When the terms of a sequence are added together, the resulting expression is called a **series**.

Example 1 □ Find the next two terms of the given sequence.

$$1, 4, 10, 19, 31, \underline{\quad}, \underline{\quad}, \cdots$$

Solution □ Sequence   1   4   10   19   31

Differences   3   6   9   12

The differences of the given sequence themselves form an arithmetic sequence with common difference 3. So the next difference will be 15, and the next term in the original sequence will be $31+15$, or 46. The term next to 46 will be $46+18$, or 64.

12-2. Arithmetic Sequences

When the difference between successive terms of a sequence is always the same, the sequence is called arithmetic.

The *n*th Term of an Arithmetic Sequence is given by

$a_n = a_1 + (n-1)d$, where

a_n is the *n*th term, a_1 is the first term, and d is the common difference.

The terms of an arithmetic sequence follow the pattern $a_1, a_1+d, a_1+2d, a_1+3d, \cdots$.

Example 2 □ The third term of an arithmetic sequence is 18, and the eighth term is 33. What is the first term of the sequence?

Solution □

$a_8 = a_1 + (8-1)d = 33$ For the eighth term, $n=8$.

$a_3 = a_1 + (3-1)d = 18$ For the third term, $n=3$.

$\qquad a_1 + 7d = 33$ First equation simplified

$- \quad a_1 + 2d = 18$ Second equation simplified

$\qquad\qquad 5d = 15$ Subtract.

$\Rightarrow \quad d = 3$

$a_1 + 7(3) = 33$ Substitute 3 for d in the first equation.

$\Rightarrow \quad a_1 = 12$ Answer

12-3. Arithmetic Series

The sum S_n of the first n terms of an arithmetic series is given by

$S_n = \dfrac{n}{2}(a_1 + a_n)$, where

a_1 is the first term, a_n is the last term, and n is the number of terms.

$S_n = \dfrac{n}{2}[2a_1 + (n-1)d]$ can be used when the value of the last term is not known.

Example 3 □ Find the sum of the positive two-digit integers that are divisible by 6.

Solution □ $12, 18, 24, \ldots, 90, 96$

The list of numbers above shows the positive two-digit integers that are divisible by 6, where $a_1 = 12$, $a_n = 96$, and $d = 6$. To find n, which is the number of terms, use the formula $a_n = a_1 + (n-1)d$.

$96 = 12 + (n-1)6 \implies n = 15$

$S_n = \dfrac{n}{2}(a_1 + a_n) = \dfrac{15}{2}(12 + 96) = 810$ Answer

12-4. Geometric Sequences

When the ratio of successive terms of a sequence is always the same, the sequence is called geometric.

The nth Term of a Geometric Sequence is given by

$a_n = a_1 \cdot r^{n-1}$, where

a_n is the nth term, a_1 is the first term, and r is the common ratio.

The terms of a geometric sequence follow the pattern $a_1, \ a_1 \cdot r, \ a_1 \cdot r^2, \ a_1 \cdot r^3, \ \cdots$.

Example 4 □ If $8, 4\sqrt{3}, 6, d,$ and e are the first five terms of a geometric sequence, what is the value of $d \cdot e$?

Solution □ $a_2 = a_1 \cdot r$

$4\sqrt{3} = 8 \cdot r \implies r = \dfrac{\sqrt{3}}{2}$

$a_4 = a_3 \cdot r \implies d = 6 \cdot \dfrac{\sqrt{3}}{2} = 3\sqrt{3}$

$a_5 = a_4 \cdot r \implies e = d \cdot \dfrac{\sqrt{3}}{2} = 3\sqrt{3} \cdot \dfrac{\sqrt{3}}{2} = \dfrac{9}{2}$

$d \cdot e = 3\sqrt{3} \cdot \dfrac{9}{2} = \dfrac{27\sqrt{3}}{2}$ Answer

12-5. Geometric Series

The sum S_n of the first n terms of a geometric series is given by

$S_n = \dfrac{a_1(1-r^n)}{1-r}$, where

a_1 is the first term, r is the common ratio ($r \neq 1$), and n is the number of terms.

Example 5 □ $5+6+7.2\ldots$

Find the sum of the first 6 terms of the geometric series shown above.

Solution   □   For the geometric series shown above, $a_1 = 5$ and $r = 1.2$.
Since we are adding up the first 6 terms, $n = 6$.

$$S_6 = \frac{5(1-(1.2)^6)}{1-1.2} = \frac{5(1-2.985984)}{-.2}$$
$$= 49.6496 \qquad \text{Answer}$$

12-6. Infinite Geometric Series $\boxed{L2}$

The sum S of an infinite geometric series is given by

$S = \dfrac{a_1}{1-r}$, where

a_1 is the first term and $|r| < 1$.

Example 6 □   Find the sum of each infinite geometric series.
a. $9-3+1-\dfrac{1}{3}\ldots$
b. $4-6+9-\ldots$

Solution   □   a. $a_1 = 9$ and $r = \dfrac{-3}{9} = -\dfrac{1}{3}$.

Since $\left|-\dfrac{1}{3}\right| < 1$, a sum exists for this infinite series.

$$S = \frac{a_1}{1-r} = \frac{9}{1-(-\frac{1}{3})} = \frac{9}{(\frac{4}{3})} = \frac{27}{4} \qquad \text{Answer}$$

b. $r = \dfrac{-6}{4} = -\dfrac{3}{2}$.

Since $\left|-\dfrac{3}{2}\right| > 1$, the series has no sum.

12-7. Sigma Notation $\boxed{L2}$

A series can be written in an abbreviated form by using the Greek letter Σ (sigma), called the **summation sign**.

The sum of n terms $S_n = a_1 + a_2 + \cdots + a_n$ can be written $S_n = \displaystyle\sum_{i=1}^{n} a_i$.

This expression is read "the sum of a_i from $i = 1$ to n." The letter i (called the **index**) takes on consecutive integer values beginning with 1 and ending with n. Any letter can be used as the index.

Summation Formulas

1. $\displaystyle\sum_{i=1}^{n} c = cn$

   (c is a constant and it does not depend on i)

2. $\displaystyle\sum_{i=1}^{n} i = \dfrac{n(n+1)}{2}$

3. $\displaystyle\sum_{i=1}^{n} i^2 = \dfrac{n(n+1)(2n+1)}{6}$

4. $\displaystyle\sum_{i=1}^{n} i^3 = \dfrac{n^2(n+1)^2}{4}$

Example 7 □   a. Use sigma notation to write the series $4 + 7 + 10 + \cdots + 37$.

b. Find the sum of $\displaystyle\sum_{i=1}^{5} (i^2 - 1)$

Solution   □   a. The series is arithmetic with $a_1 = 4$ and $d = 3$, the nth term is:

$$a_n = a_1 + (n-1)d$$
$$= 4 + (n-1)3$$
$$= 3n + 1$$

Now find n such that the last term is 37.
$$37 = 3n + 1$$
$$n = 12$$

The sigma notation for the series is $\displaystyle\sum_{i=1}^{12} (3i + 1)$.   Answer

b. $\displaystyle\sum_{i=1}^{5} (i^2 - 1) = (1^2 - 1) + (2^2 - 1) + (3^2 - 1) + (4^2 - 1) + (5^2 - 1)$

$$= 0 + 3 + 8 + 15 + 24$$
$$= 50 \qquad\qquad\qquad\qquad \text{Answer}$$

12-8. Recursive Formula $\boxed{L2}$

A recursive formula for a sequence describes how to find the nth term from the term(s) before it. Some problems give the first or the first few terms of a sequence and a recursive formula, where the nth term a_n is defined in terms of previous terms of the sequence.

Example 8 □   a. Find the first four terms of the sequence in which $a_1 = 3$ and $a_{n+1} = 2a_n + 1$.

b. Find x_3 , if $x_0 = 4$ and $x_{n+1} = \sqrt{x_n + 5}$.

Solution □ a. $a_1 = 3$ and $a_{n+1} = 2a_n + 1$ Given

$$a_{1+1} = 2a_1 + 1 \Rightarrow a_2 = 2(3) + 1 = 7 \qquad\qquad n = 1 \text{ and } a_1 = 3$$

$$a_{2+1} = 2a_2 + 1 \Rightarrow a_3 = 2(7) + 1 = 15 \qquad\quad n = 2 \text{ and } a_2 = 7$$

$$a_{3+1} = 2a_3 + 1 \Rightarrow a_4 = 2(15) + 1 = 31 \qquad n = 3 \text{ and } a_3 = 15$$

The first four terms of the sequence are 3, 7, 15, and 31.

b. $x_0 = 4$ and $x_{n+1} = \sqrt{x_n + 5}$ Given

$$x_{0+1} = \sqrt{x_0 + 5} \Rightarrow x_1 = \sqrt{4+5} = 3 \qquad\qquad n = 0 \text{ and } x_0 = 4$$

$$x_{1+1} = \sqrt{x_1 + 5} \Rightarrow x_2 = \sqrt{3+5} = \sqrt{8} \qquad\quad n = 1 \text{ and } x_0 = 3$$

$$x_{2+1} = \sqrt{x_2 + 5} \Rightarrow x_3 = \sqrt{\sqrt{8} + 5} \qquad\qquad n = 2 \text{ and } x_2 = \sqrt{8}$$

$$\approx 2.798 \qquad\qquad\qquad\qquad\quad \text{Answer}$$

12-9. Binomial Theorem $\boxed{L2}$

$$(a+b)^n = {}_nC_0 a^n b^0 + {}_nC_1 a^{n-1} b + {}_nC_2 a^{n-2} b^2 + \cdots + {}_nC_{n-1} ab^{n-1} + {}_nC_n a^0 b^n, \text{ where}$$

n is a positive integer and ${}_nC_r = \dfrac{n!}{r!(n-r)!}$.

The k th term of $(a+b)^n$ is ${}_nC_{k-1}(a)^{n-(k-1)}(b)^{(k-1)}$.

Factorial

The symbol $n!$, read as "n *factorial*," is defined as $n! = n \cdot (n-1) \cdot (n-2) \cdot \ \cdot \ \cdot \ \cdot \ \cdot 3 \cdot 2 \cdot 1$,
where n is an integer greater than 1. For example

$1! = 1$
$2! = 2 \cdot 1 = 2$
$3! = 3 \cdot 2 \cdot 1 = 6$
Zero factorial is defined as $0! = 1$.

Example 9 □   a. Expand $(x+3)^5$.   b. Find the eighth term of $(a-2b)^{12}$.

Solution □   a. $(x+3)^5 = {}_5C_0 x^5 (3)^0 + {}_5C_1 x^4 (3)^1 + {}_5C_2 x^3 (3)^2$

$$+ {}_5C_3 x^2 (3)^3 + {}_5C_4 x^1 (3)^4 + {}_5C_5 x^0 (3)^5$$

$$= 1 \cdot x^5 \cdot 1 + 5 \cdot x^4 \cdot 3 + 10x^3 \cdot 9 + 10x^2 \cdot 27 + 5 \cdot x \cdot 81 + 1 \cdot 1 \cdot 243$$

$$= x^5 + 15x^4 + 90x^3 + 270x^2 + 405x + 243$$

b. The eighth term of $(a-2b)^{12}$ is

$${}_{12}C_{(8-1)}(a)^{12-(8-1)}(-2b)^{8-1}$$

$$= {}_{12}C_7 (a)^5 (-2b)^7$$

$$= 792a^5 (-128b^7)$$

$$= -101376a^5 b^7 \qquad\qquad \text{Answer}$$

1. If the 5th term of an arithmetic sequence is 7
   and 12th term is 24.5, what is the first term of
   the sequence?

   (A) −6

   (B) −3

   (C) 1

   (D) 5

   (E) 7

2. For the geometric sequence $\dfrac{16}{9}$, $\dfrac{8}{3}$, 4, 6, . . . ,
   what is the 9th term of the sequence?

   (A) $\dfrac{27}{2}$

   (B) $\dfrac{81}{4}$

   (C) $\dfrac{243}{8}$

   (D) $\dfrac{729}{16}$

   (E) $\dfrac{2187}{32}$

3. For the arithmetic series $-5-2+1+4 \cdots$, the sum
   of the first 12 terms is

   (A) 91

   (B) 113

   (C) 138

   (D) 166

   (E) 197

4. For the geometric series $\dfrac{1}{2}-1+2-4 \cdots$, the sum
   of the first 10 terms is

   (A) 85.5

   (B) 181

   (C) −127.5

   (D) −170.5

   (E) −511.5

5. If 4, a, b, c, are the first few terms of an
   arithmetic sequence and a, b, 18, 27, are the
   first few terms of a geometric sequence, what
   is the value of c?

   (A) 8

   (B) 10

   (C) 12

   (D) 14

   (E) 16

6. The sigma notation of the arithmetic series
   $\dfrac{1}{3}+\dfrac{5}{3}+3+\dfrac{13}{3}+\cdots+19$ is $\boxed{L2}$

   (A) $\displaystyle\sum_{k=0}^{14} \dfrac{4}{3}k$

   (B) $\displaystyle\sum_{k=0}^{14} (\dfrac{4}{3}k-\dfrac{1}{3})$

   (C) $\displaystyle\sum_{k=0}^{15} (\dfrac{4}{3}k+\dfrac{1}{3})$

   (D) $\displaystyle\sum_{k=1}^{15} (\dfrac{4}{3}k-1)$

   (E) $\displaystyle\sum_{k=1}^{15} (\dfrac{4}{3}k+1)$

7. The sigma notation of the infinite geometric series
$1 - \dfrac{2}{3} + \dfrac{4}{9} - \dfrac{8}{27} + \cdots$ is $\boxed{L2}$

(A) $\displaystyle\sum_{i=1}^{\infty} (-\dfrac{2}{3})^i$

(B) $\displaystyle\sum_{i=0}^{\infty} (-\dfrac{2}{3})^i$

(C) $\displaystyle\sum_{i=0}^{\infty} -(\dfrac{2}{3})^i$

(D) $\displaystyle\sum_{i=0}^{\infty} \left[-1 + (\dfrac{2}{3})^i \right]$

(E) $\displaystyle\sum_{i=0}^{\infty} \left[1 - (-\dfrac{2}{3})^i \right]$

8. A sequence is recursively defined by
$a_n = 2a_{n-1} + 1$, for $n \geq 2$. If $a_1 = 1$, what is the
value of a_5? $\boxed{L2}$

(A) 15

(B) 21

(C) 25

(D) 28

(E) 31

9. A sequence is recursively defined by
$a_n = a_{n-1} + n$, for $n \geq 2$. If $a_1 = 0$, what is
the value of a_4? $\boxed{L2}$

(A) 5

(B) 7

(C) 9

(D) 14

(E) 20

10. Which of the following could be a_4, if $a_1 = \sqrt{3}$
and $a_n = \sqrt{2(a_{n-1})^2 - n}$ for $n \geq 2$? $\boxed{L2}$

(A) $\sqrt{6}$

(B) $\sqrt{7}$

(C) $\sqrt{8}$

(D) 3

(E) $\sqrt{10}$

11. If $\displaystyle\sum_{i=1}^{20} i^2 = 2870$, then $\displaystyle\sum_{i=1}^{20} (\dfrac{1}{2}i^2 + 10) =$ $\boxed{L2}$

(A) 1445

(B) 1560

(C) 1635

(D) 2150

(E) 2880

12. What is the sum of the infinite geometric series
$\sqrt{2} + 1 + \dfrac{\sqrt{2}}{2} + \dfrac{1}{2} \cdots$? $\boxed{L2}$

(A) $2(\sqrt{2} - 1)$

(B) $2(\sqrt{2} + 1)$

(C) $2\sqrt{2} - 3$

(D) $2\sqrt{2} + 3$

(E) There is no sum.

13. If $(n+3)! = 4!(n+2)!$, then $n =$ [L2]

(A) 7

(B) 9

(C) 11

(D) 15

(E) 21

14. $\dfrac{(n-1)^2[(n)!]^2}{n^2[(n-1)!]^2} =$ [L2]

(A) 1

(B) n

(C) $n-1$

(D) $(n-1)^2$

(E) $\dfrac{n-1}{n}$

15. $(x-y)^5 =$ [L2]

(A) $x^5 - y^5$

(B) $x^5 - x^4 y + x^3 y^2 - x^2 y^3 + xy^4 - y^5$

(C) $x^5 - 2x^4 y + 3x^3 y^2 - 3x^2 y^3 + 2xy^4 - y^5$

(D) $x^5 - 5x^4 y + 10x^3 y^2 - 10x^2 y^3 + 5xy^4 - y^5$

(E) $x^5 + 5x^4 y + 10x^3 y^2 + 10x^2 y^3 + 5xy^4 + y^5$

16. Which of the following is the coefficient of the fifth term in the expansion of $(x - \frac{1}{2})^7$? [L2]

(A) $-\dfrac{35}{16}$

(B) $-\dfrac{21}{32}$

(C) $\dfrac{35}{16}$

(D) $\dfrac{21}{32}$

(E) $\dfrac{35}{8}$

17. Which of the following is the fourth term in the expansion of $(x - y^2)^9$? [L2]

(A) $-84x^6 y^6$

(B) $-36x^6 y^6$

(C) $-126x^4 y^{10}$

(D) $84x^5 y^8$

(E) $36x^6 y^8$

Answer Key

1. B	2. D	3. C	4. D	5. E
6. D	7. B	8. E	9. C	10. A
11. C	12. B	13. E	14. D	15. D
16. C	17. A			

Answers and Explanations

1. B

Use the arithmetic sequence formula.

$a_n = a_1 + (n-1)d$

$a_5 = a_1 + (5-1)d = 7 \implies a_1 + 4d = 7$

$a_{12} = a_1 + (12-1)d = 24.5 \implies a_1 + 11d = 24.5$

By subtracting the first equation from the second equation we get $7d = 17.5 \implies d = 2.5$.

$a_1 + 4d = 7 \implies a_1 + 4(2.5) = 7 \implies a_1 = -3$

2. D

$\dfrac{16}{9}, \dfrac{8}{3}, 4, 6, \ldots,$

$a_1 = \dfrac{16}{9}$

$\dfrac{16}{9} \cdot r = \dfrac{8}{3} \implies r = \dfrac{3}{2}$

$a_n = a_1 r^{n-1}$

$a_9 = \left(\dfrac{16}{9}\right)\left(\dfrac{3}{2}\right)^{9-1} = \left(\dfrac{16}{9}\right)\left(\dfrac{3}{2}\right)^{8} = \dfrac{729}{16}$

3. C

For the arithmetic series $-5 - 2 + 1 + 4 \cdots$,

$a_1 = -5$ and $d = 3$.

The sum of the arithmetic series is given by

$S_n = \dfrac{n(a_1 + a_n)}{2}$.

$S_{12} = \dfrac{12(a_1 + a_n)}{2}$ $n = 12$

$= \dfrac{12(a_1 + (a_1 + (n-1)d))}{2}$ $a_n = a_1 + (n-1)d$

$= \dfrac{12(2a_1 + (n-1)d)}{2}$ Simplify.

$= \dfrac{12(2(-5) + (12-1)3)}{2}$ $a_1 = -5$, $d = 3$

$= \dfrac{12(-10 + 33)}{2}$

$= 138$

4. D

For the geometric series $\dfrac{1}{2} - 1 + 2 - 4 \cdots$,

$a_1 = \dfrac{1}{2}$ and $r = -2$.

The sum of the geometric series is given by

$S_n = \dfrac{a_1(1 - r^n)}{1 - r}$.

$S_{10} = \dfrac{\dfrac{1}{2}(1 - (-2)^{10})}{1 - (-2)} = \dfrac{\dfrac{1}{2}(1 - (-2)^{10})}{3} = \dfrac{1 - 2^{10}}{6}$

$= -170.5$

5. E

$a, b, 18, 27, \cdots$ form a geometric sequence

where $r = \dfrac{27}{18} = \dfrac{3}{2}$.

$b \cdot \dfrac{3}{2} = 18 \implies b = 12$

$a \cdot \dfrac{3}{2} = b \implies a \cdot \dfrac{3}{2} = 12 \implies a = 8$

Now substitute $a = 8$ and $b = 12$ into the arithmetic sequence $4, a, b, c, \cdots$ and calculate the common difference.

The common difference is 4, so $c = 16$.

6. D $\boxed{L2}$

$$\frac{1}{3}+\frac{5}{3}+3+\frac{13}{3}+\cdots+19$$

Check the first and last terms of the sigma notation in each answer choice.

(A) $\displaystyle\sum_{k=0}^{14}\frac{4}{3}k$ $a_k=\frac{4}{3}k$

$a_0=\frac{4}{3}(0)=0\neq\frac{1}{3}$. Discard choice (A).

(B) $\displaystyle\sum_{k=0}^{14}(\frac{4}{3}k-\frac{1}{3})$ $a_k=\frac{4}{3}k-\frac{1}{3}$

$a_0=\frac{4}{3}(0)-\frac{1}{3}=-\frac{1}{3}\neq\frac{1}{3}$. Discard choice (B).

(C) $\displaystyle\sum_{k=0}^{15}(\frac{4}{3}k+\frac{1}{3})$ $a_k=\frac{4}{3}k+\frac{1}{3}$

$a_0=\frac{4}{3}(0)+\frac{1}{3}=\frac{1}{3}$. $a_{15}=\frac{4}{3}(15)+\frac{1}{3}=\frac{61}{3}\neq19$.

Discard choice (C).

(D) $\displaystyle\sum_{k=1}^{15}(\frac{4}{3}k-1)$ $a_k=\frac{4}{3}k-1$

$a_1=\frac{4}{3}(1)-1=\frac{1}{3}$. $a_{15}=\frac{4}{3}(15)-1=19$.

Choice (D) is correct since both the first and last terms are the same as those in the given series.

7. B $\boxed{L2}$

$1-\frac{2}{3}+\frac{4}{9}-\frac{8}{27}+\cdots$ is an infinite geometric series,

with $a_1=1$ and $r=-\frac{2}{3}$.

Write out the first four terms of the infinite geometric series in each answer choice.

(A) $\displaystyle\sum_{i=1}^{\infty}(-\frac{2}{3})^i$

$=(-\frac{2}{3})^1+(-\frac{2}{3})^2+(-\frac{2}{3})^3+(-\frac{2}{3})^4+\cdots$

$=-\frac{2}{3}+\frac{4}{9}-\frac{8}{27}+\frac{16}{81}+\cdots$

This is not same as the given series.

(B) $\displaystyle\sum_{i=0}^{\infty}(-\frac{2}{3})^i$

$=(-\frac{2}{3})^0+(-\frac{2}{3})^1+(-\frac{2}{3})^2+(-\frac{2}{3})^3+\cdots$

$=1-\frac{2}{3}+\frac{4}{9}-\frac{8}{27}+\cdots$

This is same as the given series, so choice (B) is correct.

8. E $\boxed{L2}$

$a_n=2a_{n-1}+1$, for $n\geq2$ and $a_1=1$.

$a_2=2a_1+1=2(1)+1=3$
$a_3=2a_2+1=2(3)+1=7$
$a_4=2a_3+1=2(7)+1=15$
$a_5=2a_4+1=2(15)+1=31$

9. C $\boxed{L2}$

$a_n=a_{n-1}+n$, for $n\geq2$ and $a_1=0$.

$a_2=a_1+n=0+2=2$ $a_1=0$, $n=2$
$a_3=a_2+n=2+3=5$ $a_2=2$, $n=3$
$a_4=a_3+n=5+4=9$ $a_3=5$, $n=4$

10. A $\boxed{L2}$

$a_n=\sqrt{2(a_{n-1})^2-n}$ for $n\geq2$ and $a_1=\sqrt{3}$.

$a_2=\sqrt{2(a_1)^2-n}=\sqrt{2(\sqrt{3})^2-2}=\sqrt{4}=2$
$a_3=\sqrt{2(a_2)^2-n}=\sqrt{2(2)^2-3}=\sqrt{5}$
$a_4=\sqrt{2(a_3)^2-n}=\sqrt{2(\sqrt{5})^2-4}=\sqrt{6}$

11. C $\boxed{L2}$

Given $\displaystyle\sum_{i=1}^{20} i^2 = 2870$

$\displaystyle\sum_{i=1}^{20}\left(\frac{1}{2}i^2 + 10\right)$

$= \displaystyle\sum_{i=1}^{20}\frac{1}{2}i^2 + \sum_{i=1}^{20}10$

$= \dfrac{1}{2}\displaystyle\sum_{i=1}^{20}i^2 + \sum_{i=1}^{20}10$

$= \dfrac{1}{2}(2870) + (10 \cdot 20) \qquad \displaystyle\sum_{i=1}^{20}i^2 = 2870 \,, \sum_{i=1}^{20}10 = 10 \cdot 20$

$= 1635$

12. B $\boxed{L2}$

For the infinite geometric series

$\sqrt{2} + 1 + \dfrac{\sqrt{2}}{2} + \dfrac{1}{2}\ \cdots$

$a_1 = \sqrt{2}$ and $r = \dfrac{1}{\sqrt{2}}$.

The sum of the infinite geometric series is given

by $S = \dfrac{a_1}{1-r}$.

$S = \dfrac{\sqrt{2}}{1 - \dfrac{1}{\sqrt{2}}} = \dfrac{(\sqrt{2})\sqrt{2}}{(1 - \dfrac{1}{\sqrt{2}})\sqrt{2}} = \dfrac{2}{\sqrt{2}-1}$

$= \dfrac{2(\sqrt{2}+1)}{(\sqrt{2}-1)(\sqrt{2}+1)} = \dfrac{2(\sqrt{2}+1)}{2-1} = 2(\sqrt{2}+1)$

13. E $\boxed{L2}$

$(n+3)! = 4!(n+2)!$

$\dfrac{(n+3)!}{(n+2)!} = 4!$ \qquad Divide both sides by $(n+2)!$.

$\dfrac{(n+3)\,(n+2)\,(n+1)\ \cdots\ \cancel{3}\cdot\cancel{2}\cdot\cancel{1}}{(n+2)\,(n+1)\,(\cancel{n})\ \cdots\ \cancel{3}\cdot\cancel{2}\cdot\cancel{1}} = 4!$

$n+3 = 4!$
$n+3 = 4\cdot3\cdot2\cdot1$
$n = 21$

14. D $\boxed{L2}$

$\dfrac{(n-1)^2[(n)!]^2}{n^2[(n-1)!]^2} = \dfrac{(n-1)^2}{n^2}\cdot\left[\dfrac{(n)!}{(n-1)!}\right]^2$

$= \dfrac{(n-1)^2}{n^2}\cdot\left[\dfrac{(n)\,\cancel{(n-1)(n-1)\cdots 3\cdot2\cdot1}}{\cancel{(n-1)(n-1)\cdots 3\cdot2\cdot1}}\right]^2$

$= \dfrac{(n-1)^2}{n^2}\cdot n^2$

$= (n-1)^2$

15. D $\boxed{L2}$

$(x-y)^5$

$= {}_5C_0(x)^5(-y)^0 + {}_5C_1(x)^4(-y)^1 + {}_5C_2(x)^3(-y)^2$
$\quad + {}_5C_3(x)^2(-y)^3 + {}_5C_4(x)^1(-y)^4 + {}_5C_5(x)^0(-y)^5$

$= x^5 - 5x^4y + 10x^3y^2 - 10x^2y^3 + 5xy^4 - y^5$

16. C $\boxed{L2}$

The k th term of $(a+b)^n$ is

${}_nC_{(k-1)}(a)^{n-(k-1)}(b)^{(k-1)}$.

The fifth term in the expansion of $\left(x-\dfrac{1}{2}\right)^7$ is

${}_7C_{(5-1)}(x)^{7-(5-1)}\left(-\dfrac{1}{2}\right)^{(5-1)}$

$= {}_7C_4(x)^3\left(-\dfrac{1}{2}\right)^4$

$= 35x^3\cdot\dfrac{1}{16}$

$= \dfrac{35}{16}x^3$

The coefficient of the fifth term is $\dfrac{35}{16}$.

17. A $\boxed{L2}$

The k th term of $(a+b)^n$ is

${}_nC_{(k-1)}(a)^{n-(k-1)}(b)^{(k-1)}$.

The fourth term in the expansion of $(x - y^2)^9$ is

$$_9C_{(4-1)}(x)^{9-(4-1)}(-y^2)^{(4-1)}$$

$$= {}_9C_3(x)^6(-y^2)^3$$

$$= 84x^6(-y^6)$$

$$= -84x^6y^6$$

CHAPTER 13
Logic and Probability

13-1. Sets

A **set** is a collection of distinct objects.

The objects of a set are called its **elements** or **members**.

Intersection and Union of Two Sets

Let A and B be any two sets. The **intersection** of A and B, written as $A \cap B$, is defined as the set consisting of those elements that are in **both A and B**. The **union** of A and B, written as $A \cup B$, is defined as the set consisting of those elements that belong to **either A or B, or both**.

Venn Diagram

A Venn diagram represents sets as circles enclosed in a rectangle, which represents the universal set.

The Venn diagram at the right shows sets A and B, where $A = \{1,3,5,7,9\}$ and $B = \{2,3,5,7,11\}$. The intersection and union of the two sets are denoted as $A \cap B = \{3,5,7\}$ and $A \cup B = \{1,2,3,5,7,9,11\}$.

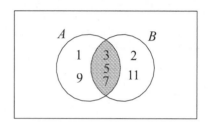

Example 1 □   A die is tossed three times. Let A be the event that the die shows prime numbers, B be the event that the die shows even numbers, and C be the event that the die shows odd numbers. Find $A \cup B$, $A \cap C$, and $B \cap C$.

Solution   □ $A = \{2,3,5\}$, $B = \{2,4,6\}$ and $C = \{1,3,5\}$

$A \cup B = \{2,3,4,5,6\}$

$A \cap C = \{3,5\}$

$B \cap C = \{\varnothing\}$ (Set B and Set C don't have any elements in common.) ■

13-2. Conditional Statements and Related Statements

If-then statements are called **conditional statements**.

From a conditional statement come several related statements, called a contrapositive, converse, and inverse.

Related If-Then Statements

Given statement :	If p, then q.
Contrapositive :	If not q, then not p.
Converse :	If q, then p.
Inverse :	If not p, then not q.

A statement and its contrapositive are logically equivalent, but a statement is not logically equivalent to its converse or to its inverse.

Thus if a given statement is true its contrapositive is also true, but its converse and inverse are not necessarily true.

Example 2 □ Write the contrapositive and the converse of each given statement.

   a. If a figure is a square, then it has four sides.

   b. If $x^3 = 27$, then $x = 3$.

Solution □ a. Statement: If a figure is a square, then it has four sides.

   Contrapositive: If a figure does not have four sides, then it is not a square.

   Converse: If a figure has four sides, then it is a square.

   The given statement and its contrapositive are true. But the converse is not necessarily true.

   b. Statement: If $x^3 = 27$, then $x = 3$.
   Contrapositive: If $x \neq 3$, then $x^3 \neq 27$.
   Converse: If $x = 3$, then $x^3 = 27$.

   The given statement is true. The contrapositive and the converse are also true.   ■

13-3. Indirect Proof and Negation

An **indirect proof** is a proof by contradiction. The first step in writing an indirect proof is to assume that the desired conclusion is not true. On the SAT, you will be asked only for the assumption that could serve as the first step of an indirect proof.

A denial of a statement is called a **negation**. Some examples of negation are shown below.

Statements		Negations
You live in Canada.	⇔	You do not live in Canada.
All people are happy.	⇔	Some people are not happy.
Someone has a laptop computer.	⇔	No one has a laptop computer.

Example 3 □ a. Write an assumption that could begin an indirect proof of the following statement:
   If $x + 5 = 12$, then $x = 7$.

   b. Write the negation of each statement:

   A bear is an animal.

   Some people have no printer.

Solution □ a. Assume that $x \neq 7$.

   b. A bear is not an animal.

   Every person has a printer.   ■

13-4. The Counting Principle

If an event can occur in m different ways and another event can occur in n different ways, then there are $m \times n$ total ways that both events can occur.

Example 4 □ On a survey there are 6 multiple-choice questions with 4 possible answers each. In how many ways can the 6 questions be answered?

Solution □ Each question can be answered 4 different ways. So there are
$$4 \cdot 4 \cdot 4 \cdot 4 \cdot 4 \cdot 4 = 4,096$$
possible ways the questions can be answered.

13-5. Permutation

When a group of objects or people is arranged in a certain order, the arrangement is called a permutation.

The number of permutations of n distinct objects taken r at a time is defined as follows:

$$_nP_r = \frac{n!}{(n-r)!}$$

Permutations with Repetition

The number of permutations of n objects of which p are alike and q are alike is $\dfrac{n!}{p!q!}$.

This rule can be extended for any number of objects that are repeated.

Example 5 □ a. In how many ways can 7 people be seated if there are 4 chairs in a row?

b. In how many ways can the letters of the word MISSISSIPPI be arranged?

Solution □ a. $_7P_4 = \dfrac{7!}{(7-4)!} = \dfrac{7!}{3!} = \dfrac{7 \cdot 6 \cdot 5 \cdot 4 \cdot 3 \cdot 2 \cdot 1}{3 \cdot 2 \cdot 1} = 840$ Answer

b. There are 11 letters, of which 4 are S's, 4 are I's, and 2 are P's.

$\dfrac{11!}{4!4!2!} = 34650$ Answer

13-6. Combination

When a group of objects or people is selected, and the order is not important, the selection is called a combination.

The number of combinations of n distinct objects taken r at a time is defined as follows:

$$_nC_r = \frac{n!}{r!(n-r)!}$$

The basic difference between a permutation and a combination is that **order is considered** in a permutation and **order is not considered** in a combination.

Example 6 □ How many different committees of 3 juniors and 2 sophomores can be formed from 6 juniors and 5 sophomores?

Solution □ $\underbrace{{}_6C_3}_{\substack{\text{combinations of 3 juniors that}\\\text{can be chosen from 6 juniors}}}$ · $\underbrace{{}_5C_2}_{\substack{\text{combinations of 2 sophomores that}\\\text{can be chosen from 5 sophomores}}}$ Counting principle

$= 20 \cdot 10$

$= 200$ Answer

13-7. Probability

If an event can succeed in s ways and fail in f ways, then the probabilities of success $P(s)$ and of failure $P(f)$ are as follows:

$$P(s) = \frac{s}{s+f} \qquad P(f) = \frac{f}{s+f}$$

If the outcome of one event *does not affect* the outcome of another event, then the events are called **independent events**.

If the outcome of one event *does affect* the outcome of another event, then the events are called **dependent events**.

Example 7 □ A box contains 5 red, 2 green, and 3 blue balls.

a. Find the probability of selecting a red ball then a green, if the first ball is replaced before the second one is chosen.

b. Find the probability of selecting a red ball then a green, if the balls selected are not replaced before the next one is chosen.

Solution □ a. This event is **independent** since the selection of the second ball does not depend on the results of the first selection.

$P(\text{red}) = \dfrac{5}{10}$ Probability of choosing a red ball out of 10 balls.

$P(\text{green}) = \dfrac{2}{10}$ Probability of choosing a green ball out of 10 balls.

$P(\text{red, then green}) = \dfrac{5}{10} \cdot \dfrac{2}{10} = \dfrac{1}{10}$ Answer

b. This event is **dependent** since the selection of the second ball depends on the results of the first selection.

$P(\text{red}) = \dfrac{5}{10}$ Probability of choosing a red ball out of 10 balls.

$P(\text{green}) = \dfrac{2}{9}$ Probability of choosing a green ball out of 9 balls.

$P(\text{red, then green}) = \dfrac{5}{10} \cdot \dfrac{2}{9} = \dfrac{1}{9}$ Answer

<u>Note</u>: If a question does not mention replacement you can assume that the selection is not replaced.

13-8. Area Probability

If a region S is in the interior of region T, and a point is chosen at random in region T, then the probability that the chosen point will be in region S is

$$\frac{\text{area of region } S}{\text{area of region } T}.$$

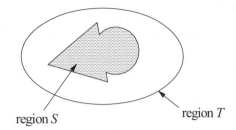

region S region T

Example 8 □ Darts are thrown at a 96-in^2 rectangle which contains a shaded region as shown at the right.
Of the 50 darts which hit the rectangle, 12 hit the shaded region. What is the estimated area of this region?

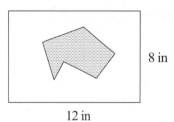

8 in

12 in

Solution □ Let $x =$ the area of the shaded region.

$$\frac{x}{\text{area of the rectangle}} \approx \frac{12}{50}$$

$$\frac{x}{96} \approx \frac{12}{50} \;\Rightarrow\; x \approx 23 \text{ in}^2 \qquad \text{Answer}$$

13-9. Categorized Table by Properties

A categorized table can be used to find the probability of an event.

Example 9 □ The table at the right shows a survey of 120 volunteers at the county hospital. If a volunteer is selected at random, what is the probability that the volunteer is a male over 20 years of age?

	Under 20	Over 20	Total
Male	27	b	
Female		34	
Total	57	a	120

Solution □ The total number of people over 20, a, is $120 - 57 = 63$.

Then the number of males over 20, b, is $63 - 34 = 29$.

P(male over 20 years of age)

$$= \frac{\text{\# of males over 20 years of age}}{\text{total \# of people}}$$

$$= \frac{29}{120} \qquad \text{Answer}$$

1. An auto manufacturer produces 3 models, each available in 5 different colors, with 4 different interior colors, and 3 different interior fabrics. How many varieties of automobiles are available?

   (A) 12

   (B) 60

   (C) 120

   (D) 180

   (E) 240

2. An indirect proof of the statement "If Brian is not here, then he is in Canada" could begin with the assumption that

   (A) Brian is in Canada.

   (B) Brian is not in Canada.

   (C) Brian is in France.

   (D) Brian is here.

   (E) Brian is not here.

$$A = \{2, 3, 4\}$$
$$B = \{H, I, J, K, L\}$$
$$C = \{4, 5, 6, 7, 8, 9\}$$

3. If a can be any number in set A above, b can be any letter in set B, and c can be any number in set C, how many different combinations of abc are possible?

   (A) 14

   (B) 21

   (C) 75

   (D) 90

   (E) 150

4. The probability of event A occurring is $\frac{2}{5}$ and the probability of event B occurring is $\frac{1}{3}$. What is the probability that both events A and B are occurring simultaneously?

   (A) $\frac{2}{15}$

   (B) $\frac{3}{8}$

   (C) $\frac{3}{5}$

   (D) $\frac{2}{3}$

   (E) $\frac{11}{15}$

5. A bag contains 3 red, 4 blue, and 5 yellow marbles. If two marbles are selected in succession, without replacement, what is the probability that neither is yellow?

   (A) $\frac{7}{22}$

   (B) $\frac{5}{11}$

   (C) $\frac{6}{11}$

   (D) $\frac{20}{33}$

   (E) $\frac{2}{3}$

6. A student body of 6 juniors and 4 sophomores is to be chosen from a group of 20 juniors and 10 sophomores. How many different student bodies can be formed?

(A) 24

(B) 50

(C) 4800

(D) 1,017,450

(E) 81,396,00

7. The probability of rain on a certain day is 12% in Greendale and 35% in Santa Rosa. What is the probability that it will rain in neither town?

(A) 0.04

(B) 0.31

(C) 0.44

(D) 0.57

(E) 0.62

8. In how many ways can 12 people be divided into two groups, one with 7 people and the other with 5 people?

(A) 72

(B) 616

(C) 792

(D) 1,584

(E) 3,960

9. A certain club with 20 members is operated by two committees. There are 5 members in committee A and 7 members in committee B. If the two committees have 3 members in common, what is the probability that a person chosen at random will not belong to either committee?

(A) $\dfrac{3}{10}$

(B) $\dfrac{7}{20}$

(C) $\dfrac{3}{8}$

(D) $\dfrac{9}{20}$

(E) $\dfrac{11}{20}$

10. A bag contains 5 red, 6 blue, and 9 green marbles. If three marbles are selected in succession, without replacement, what is the probability that all three are the same color?

(A) $\dfrac{1}{15}$

(B) $\dfrac{1}{12}$

(C) $\dfrac{1}{10}$

(D) $\dfrac{1}{9}$

(E) $\dfrac{1}{8}$

11. Given: If you can't bicycle, then I can't run.

Which of the following statements is equivalent to the given statement?

(A) If you can bicycle, then I can run.

(B) If you can run, then I can bicycle.

(C) If you can't run, then I can't bicycle.

(D) If I can run, then you can bicycle.

(E) If I can't run, then you can't bicycle.

12. In how many ways can 3 identical green chairs, 4 identical red chairs, and 5 identical blue chairs be arranged in a row?

(A) 60

(B) 1,507

(C) 27, 720

(D) 7,983,360

(E) 86,248,800

13. How many different 8 digit numbers can be formed by rearranging the digits in the number 03062006?

(A) 840

(B) 1,680

(C) 5,040

(D) 20,160

(E) 40,320

14. Among the members in a certain gym, 58% are females and 62% are 30 years or older. If 18% of the members are males under 30, what is the probability when a gym member is randomly selected that the person is under 30, a female, or both?

(A) 0.46

(B) 0.52

(C) 0.58

(D) 0.64

(E) 0.76

15. In a box, each of 26 balls is marked with letters from A to Z. If the balls are chosen randomly from the box without replacement, what is the probability of choosing 4 consonants and 2 vowels?

(A) 0.21

(B) 0.26

(C) 0.32

(D) 0.35

(E) 0.38

Answer Key

1. D	2. B	3. D	4. A	5. A
6. E	7. D	8. C	9. E	10. C
11. D	12. C	13. A	14. E	15. B

Answers and Explanations

1. D

Use the counting principle.
$3 \cdot 5 \cdot 4 \cdot 3 = 180$

2. B

The first step in writing an indirect proof is to assume that the desired conclusion is *not* true.

Indirect proof of the given statement could begin with "Assume that Brian is not in Canada."

3. D

Use the counting principle.
$3 \cdot 5 \cdot 6 = 90$

4. A

The probability that both events A and B are occurring simultaneously is $\dfrac{2}{5} \cdot \dfrac{1}{3}$, or $\dfrac{2}{15}$.

5. A

There are 3 red, 4 blue, and 5 yellow marbles in a bag.

$$\boxed{\dfrac{7}{12}} \quad \times \quad \boxed{\dfrac{6}{11}} \quad = \dfrac{7}{22}$$

↑ Out of 12 marbles in the bag, 7 are not yellow.   ↑ Out of 11 marbles left in the bag, 6 are not yellow.

6. E

The number of ways of choosing 6 juniors from a group of 20 juniors is $_{20}C_6$.

The number of ways of choosing 4 sophomores from a group of 10 sophomores is $_{10}C_4$.

$_{20}C_6 \cdot {}_{10}C_4 = 8,139,600$

7. D

If the probability of rain on a certain day in Greendale is 12%, then the probability it will not rain is 88%.

If the probability of rain on a certain day in Santa Rosa is 35%, then the probability it will not rain is 65%.

The probability that it will rain in neither town is $0.88 \times 0.65 = 0.572$.

8. C

When you choose 7 people to be in the first group, the remaining 5 people will automatically form the other group. Thus the number of ways to divide the 12 people into two groups is equal to $_{12}C_7$, or 792.

9. E

Draw a Venn diagram.

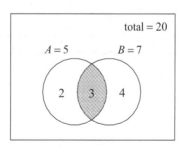

There are $5 + 7 - 3$, or 9 members, who belong to either committee. There are $20 - 9$, or 11 members, who do not belong to either committee.

$P(\text{who do not belong to either committee}) = \dfrac{11}{20}$

10. C

There are 5 red, 6 blue, and 9 green marbles in a bag. If all three marbles selected are the same color, the possible outcomes are

$\boxed{R}\boxed{R}\boxed{R}$, $\boxed{B}\boxed{B}\boxed{B}$, and $\boxed{G}\boxed{G}\boxed{G}$.

P(choosing 3 red marbles in succession)

| 5 red marbles are in the bag. | 4 red marbles are left in the bag. | 3 red marbles are left in the bag. |

$$= \frac{\overset{5}{\cancel{}}}{\underset{\text{20 marbles are in the bag.}}{20}} \times \frac{\overset{4}{\cancel{}}}{\underset{\text{19 marbles are left in the bag.}}{19}} \times \frac{\overset{3}{\cancel{}}}{\underset{\text{18 marbles are left in the bag.}}{18}} = \frac{1}{114}$$

P(choosing 3 blue marbles in succession)

$$= \frac{6}{20} \cdot \frac{5}{19} \cdot \frac{4}{18} = \frac{1}{57}$$

P(choosing 3 green marbles in succession)

$$= \frac{9}{20} \cdot \frac{8}{19} \cdot \frac{7}{18} = \frac{7}{95}$$

P(choosing 3 marbles of the same color

in succession)

$$= \frac{1}{114} + \frac{1}{57} + \frac{7}{95} = \frac{1}{10}$$

11. D

A statement and its contrapositive are logically equivalent.

Given statement: If p, then q.
Contrapositive: If not q, then not p.

Statement: If you can't bicycle, then I can't run.
Contrapostive: If I can run, then you can bicycle.

12. C

The number of permutations of n objects of which p are alike, q are alike, and r are alike is $\dfrac{n!}{p!\,q!\,r!}$.

There are 3 green, 4 red, and 5 blue chairs, for a total of 12 chairs.

$$\frac{12!}{3!4!5!} = 27,720$$

13. A

The number of permutations of 8 objects of which 4 are alike and 2 are alike is $\dfrac{8!}{4!2!} = 840$.

14. E

Let the total $= 100$.
Use a categorized table.

	Under 30	30 or older	Total
Male	18		
Female	(b)		58
Total	(a)	62	100

58 members are female, 62 members are 30 years or older, and 18 members are males under 30.

(a) Members under 30 years of age
$= 100 - 62 = 38$

(b) Females under 30 years of age
$= 38 - 18 = 20$

The number of gym members who are under 30 years, female, or both
= the number of members under 30 years

+ the number of females

− the number of females under 30 years

(Subtract the number of females under 30 so they are not counted twice.)

$\Rightarrow\ 38 + 58 - 20 = 76$

P(under 30 years, female, or both)

$$= \frac{76}{100} = 0.76$$

15. B

| number of ways of choosing 4 consonants out of 21 consonants | number of ways of choosing 2 vowels out of 5 vowels |

$$\frac{\overbrace{{}_{21}C_4}\ \cdot\ \overbrace{{}_5C_2}}{\underbrace{{}_{26}C_6}} \approx 0.26$$

number of ways of choosing 6 letters out of 26 letters

CHAPTER 14
Data Interpretation, Averages, and Percents

14-1. Mean, Median, and Mode

$$\textbf{Mean} = \frac{\text{The sum of the values in a set of data}}{\text{The number of values in a set of data}}$$

The mean is also called the arithmetic average.

The sum of the values = mean × the number of values

The **median** of a set of data is the middle value. If there are two middle values, the median is the mean of the two values.

The **mode** of a set of data is the value that appears most frequently. Some sets of data have more than one mode, and others have no mode. In the set of data {3, 7, 9, 12, 20, 27}, there is no mode since each number appears only once. In the set of data {4, 5, 5, 8, 18, 18, 35}, the modes are 5 and 18, since both numbers appear twice.

Example 1 □ What is the positive difference between the median and the mean of the numbers 17, 21, 21, 33, 38, and 56?

Solution □ $\text{Median} = \dfrac{21+33}{2} = 27$

$\text{Mean} = \dfrac{17+21+21+33+38+56}{6} = 31$

$\text{Mean} - \text{Median} = 31 - 27 = 4$ Answer

14-2. Weighted Average of Two Groups

$$\textbf{Weighted Average of Two Groups} = \frac{\left\{\begin{array}{c}\text{Sum of the values}\\\text{of group 1}\end{array}\right\} + \left\{\begin{array}{c}\text{Sum of the values}\\\text{of group 2}\end{array}\right\}}{\text{Total number of values}}$$

Sum of the values of group 1 = mean of group 1 × number of values in group 1

Sum of the values of group 2 = mean of group 2 × number of values in group 2

Example 2 □ In a Spanish class of 15 boys and 12 girls, the average (arithmetic mean) test score of the class was 78. If the average score of the 15 boys was 75, what was the average score of the 12 girls?

Solution □ Let $x =$ the average score of 12 girls

$78 = \dfrac{(15 \cdot 75) + 12x}{15 + 12}$ Weighted average formula

$x = 81.75$ Answer

14-3. Percent Increase and Percent Decrease

$$\textbf{Percent Increase} = \frac{\text{Amount of Increase}}{\text{Original Amount}} \qquad \textbf{Percent Decrease} = \frac{\text{Amount of Decrease}}{\text{Original Amount}}$$

Example 3   □   An initial sample of 12 bacteria increased to 120 bacteria in 24 hours. What was the percent increase?

Solution   □   Percent increase $= \dfrac{\text{Amount of increase}}{\text{Original amount}} = \dfrac{120-12}{12} = 9$

Therefore the bacteria increased by 900%.

14-4. Stem-and-Leaf Plots and Box-and-Whisker Plots

A **stem-and-leaf plot** organizes data by putting numbers in order. The leaf is the last digit of each value and the stem is the remaining digit(s). The key shows how to read the stem-and-leaf plot. In the plot at the right, the first line shows the values 20, 23, 25, 28, and 29.

$$
\begin{array}{r|l}
2 & 0\ 3\ 5\ 8\ 9 \\
\text{stems} \rightarrow \quad 3 & 0\ 4\ 6\ 8 \quad \leftarrow \text{leaves} \\
4 & 1\ 3
\end{array}
$$

$3\mid 5 = 35 \quad \leftarrow$ key

A **box-and-whisker plot** displays the distribution of data items along a number line. Quartiles divide the data into four equal parts. The median is the **middle quartile**. The **lower quartile** is the median of the lower half of the data and the **upper quartile** is the median of the upper half of the data. The **interquartile range** is the difference between the upper and lower quartiles.

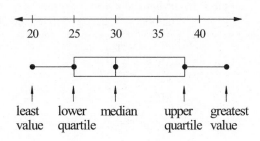

Example 4   □   The stem-and-leaf plot at the right shows a basketball team's scores for all of the games last season.

$$
\begin{array}{r|l}
5 & 4\ 7\ 8\ 9 \\
6 & 2\ 3\ 3\ 5\ 6\ 8\ 8 \\
7 & 1\ 2\ 4\ 5\ 8\ 9
\end{array}
$$

$5\mid 2 = 52$

a. What percent of the scores are more than 70 points?

b. Find the lower quartile, median, and upper quartile of the scores.

Solution   □   a. 17 basketball scores are represented in the stem-and-leaf plot. 6 of the scores are more than 70 points.

$\dfrac{6}{17} \approx 35\%$ Answer

b. Arrange the data in order from least to greatest.

$\underbrace{54,\ 57,\ 58,\ 59,\ 62,\ 63,\ 63,\ 65,}_{\text{lower half}} \quad \underbrace{66}_{\text{median}}\ ,\ \underbrace{68,\ 68,\ 71,\ 72,\ 74,\ 75,\ 78,\ 79}_{\text{upper half}}$

Lower quartile $= \dfrac{59+62}{2} = 60.5$ Answer

Median $= 66$ Answer

Upper quartile $= \dfrac{72+74}{2} = 73$ Answer

14-5. Scatter Plots

A **scatter plot** is a coordinate graph containing points that represent real-life data. When the data is collected, usually there is no single line that passes through all the data points, but we can approximate a linear relationship by finding a line that best fits the data. This is called the **line of best fit**.

Positive Correlation   Negative Correlation   No Correlation

Example 5 □   The scatter plot at the right shows the age of and the number of movies attended by a sample of 18 students. What percent of these students are more than 20 years old and attended less than 10 movies?

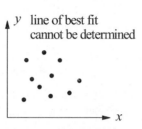

Solution   □   The scatter plot shows 6 persons are more than 20 years old and attended less than 10 movies.

$$\frac{6}{18} \approx 0.33 \quad \Rightarrow \quad 33\,\% \qquad \text{Answer}$$

14-6. Bar Graphs, Histograms, and Line Graphs

On a **bar graph**, one axis is labeled with a numerical scale and the other is labeled with categories. The height of each bar shows its value. A **histogram** is a type of bar graph that displays a frequency distribution.

A **line graph** shows the values and direction of change for certain data over a period of time.

Example 6 □   According to the graph at the right, what is the average number of computers per household?

Number of Computers in a Household

Solution   □   Total # of computers
$$= 1\cdot2 + 2\cdot5 + 3\cdot7 + 4\cdot4 + 5\cdot2 + 6\cdot1$$
$$= 65$$

$$\text{Average \# of computers} = \frac{65}{21}$$

$$\approx 3.1 \qquad \text{Answer}$$

14-7. Circle Graphs (Pie Charts)

A **circle graph** is used to represent data expressed as part of a whole.
The entire circle represents the whole, or 100%, of the data. Each section is
labeled with a category name, accompanied by the corresponding percentage.

Example 7 □   The pie chart at the right shows
compact discs owned by a student.

    a. Find the measure of the central angle
       of the sector representing jazz.

    b. What percent of the CDs are
       classical?

Types of Compact Discs

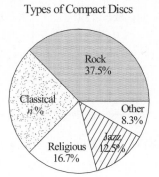

Solution   □   a. $360° \times 0.125 = 45°$ Answer

    b. In a circle graph the entire circle
       represents 100%.

      $n + 37.5 + 8.3 + 12.5 + 16.7 = 100$
      $\Rightarrow\ n = 25\%$ Answer

14-8. Standard Deviation $\boxed{L2}$

The variance, denoted σ^2, and the standard deviation of a data set $\{x_1,\ x_2,\ \cdots,\ x_n,\}$ are
defined as follows:

$$\textbf{Variance} = \sigma^2 = \frac{(x_1 - M)^2 + (x_2 - M)^2 + \cdots + (x_n - M)^2}{n}\ ,\ \text{where } M \text{ is the mean of } n \text{ numbers.}$$

$$\textbf{Standard deviation} = \sqrt{\sigma^2} = \sqrt{\frac{(x_1 - M)^2 + (x_2 - M)^2 + \cdots + (x_n - M)^2}{n}}$$

In a data set, if the same number k is added to each number, the mean is increased by k, while
the range and the standard deviation are unchanged. If each number in a data set is multiplied
by the same number k, the mean, range, and standard deviation are all multiplied by k.

Example 8 □   Find the standard deviation of the data set $\{4,\ 7,\ 11,\ 14,\ 24\}$.

Solution   □ $\text{Mean} = \dfrac{4 + 7 + 11 + 14 + 24}{5} = 12$

$$\text{Standard deviation} = \sqrt{\frac{(4-12)^2 + (7-12)^2 + (11-12)^2 + (14-12)^2 + (24-12)^2}{5}}$$

$$\approx 6.9 \qquad \text{Answer}$$

```
3 | 2 6
4 | 0 2 5 9
5 | 3 8 9
4 | 8  = 48
```

1. In the stem-and-leaf plot above, what is the positive difference between the mean and the median of the values?

(A) 1

(B) 2

(C) 3

(D) 4

(E) 5

2. The average (arithmetic mean) score of 6 golfers was 92 and the average score of 12 other golfers was 98. What was the average score of all 18 golfers?

(A) 93

(B) 94

(C) 95

(D) 96

(E) 97

3. A student has an average (arithmetic mean) score of 76 points for 5 previous tests. What is the total score this student needs in the next two tests, in order to have an average of 80 for all 7 tests?

(A) 172

(B) 176

(C) 180

(D) 184

(E) 188

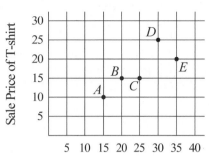

4. The scatter plot above shows the regular price and sale price of 5 T-shirts at a certain department store. For which T-shirt is the percent decrease from regular to sale price the greatest?

(A) A

(B) B

(C) C

(D) D

(E) E

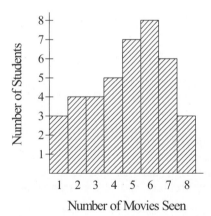

5. The graph above shows the number of movies seen by 40 students last year. What percentage of the students attended 5 or more movies last year?

(A) 52%

(B) 55%

(C) 60%

(D) 64%

(E) 68%

6. In a data set of 40 numbers, the average (arithmetic mean) of the first 30 numbers was 12 and the average of all 40 numbers was *x*. If the least number in the data set of the last 10 numbers was 2 and the greatest was 18, then which of the following inequalities is true?

(A) $9.5 \leq x \leq 13.5$

(B) $10 \leq x \leq 14.5$

(C) $10 \leq x \leq 16$

(D) $12 \leq x \leq 16.5$

(E) $12 \leq x \leq 18$

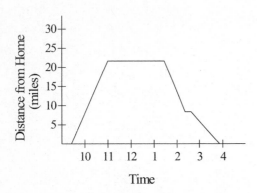

7. The graph above shows the relationship between the time and the distance of Kay's car from her home on Saturday. Which of the following could be a description of her trip?

(A) Kay leaves a park after a picnic, drives toward her home, and makes a stop for gas.

(B) Kay leaves home, drives to a park for a picnic, then drives toward home, stops for gas, and returns home.

(C) Kay leaves home, drives to a park for a picnic, then drives to her friend's house, and stays there.

(D) Kay leaves home, drives to a park, then drives to the grocery store, and then drives back to the park.

(E) Kay leaves home, stops for gas, then drives to the grocery store, and then stays at the park.

8. An engineer boards a commuter train at a station near his home, rides the train for 45 minutes, and arrives at the LA station. He waits 10 minutes to take a bus to his office near downtown LA. The bus ride to his office takes 15 minutes. Which of the following graphs could correctly represent his trip?

(A)

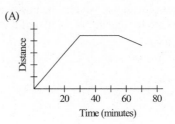

(B)

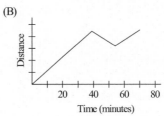

(C)

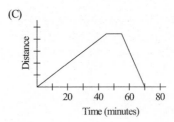

(D)

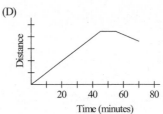

(E)

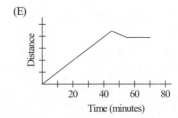

9. The average (arithmetic mean) of a set of n integers is 9, and the average of the n integers and 42 is 12. What is the value of n?

(A) 6

(B) 7

(C) 8

(D) 9

(E) 10

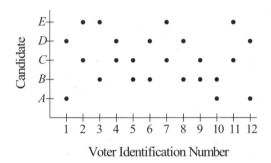

Voter Identification Number

10. The graph above shows how 12 different voters voted for 5 different candidates. Each voter voted for exactly two candidates. The two candidates receiving the most votes were the winners. What fraction of the total number of votes cast did the two winners together receive?

(A) $\dfrac{1}{3}$

(B) $\dfrac{3}{8}$

(C) $\dfrac{5}{12}$

(D) $\dfrac{1}{2}$

(E) $\dfrac{7}{12}$

11. Darol has a batting average of 0.258 after finishing 60% of the regular season games. If he wants to finish the entire season with a batting average of 0.280, what must be his batting average, to the nearest thousandth, for the remainder of the season?

(A) 0.302

(B) 0.313

(C) 0.317

(D) 0.323

(E) 0.329

7	5 8
8	1 3 5 7
9	2

$8 \mid 2 = 82$

12. What is the standard deviation of the data shown in the stem-and-leaf plot above? $\boxed{L2}$

(A) 4.4

(B) 4.8

(C) 5.3

(D) 5.7

(E) 6.2

Answer Key

1. A   2. D   3. C   4. E   5. C

6. A   7. B   8. D   9. E   10. D

11. B   12. C

Answers and Explanations

1. A

$$
\begin{array}{c|l}
3 & 2\ 6 \\
4 & 0\ 2\ 5\ 9 \\
5 & 3\ 8\ 9 \\
4 & 8\ =48
\end{array}
$$

Arrange the data in order from least to greatest:

$32, 36, 40, 42, 45, 49, 53, 58, 59$

The average (arithmetic mean)

$$= \frac{32+36+40+42+45+49+53+58+59}{9} = 46.$$

The median is 45.

The difference between the mean and the median $= 46 - 45 = 1$.

2. D

Weighted Average of Two Groups

$$= \frac{\left\{\begin{array}{c}\text{Sum of the values}\\\text{of group 1}\end{array}\right\} + \left\{\begin{array}{c}\text{Sum of the values}\\\text{of group 2}\end{array}\right\}}{\text{Total number of values}}$$

Average of all 18 golfers

$$= \frac{6\cdot 92 + 12\cdot 98}{6+12}$$

$$= 96$$

3. C

Let x = the total score needed in the next two tests.

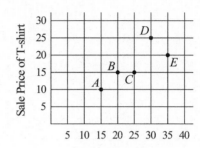

$$
\underbrace{80}_{\substack{\text{average scores}\\\text{of 7 tests}}} = \frac{\overbrace{5\cdot 76}^{\substack{\text{sum of the scores}\\\text{of 5 previous tests}}} + \overbrace{x}^{\substack{\text{sum of the scores he}\\\text{needs for next 2 tests}}}}{7}
$$

$$7\cdot 80 = 5\cdot 76 + x \implies 560 = 380 + x$$
$$x = 180$$

4. E

Use the percent decrease formula.

(A) Regular price $= 15$, Sale price $= 10$

$$\text{Percent discount} = \frac{15-10}{15} = \frac{1}{3} = 33\%$$

(B) Regular price $= 20$, Sale price $= 15$

$$\text{Percent discount} = \frac{20-15}{20} = \frac{1}{4} = 25\%$$

(C) Regular price $= 25$, Sale price $= 15$

$$\text{Percent discount} = \frac{25-15}{25} = \frac{2}{5} = 40\%$$

(D) Regular price $= 30$, Sale price $= 25$

$$\text{Percent discount} = \frac{30-25}{30} = \frac{1}{6} = 16.6\%$$

(E) Regular price $= 35$, Sale price $= 20$

$$\text{Percent discount} = \frac{35-20}{35} = \frac{3}{7} = 42.9\%$$

Choice (E) has the greatest percent decrease.

5. C

The number of students who attended 5 or more movies $= 7+8+6+3 = 24$.

The percentage of students who attended 5 or more movies $= \dfrac{24}{40} = 60\%$.

6. A

Sum of the first 30 numbers $= 30 \cdot 12 = 360$

Sum of all 40 numbers $= 40x$

Sum of the last 10 numbers $= 40x - 360$

Average of the last 10 numbers

$= \dfrac{40x - 360}{10} = 4x - 36$

The least number in the data set was 2 and the greatest was 18, therefore

$2 \le 4x - 36 \le 18 \implies 38 \le 4x \le 54$

$\implies \dfrac{38}{4} \le x \le \dfrac{54}{4} \implies 9.5 \le x \le 13.5$

7. B

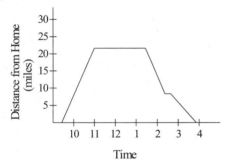

The graph shows that she started the trip from her home, since the distance from home was 0. Eliminate choice (A). She arrived somewhere at 11:00 and stayed there for about two and a half hours. She then drove back toward her house, stopping somewhere in between for a short time, before finally arriving at her house.

Choice (B) is correct since it states that she returns home at the end of her trip.

8. D

After riding the train for 45 minutes, the engineer arrives at the LA station then waits at the bus stop for 10 minutes. Eliminate choices (B) and (E), since the graphs do not show a 10-minute stay at the same place. Also eliminate choice (A), since it shows a 25-minute stay at the same place. The graph in choice (C) shows that the engineer arrives at home, not his office.

Choice (D) is correct.

9. E

The sum of the set of n integers is $9n$.

The average of n integers and 42 is 12.

$$\underset{\substack{\text{There are } n+1 \text{ numbers.}}}{\dfrac{\overset{\text{sum of } n \text{ integers and 42}}{\overbrace{9n + 42}}}{\underbrace{n + 1}}} = 12$$

$9n + 42 = 12(n + 1)$

$9n + 42 = 12n + 12 \implies 3n = 30$

$\implies n = 10$

10. D

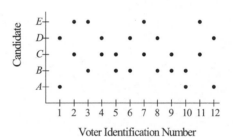

Voter Identification Number

Number of votes candidate A received $= 3$.
Number of votes candidate B received $= 6$.
Number of votes candidate C received $= 6$.
Number of votes candidate D received $= 5$.
Number of votes candidate E received $= 4$.

The two winners are candidate B and candidate C. Together they received $6 + 6$, or 12, votes.

$$\dfrac{\text{\# of votes for the two winners}}{\text{total \# of votes}} = \dfrac{12}{24} = \dfrac{1}{2}$$

11. B

Let $x =$ Darol's batting average for the remainder of the season.

batting average for the first 60% of the season		batting average for the remaining 40% of the season		batting average for the entire season

$0.6 \times \overbrace{0.258} + 0.4 \times \overbrace{x} = \overbrace{0.280}$

$0.1548 + 0.4x = 0.28$

$0.4x = 0.1252$

$x = 0.313$

12. C $\boxed{L2}$

Arrange the data in order from least to greatest:
75, 78, 81, 83, 85, 87, 92

The average (arithmetic mean)
$$= \frac{75 + 78 + 81 + 83 + 85 + 87 + 92}{7} = 83$$

$$\begin{aligned} \text{Variance} &= [(75-83)^2 + (78-83)^2 + (81-83)^2 \\ &\quad + (83-83)^2 + (85-83)^2 + (87-83)^2 \\ &\quad + (92-83)^2] \div 7 \\ &\approx 27.7 \end{aligned}$$

$$\begin{aligned} \text{Standard deviation} &= \sqrt{\text{variance}} \\ &= \sqrt{27.7} \\ &\approx 5.26 \end{aligned}$$

CHAPTER 15
Additional Topics

15-1. Defined Operations with Special Symbols

For some problems on the SAT, test-makers will use their own special symbols to define their own operations. Approach these new symbols and definitions as you would a function. The key to this type of question is to read the definition carefully and make substitutions.

Suppose you are given an equation $x \otimes = \dfrac{\sqrt{x-1}}{2}$, which is defined by a special symbol $\otimes$.

You can solve this equation as you would $f(x) = \dfrac{\sqrt{x-1}}{2}$.

> Example 1 □ For all real numbers m, where $m \neq 0$, let the operation $*$ be defined as $m^* = \dfrac{m-1}{m}$. What is the value of $((-2)^*)^*$?

> Solution □ $((-2)^*)^* = (\dfrac{-2-1}{-2})^*$ Substitution: $(-2)^* = \dfrac{-2-1}{-2}$.
>
> $= (3/2)^*$ Simplify.
>
> $= \dfrac{3/2-1}{3/2}$ Substitution: $(3/2)^* = \dfrac{3/2-1}{3/2}$.
>
> $= \dfrac{1}{3}$ Answer

15-2. Matrices

A **matrix** is a rectangular array of real numbers.
The **rows** of a matrix run horizontally, and the **columns** run vertically.
Each number in a matrix is called an **element**.
A matrix with m rows and n columns has **dimensions** $m \times n$.

$\begin{bmatrix} 3 & -4 & 6 \\ 2 & 5 & 11 \end{bmatrix} \Leftarrow$ 2 rows

⇑
3 columns

The dimensions of the matrix are 2×3.

The element in row 2, column 3 is 11.

Matrix Multiplication

The product of two matrices is found by multiplying rows and columns. Two matrices can be multiplied only if the number of columns in one matrix equals the number of rows in the other matrix.

If $R = \begin{bmatrix} r_1 & r_2 & r_3 \end{bmatrix}$ and $C = \begin{bmatrix} c_1 \\ c_2 \\ c_3 \end{bmatrix}$, then the product of R and C is the number $r_1 c_1 + r_2 c_2 + r_3 c_3$.

Multiplying a matrix with m rows and n columns by a matrix with n rows and p columns yields a matrix with m rows and p columns: $M_{m \times n} \cdot M_{n \times p} = M_{m \times p}$.

Example 2 □   Find the products of the following matrices.

a. $\begin{bmatrix} 3 \\ 2 \end{bmatrix} \cdot \begin{bmatrix} 4 & 5 \\ 3 & 10 \end{bmatrix}$ b. $\begin{bmatrix} -2 & 8 \\ 5 & 3 \end{bmatrix} \cdot \begin{bmatrix} 4 \\ 3 \end{bmatrix}$ c. $\begin{bmatrix} 6 & -1 \\ 5 & 8 \end{bmatrix} \cdot \begin{bmatrix} 4 & 9 \\ -2 & 3 \end{bmatrix}$

d. $\begin{bmatrix} 12 & 16 & 24 \end{bmatrix} \cdot \begin{bmatrix} 25 & 14 & 6 \\ 15 & 11 & 8 \\ 9 & 7 & 5 \end{bmatrix}$

Solution □ a. $\begin{bmatrix} 3 \\ 2 \end{bmatrix} \cdot \begin{bmatrix} 4 & 5 \\ 3 & 10 \end{bmatrix} = \begin{bmatrix} 3\cdot 4 + 3\cdot 3 & 3\cdot 5 + 3\cdot 10 \\ 2\cdot 4 + 2\cdot 3 & 2\cdot 5 + 2\cdot 10 \end{bmatrix} = \begin{bmatrix} 21 & 45 \\ 14 & 30 \end{bmatrix}$ $M_{2\times1} \cdot M_{2\times2} = M_{2\times2}$

b. $\begin{bmatrix} -2 & 8 \\ 5 & 3 \end{bmatrix} \cdot \begin{bmatrix} 4 \\ 3 \end{bmatrix} = \begin{bmatrix} -2\cdot 4 + 8\cdot 3 \\ 5\cdot 4 + 3\cdot 3 \end{bmatrix} = \begin{bmatrix} 16 \\ 29 \end{bmatrix}$ $M_{2\times2} \cdot M_{2\times1} = M_{2\times1}$

c. $\begin{bmatrix} 6 & -1 \\ 5 & 8 \end{bmatrix} \cdot \begin{bmatrix} 4 & 9 \\ -2 & 3 \end{bmatrix} = \begin{bmatrix} 6\cdot 4 + (-1)(-2) & 6\cdot 9 + (-1)3 \\ 5\cdot 4 + 8(-2) & 5\cdot 9 + 8\cdot 3 \end{bmatrix}$

$= \begin{bmatrix} 26 & 51 \\ 4 & 69 \end{bmatrix}$ $M_{2\times2} \cdot M_{2\times2} = M_{2\times2}$

d. $\begin{bmatrix} 12 & 16 & 24 \end{bmatrix} \cdot \begin{bmatrix} 25 & 14 & 6 \\ 15 & 11 & 8 \\ 9 & 7 & 5 \end{bmatrix}$

$= \begin{bmatrix} 12\cdot 25 + 16\cdot 15 + 24\cdot 9 & 12\cdot 14 + 16\cdot 11 + 24\cdot 7 & 12\cdot 6 + 16\cdot 8 + 24\cdot 5 \end{bmatrix}$

$= \begin{bmatrix} 756 & 512 & 320 \end{bmatrix}$ $M_{1\times3} \cdot M_{3\times3} = M_{1\times3}$ ■

15-3. Parametric Equations $\boxed{L2}$

If $f(t)$ and $g(t)$ are both given as functions of a third variable t, where t is a real number, then the equations $x = f(t)$ and $y = g(t)$ are called **parametric equations**.

To write parametric equations as a single equation in terms of x and y, solve for t in one equation, and substitute the result into the second equation. Then you can find an equation in terms of x and y. If the parametric equations involve sines and cosines, use the trigonometric identities.

Example 3 □   a. If $x = t - 1$ and $y = t^2 + 1$, what is y in terms of x?

b. Write an equation in terms of x and y, if $x = \cos t$ and $y = \sin t$.

Solution	□	a.	$x = t - 1$	Parametric equation for x.
			$t = x + 1$	Solve for t.
			$y = t^2 + 1$	Parametric equation for y.
			$y = (x+1)^2 + 1$	Substitute $x + 1$ for t.
			$y = x^2 + 2x + 2$	Simplify.

		b.	$x = \cos t$	Parametric equation for x.
			$x^2 = \cos^2 t$	Square both sides.
			$y = \sin t$	Parametric equation for y.
			$y^2 = \sin^2 t$	Square both sides.
			$\cos^2 t + \sin^2 t = 1$	Trigonometric identity
			$x^2 + y^2 = 1$	Substitution

15-4. Limits of Algebraic Functions $\boxed{L2}$

If $f(x)$ is an algebraic function, then $\lim\limits_{x \to c} f(x) = f(c)$ provided $f(c)$ is defined.

Suppose $f(x) = x^2 - 3x + 2$. Then $\lim\limits_{x \to 4} f(x) = f(4) = 4^2 - 3 \cdot 4 + 2 = 6$, which

we read "the limit of $f(x)$ as x approaches 4 is 6."

Strategies for Finding Limits

1) If the function is defined at c, make a **direct substitution**.

2) If the rational function is not defined at c, **factor and divide out common factors**, then make a direct substitution.

3) If the rational function is not defined at c, you can also **rationalize the numerator of a rational expression**, then make a direct substitution.

Example 4 □ Find the limits.

a. $\lim\limits_{x \to 5} \dfrac{2x}{\sqrt{x+4}}$ b. $\lim\limits_{x \to 2} \dfrac{x^2 + 2x - 3}{x - 1}$ c. $\lim\limits_{x \to 0} \dfrac{\sqrt{x+4} - 2}{x}$

Solution	□	a.	$\lim\limits_{x \to 5} \dfrac{2x}{\sqrt{x+4}} = \dfrac{2 \cdot 5}{\sqrt{5+4}}$	Make a direct substitution.
			$= \dfrac{10}{3}$	Answer

		b.	$\lim\limits_{x \to 1} \dfrac{x^2 + 2x - 3}{x - 1} = \dfrac{1^2 + 2 \cdot 1 - 3}{1 - 1} = \dfrac{0}{0}$	Direct substitution fails.
			$\lim\limits_{x \to 1} \dfrac{x^2 + 2x - 3}{x - 1} = \lim\limits_{x \to 1} \dfrac{(x - 1)(x + 3)}{x - 1}$	Factor and divide out common factors.
			$= \lim\limits_{x \to 1} (x + 3)$	Simplify.
			$= 1 + 3 = 4$	Make a direct substitution.

c. $\lim\limits_{x \to 0} \dfrac{\sqrt{x+4}-2}{x} = \dfrac{\sqrt{0+4}-2}{0} = \dfrac{0}{0}$ Direct substitution fails.

$$\lim\limits_{x \to 0} \frac{\sqrt{x+4}-2}{x}$$

$= \lim\limits_{x \to 0} \dfrac{(\sqrt{x+4}-2)(\sqrt{x+4}+2)}{x(\sqrt{x+4}+2)}$ Rationalize the numerator.

$= \lim\limits_{x \to 0} \dfrac{(x+4)-4}{x(\sqrt{x+4}+2)}$ Simplify.

$= \lim\limits_{x \to 0} \dfrac{\cancel{x}}{\cancel{x}(\sqrt{x+4}+2)}$ Divide out like factors.

$= \lim\limits_{x \to 0} \dfrac{1}{(\sqrt{x+4}+2)}$ Simplify.

$= \dfrac{1}{(\sqrt{0+4}+2)}$ Make a substitution. $(x = 0)$

$= \dfrac{1}{\sqrt{4}+2} = \dfrac{1}{4}$ Answer ▪

15-5. Limits at Infinity $\boxed{L2}$

Let $f(x)$ be a function defined on some interval (c, ∞) and L be a real number.

1. The statement $\lim\limits_{x \to \infty} f(x) = L$ means that the values of $f(x)$ become arbitrarily close to L when x gets larger without bound.

2. The statement $\lim\limits_{x \to -\infty} f(x) = L$ means that the values of $f(x)$ become arbitrarily close to L when x gets smaller without bound.

Guidelines for Finding Limits at Infinity of Rational Functions

Let N be the degree of the numerator and D be the degree of the denominator.

1. If $N < D$, then the limit of the rational function is 0.

2. If $N = D$, then the limit of the rational function is the ratio of the leading coefficients.

3. If $N > D$, then the limit of the rational function does not exist.

Example 5 □   Find the limits.

a. $\lim\limits_{x \to \infty} \dfrac{2x}{x^2 - 1}$ b. $\lim\limits_{x \to \infty} \dfrac{4x^2 - x + 7}{3x^2 + 1}$ c. $\lim\limits_{x \to \infty} \dfrac{x^3 + 6x^2 - 11}{4x^2 + 1}$.

Solution   □   a. $\lim\limits_{x\to\infty}\dfrac{2x}{x^2-1}$

$(N < D.)$

$= \lim\limits_{x\to\infty}\dfrac{2x\big/x^2}{(x^2/x^2)-(1/x^2)}$

Divide the numerator and denominator by x^2, which is the highest power of x.

$= \lim\limits_{x\to\infty}\dfrac{2/x}{1-1/x^2}$

Simplify.

$= \dfrac{0}{1-0}$

As $x\to\infty$, $\dfrac{2}{x}\to 0$ and $\dfrac{1}{x^2}\to 0$.

$= \dfrac{0}{1} = 0$

Answer

b. $\lim\limits_{x\to\infty}\dfrac{4x^2-x+7}{3x^2+1}$

$(N = D.$ The leading coefficients are 4 and 3.$)$

$= \lim\limits_{x\to\infty}\dfrac{\dfrac{4x^2}{x^2}-\dfrac{x}{x^2}+\dfrac{7}{x^2}}{\dfrac{3x^2}{x^2}+\dfrac{1}{x^2}}$

Divide the numerator and denominator by x^2.

$= \lim\limits_{x\to\infty}\dfrac{4-\dfrac{1}{x}+\dfrac{7}{x^2}}{3+\dfrac{1}{x^2}}$

Simplify.

$= \dfrac{4-0+0}{3+0}$

As $x\to\infty$, $\dfrac{1}{x}\to 0$, $\dfrac{7}{x^2}\to 0$ and $\dfrac{1}{x^2}\to 0$.

$= \dfrac{4}{3}$

Answer

c. $\lim\limits_{x\to\infty}\dfrac{x^3+6x^2-11}{4x^2+1}$

$(N > D.)$

$= \lim\limits_{x\to\infty}\dfrac{\dfrac{x^3}{x^3}+\dfrac{6x^2}{x^3}-\dfrac{11}{x^3}}{\dfrac{4x^2}{x^3}+\dfrac{1}{x^3}}$

Divide the numerator and denominator by x^3.

$= \lim\limits_{x\to\infty}\dfrac{1+\dfrac{6}{x}-\dfrac{11}{x^3}}{\dfrac{4}{x}+\dfrac{1}{x^3}}$

Simplify.

$= \dfrac{1}{0}$

As $x\to\infty$, $\dfrac{6}{x}\to 0$, $\dfrac{11}{x^3}\to 0$, $\dfrac{4}{x}\to 0$ and $\dfrac{1}{x^3}\to 0$.

$= \infty$ (Undefined)

Answer

1. For all positive real numbers a, let the operation $*$ be defined as $a* = 2^a$. If $b* = 16$ and $b = c*$, what is the value of c?

   (A) 0

   (B) 1

   (C) 2

   (D) 3

   (E) 4

2. For all real numbers x and y, let the operation $\odot$ be defined as $x \odot y = 2^{x+y}$. If $x \odot 3 = 32$, what is the value of x?

   (A) 2

   (B) 3

   (C) 4

   (D) 5

   (E) 6

3. $\begin{bmatrix} 8 & 12 \\ 5 & 14 \end{bmatrix} \cdot \begin{bmatrix} 15 & 7 \\ 6 & 11 \end{bmatrix} =$

   (A) $\begin{bmatrix} 380 \\ 348 \end{bmatrix}$

   (B) $\begin{bmatrix} 380 & 348 \end{bmatrix}$

   (C) $\begin{bmatrix} 204 & 180 \\ 173 & 184 \end{bmatrix}$

   (D) $\begin{bmatrix} 192 & 188 \\ 159 & 189 \end{bmatrix}$

   (E) $\begin{bmatrix} 150 & 264 \\ 111 & 238 \end{bmatrix}$

4. $\begin{bmatrix} 8 & 14 & 19 \end{bmatrix} \cdot \begin{bmatrix} 4 & 7 \\ 8 & 10 \\ 15 & 9 \end{bmatrix} =$

   (A) $\begin{bmatrix} 429 \\ 367 \end{bmatrix}$

   (B) $\begin{bmatrix} 429 & 367 \end{bmatrix}$

   (C) $\begin{bmatrix} 88 \\ 252 \\ 456 \end{bmatrix}$

   (D) $\begin{bmatrix} 32 & 56 \\ 112 & 190 \\ 285 & 171 \end{bmatrix}$

   (E) $\begin{bmatrix} 32 & 112 & 285 \\ 56 & 190 & 171 \end{bmatrix}$

5. If $x = 1 - \dfrac{1}{t}$ and $y = t + 1$, what is y in terms of x?

   $\boxed{L2}$

   (A) $y = 2 - \dfrac{1}{x}$

   (B) $y = \dfrac{2+x}{1-x}$

   (C) $y = \dfrac{x-2}{x+1}$

   (D) $y = \dfrac{x+2}{x+1}$

   (E) $y = \dfrac{x-2}{x-1}$

6. A curve is represented by the parametric equations $x = 2\cos t$ and $y = 2\sin t$, where t is the parameter. Which of the following is the equation of the curve in terms of x and y? $\boxed{L2}$

(A) $x^2 + y^2 = \dfrac{1}{4}$

(B) $x^2 + y^2 = \dfrac{1}{2}$

(C) $x^2 + y^2 = 1$

(D) $x^2 + y^2 = 2$

(E) $x^2 + y^2 = 4$

7. If a curve is represented by the parametric equations $x = 8\cos^3 \theta$ and $y = 8\sin^3 \theta$, which of the following is the equation of the curve in terms of x and y? $\boxed{L2}$

(A) $x^{\frac{2}{3}} + y^{\frac{2}{3}} = 4$

(B) $x^{\frac{1}{3}} + y^{\frac{1}{3}} = 8$

(C) $x^3 + y^3 = 8$

(D) $x^2 + y^2 = 2\sqrt{2}$

(E) $x^2 + y^2 = 8$

8. $\displaystyle\lim_{x \to 3} \dfrac{x^2 - 9}{x - 3} =$ $\boxed{L2}$

(A) $\dfrac{1}{3}$

(B) 2

(C) 3

(D) 6

(E) The limit does not exist.

9. If $f(x) = \dfrac{x - 2}{x^2 - 4}$, what value does $f(x)$ approach as x approaches 2? $\boxed{L2}$

(A) $\dfrac{1}{4}$

(B) $\dfrac{1}{2}$

(C) 2

(D) 4

(E) It does not approach any single number.

10. $\displaystyle\lim_{x \to -1} \dfrac{x^2 - 2x - 3}{x^2 - 4x - 5} =$ $\boxed{L2}$

(A) $\dfrac{1}{3}$

(B) $\dfrac{2}{3}$

(C) $\dfrac{3}{2}$

(D) 3

(E) The limit does not exist.

11. $\displaystyle\lim_{x \to \infty} \dfrac{x}{3x - 3} =$ $\boxed{L2}$

(A) $\dfrac{1}{3}$

(B) $\dfrac{1}{2}$

(C) 3

(D) 6

(E) The limit does not exist.

12. $\lim\limits_{x \to \infty} \dfrac{3x}{\sqrt{x^2+1}} =$ $\boxed{L2}$

(A) 0

(B) $\dfrac{1}{3}$

(C) 3

(D) 9

(E) The limit does not exist.

13. $\lim\limits_{x \to \infty} (10 + \dfrac{5}{x}) =$ $\boxed{L2}$

(A) 0

(B) 5

(C) 10

(D) 15

(E) The limit does not exist.

14. $\lim\limits_{x \to \infty} \dfrac{\sqrt{9x^2+5}-6}{3x} =$ $\boxed{L2}$

(A) 0

(B) 1

(C) $\sqrt{6}$

(D) 3

(E) The limit does not exist.

Answer Key

1. C	2. A	3. D	4. B	5. E
6. E	7. A	8. D	9. A	10. B
11. A	12. C	13. C	14. B	

Answers and Explanations

1. C

$$a* = 2^a \;\Rightarrow\; b* = 2^b$$
$$b* = 16 \;\Rightarrow\; 16 = 2^b \;\Rightarrow\; b = 4$$
$$b = c* \;\Rightarrow\; 4 = 2^c \;\Rightarrow\; c = 2$$

2. A

$x \odot y = 2^{x+y}$	Defined operation
$x \odot 3 = 2^{x+3}$	Substitute 3 for y.
$x \odot 3 = 32$	Given
$32 = 2^{x+3}$	Substitution
$2^5 = 2^{x+3}$	$32 = 2^5$
$5 = x + 3$	Property of equality
$x = 2$	Solve for x.

3. D

$$\begin{bmatrix} 8 & 12 \\ 5 & 14 \end{bmatrix} \cdot \begin{bmatrix} 15 & 7 \\ 6 & 11 \end{bmatrix} = \begin{bmatrix} 8\cdot15+12\cdot6 & 8\cdot7+12\cdot11 \\ 5\cdot15+14\cdot6 & 5\cdot7+14\cdot11 \end{bmatrix}$$

$$= \begin{bmatrix} 192 & 188 \\ 159 & 189 \end{bmatrix} \qquad M_{2\times2} \cdot M_{2\times2} = M_{2\times2}$$

4. B

$$[8 \quad 14 \quad 19] \cdot \begin{bmatrix} 4 & 7 \\ 8 & 10 \\ 15 & 9 \end{bmatrix}$$

$$= [8\cdot4+14\cdot8+19\cdot15 \quad 8\cdot7+14\cdot10+19\cdot9]$$

$$= [429 \quad 367] \qquad M_{1\times3} \cdot M_{3\times2} = M_{1\times2}$$

5. E $\boxed{L2}$

$x = 1 - \dfrac{1}{t}$	Given equation
$x - 1 = -\dfrac{1}{t}$	Solve for t.
$t(x-1) = (-\dfrac{1}{t})(t)$	
$t(x-1) = -1$	
$t = \dfrac{-1}{x-1}$	
$y = t + 1$	Given equation
$y = \dfrac{-1}{x-1} + 1$	Substitute $t = \dfrac{-1}{x-1}$.
$y = \dfrac{-1}{x-1} + \dfrac{x-1}{x-1}$	$\dfrac{x-1}{x-1} = 1$
$y = \dfrac{x-2}{x-1}$	Simplify.

6. E $\boxed{L2}$

$x = 2\cos t$	First equation
$x^2 = 4\cos^2 t$	First equation squared
$y = 2\sin t$	Second equation
$y^2 = 4\sin^2 t$	Second equation squared
$x^2 + y^2 = 4\cos^2 t + 4\sin^2 t$	Add x^2 and y^2.
$x^2 + y^2 = 4(\cos^2 t + \sin^2 t)$	Factor.
$x^2 + y^2 = 4$	$\cos^2 t + \sin^2 t = 1$

7. A $\boxed{L2}$

$$x = 8\cos^3\theta \;\Rightarrow\; x = (2\cos\theta)^3 \;\Rightarrow\; x^{\frac{1}{3}} = 2\cos\theta$$

$$\Rightarrow\; (x^{\frac{1}{3}})^2 = (2\cos\theta)^2 \;\Rightarrow\; x^{\frac{2}{3}} = 4\cos^2\theta$$

$$y = 8\sin^3\theta \;\Rightarrow\; y = (2\sin\theta)^3 \;\Rightarrow\; y^{\frac{1}{3}} = 2\sin\theta$$

$$\Rightarrow\; (y^{\frac{1}{3}})^2 = (2\sin\theta)^2 \;\Rightarrow\; y^{\frac{2}{3}} = 4\sin^2\theta$$

$$x^{\frac{2}{3}} + y^{\frac{2}{3}} = 4\cos^2\theta + 4\sin^2\theta$$

$$= 4(\cos^2\theta + \sin^2\theta)$$

$$= 4$$

8. D $\boxed{L2}$

$$\lim_{x\to 3}\frac{x^2-9}{x-3}$$

$$=\frac{3^2-9}{3-3}=\frac{0}{0}$$ Direct substitution fails.

$$\lim_{x\to 3}\frac{x^2-9}{x-3}$$

$$=\lim_{x\to 3}\frac{(x+3)\,\cancel{(x-3)}}{\cancel{x-3}}$$ Factor and divide.

$$=\lim_{x\to 3}(x+3)$$
$$=3+3=6$$ Make the substitution.

9. A $\boxed{L2}$

$$\lim_{x\to 2} f(x)$$

$$=\lim_{x\to 2}\frac{x-2}{x^2-4}$$

$$=\lim_{x\to 2}\frac{\cancel{x-2}}{(x+2)\cancel{(x-2)}}$$ Factor and cancel.

$$=\lim_{x\to 2}\frac{1}{x+2}$$

$$=\frac{1}{2+2}=\frac{1}{4}$$ Substitute 2 for x.

10. B $\boxed{L2}$

$$\lim_{x\to -1}\frac{x^2-2x-3}{x^2-4x-5}=\lim_{x\to -1}\frac{(x+1)(x-3)}{(x+1)(x-5)}$$

$$=\lim_{x\to -1}\frac{x-3}{x-5}=\frac{-1-3}{-1-5}=\frac{-4}{-6}=\frac{2}{3}$$

11. A $\boxed{L2}$

$$\lim_{x\to \infty}\frac{x}{3x-3}$$

$$=\lim_{x\to \infty}\frac{x/x}{3x/x-3/x}$$ Divide the numerator and denominator by x.

$$=\lim_{x\to \infty}\frac{1}{3-3/x}$$ Simplify.

$$=\frac{1}{3-0}=\frac{1}{3}$$ As $x\to\infty$, $\frac{3}{x}\to 0$.

12. C $\boxed{L2}$

$$\lim_{x\to \infty}\frac{3x}{\sqrt{x^2+1}}$$

$$=\lim_{x\to \infty}\frac{3x\div x}{(\sqrt{x^2+1})\div x}$$ Divide the numerator and denominator by x.

$$=\lim_{x\to \infty}\frac{3}{(\sqrt{\frac{x^2}{x^2}+\frac{1}{x^2}})}$$ $x=\sqrt{x^2}$

$$=\lim_{x\to \infty}\frac{3}{(\sqrt{1+\frac{1}{x^2}})}$$

$$=3$$ As $x\to\infty$, $\frac{1}{x^2}\to 0$.

13. C $\boxed{L2}$

$$\lim_{x\to \infty}(10+\frac{5}{x})=10$$ As $x\to\infty$, $\frac{5}{x}\to 0$.

14. B $\boxed{L2}$

$$\lim_{x\to \infty}\frac{\sqrt{9x^2+5}-6}{3x}$$

$$=\lim_{x\to \infty}\frac{(\sqrt{9x^2+5}-6)\div x}{3x\div x}$$ Divide the numerator and denominator by x.

$$=\lim_{x\to \infty}\frac{(\sqrt{\frac{9x^2}{x^2}+\frac{5}{x^2}}-\frac{6}{x})}{3}$$ $x=\sqrt{x^2}$

$$=\lim_{x\to \infty}\frac{(\sqrt{9+\frac{5}{x^2}}-\frac{6}{x})}{3}$$

$$=\frac{\sqrt{9}}{3}$$ As $x\to\infty$, $\frac{5}{x^2}\to 0$,

$$=1$$ $\frac{6}{x}\to 0$.

II. Geometry

CHAPTER 16
Lines and Angles

16-1. Lines, Rays, and Segments

A **line** is a straight arrangement of points that extends forever in opposite directions.
You can name a line using any two points on the line.

Written as: line PQ or $\overleftrightarrow{PQ}$.

A **segment** is a part of a line that consists of two endpoints and all points in between.
You can name a segment using its endpoints.

Written as: segment PQ or $\overline{PQ}$.

A **ray** is a part of a line that has one endpoint and extends forever in one direction.
You can name a ray using its endpoint and one other point on the ray.

Two rays $\overrightarrow{RP}$ and $\overrightarrow{RQ}$ are called **opposite rays** if R is between P and Q.

Written as:

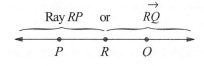

The **length** of $\overline{PQ}$, written as PQ, is the distance between point P and point Q.

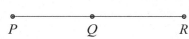

Segment Addition Postulate
If Q is between P and R, then $PQ + QR = PR$.

Example 1 ☐ Points P, Q, R, and S lie on a line as shown below.

Find the intersection of ray QS and ray RP.

Solution ☐ The endpoint of ray QS is Q and the endpoint of ray RP is R.
The intersection of the rays is the segment QR.

16-2. Midpoint and Segment Bisector

If M is the **midpoint** of $\overline{PQ}$,
then $PM = MQ = \dfrac{1}{2}PQ$.

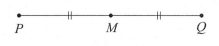

A **segment bisector** is a line or a segment that intersects a segment at its midpoint.

Example 2 □   On the number line below, if point M is the midpoint of $\overline{PQ}$ and N is the midpoint of $\overline{MQ}$, what is the length of $\overline{NQ}$?

$$
\begin{array}{cccc}
P & M & N & Q \\
-6 & x & & 5x
\end{array}
$$

Solution   □ $PM = MQ$, since M is the midpoint of PQ.

$x-(-6)=5x-x \;\Rightarrow\; x+6=4x \;\Rightarrow\; x=2 \;\Rightarrow\; PM = MQ = 8$

$NQ = \dfrac{1}{2}MQ$, since N is the midpoint of MQ.

$NQ = \dfrac{1}{2}MQ = \dfrac{1}{2}(8) = 4$ Answer

16-3. Angle Addition Postulate and Angle Bisector

Angle Addition Postulate

If C is in the interior of $\angle AOB$, then
$m\angle AOB = m\angle AOC + m\angle COB$.

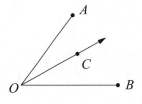

An **angle bisector** divides an angle into two congruent angles.

If $\overrightarrow{OC}$ is the angle bisector of $\angle AOB$, then

$m\angle AOC = m\angle COB = \dfrac{1}{2}m\angle AOB$.

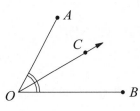

Example 3 □   In the diagram at the right, $\overrightarrow{OD}$ bisects $\angle COE$. If $m\angle BOD = 90$ and $m\angle COE = 68$, what is the measure of $\angle BOC$?

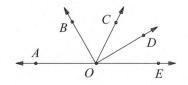

Solution   □ $m\angle COD = \dfrac{1}{2}m\angle COE$ $\overrightarrow{OD}$ bisects $\angle COE$.

$m\angle COD = \dfrac{1}{2}(68) = 34$ Substitution

$m\angle BOD = m\angle BOC + m\angle COD$ Angle addition postulate

$90 = m\angle BOC + 34$ Substitution

$m\angle BOC = 56$ Answer

16-4. Special Pairs of Angles

When two lines intersect, they form two
pairs of **vertical angles**.

Vertical angles are congruent (denoted by

the symbol ≅).

$\angle 1 \cong \angle 3$ and $\angle 2 \cong \angle 4$, and
$m\angle 1 = m\angle 3$ and $m\angle 2 = m\angle 4$.

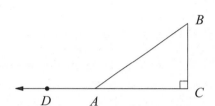

Two angles whose measures have a sum
of 180 are called **supplementary angles**.
$\angle DAB$ and $\angle BAC$ are supplementary.

Two angles whose measures have a sum
of 90 are called **complementary angles**.
$\angle B$ and $\angle BAC$ are complementary.

Example 4 □   a. The measure of an angle is 24 more than twice its complement.
Find the measure of the angle.

Solution   □   a. Let x = the measure of an angle. Then $90 - x$ = the measure of
its complement.

The measure of an angle	twice its complement	24 more than
x	$= 2(90 - x)$	$+24$

$$x = 180 - 2x + 24$$
$$x = 68 \qquad \text{Answer}$$

16-5. Properties of Parallel Lines

For two parallel lines ℓ and m which are cut by a transversal t:

1) **Corresponding angles** are equal
in measure.
$m\angle 1 = m\angle 5 \quad m\angle 2 = m\angle 6$
$m\angle 3 = m\angle 7 \quad m\angle 4 = m\angle 8$

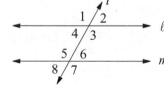

2) **Alternate interior angles** are equal
in measure.

$m\angle 3 = m\angle 5 \quad m\angle 4 = m\angle 6$

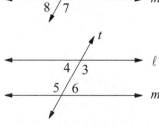

3) **Alternate exterior angles** are equal
in measure.

$m\angle 1 = m\angle 7 \quad m\angle 2 = m\angle 8$

4) **Consecutive interior (same-side interior) angles** are supplementary.

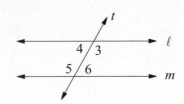

$$m\angle 3 + m\angle 6 = 180° \qquad m\angle 4 + m\angle 5 = 180°$$

Perpendicular Transversal Theorem

If a transversal is perpendicular to one of two parallel lines, then it is also perpendicular to the other.

If $\ell \parallel m$ and $\ell \perp t$, then $m \perp t$.

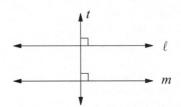

Example 5 ☐ In the figure at the right, $j \perp m$, $k \parallel \ell$, and $m \parallel n$. Find the values of a, b, c, and d.

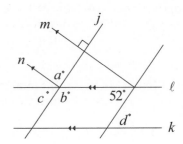

Solution ，☐ $a = 90$ $\perp$ transversal theorem

$b + 52 = 180$ Consecutive interior angles
$\Rightarrow b = 128$ are supplementary.

$c = 52$ Corresponding angles
are equal in measure.

$d = 52$ Alternate interior angles
are equal in measure.

16-6. Transformations

Translations

A transformation that moves all points the same distance in the same direction is called a translation.

If point $P(x, y)$ moves h units to the right and k units up, $P(x, y) \rightarrow P'(x + h, y + k)$.

In the figure at the right, point P is translated 5 units to the right and 3 units down.

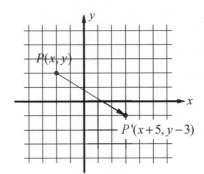

Reflections

If point $P(x, y)$ is reflected about the y-axis, then the y-axis is a **line of reflection** or a **line of symmetry**, and $P(x, y) \rightarrow P'(-x, y)$.

If point $P(x, y)$ is reflected about the x-axis, then the x-axis is a line of reflection or a line of symmetry, and $P(x, y) \rightarrow P'(x, -y)$.

In the figure at the right point P' is a reflection of P about the y-axis, and P'' is a reflection of P about the x-axis.

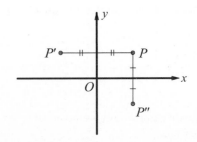

Rotations

If point $P(x, y)$ is rotated $90°$ clockwise about the origin, $P(x, y) \rightarrow P'(y, -x)$.

If point $P(x, y)$ is rotated $90°$ counterclockwise about the origin, $P(x, y) \rightarrow P'(-y, x)$.

If point $P(x, y)$ is rotated $180°$ about the origin, $P(x, y) \rightarrow P'(-x, -y)$. **Point symmetry** is another name for $180°$ rotational symmetry.

In the figure at the right, rotating point $P(5, 3)$ $90°$ clockwise, $90°$ counterclockwise, and $180°$ about the origin creates the rotation images points Q, R, and S, respectively.

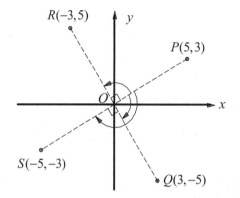

Example 6 □ Point P' is located by beginning at $P(3, 2)$ and moving 2 units up and 5 units to the left. If point P'' is the rotated image of point P' with respect to the origin, what are the coordinates of point P''?

Solution □ Subtract 5 from the x-coordinate and add 2 to the y-coordinate. $P(3, 2) \rightarrow P'(-2, 4)$ Since P'' is created by rotating point P' about the origin, $P(x, y) \rightarrow P'(-x, -y)$.

$P'(-2, 4) \rightarrow P''(2, -4)$

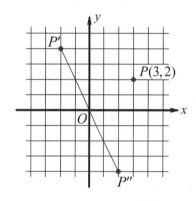

16-7. Locus

A figure is a locus if it is the set of all points, and only those points, that satisfy given conditions.

When solving locus problems, follow these steps:
1) Draw the given figure.
2) Locate some of the points that satisfy the given conditions.
3) Draw a smooth geometric figure connecting the points and describe the pattern of the points.

Example 7 □ What is the locus of points in a plane that are equidistant from two points P and Q?

Solution □ The locus of points equidistant from the two given points P and Q is the perpendicular bisector of $\overline{PQ}$.

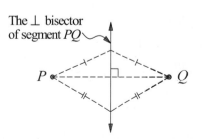

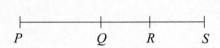

Figure 1

1. In Figure 1 if $PR = 3x + 5$, $RS = x + 8$, and $PS = 3RS$, what is the length of $\overline{PS}$?

(A) 32

(B) 38

(C) 46

(D) 52

(E) 57

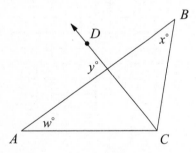

Figure 2

2. In Figure 2, if $\overrightarrow{CD}$ bisects $\angle ACB$, what is y in terms of w and x?

(A) $180 - (w + x)$

(B) $90 - (w + x)$

(C) $90 - (\dfrac{w - x}{2})$

(D) $90 + \dfrac{w - x}{2}$

(E) $90 - (\dfrac{w + x}{2})$

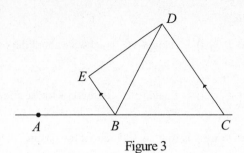

Figure 3

3. In Figure 3, $\overline{BE}$ bisects $\angle ABD$ and $\overline{BE} \parallel \overline{CD}$. If $m\angle ABE = x$, what is the measure of $\angle BDC$ in terms of x?

(A) x

(B) $90 - x$

(C) $180 - 2x$

(D) $90 - \dfrac{x}{2}$

(E) $2x - 90$

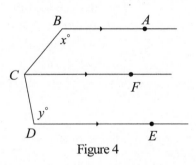

Figure 4

4. In Figure 4 $\overline{AB} \parallel \overline{CF} \parallel \overline{DE}$, $m\angle ABC = x$, and $m\angle CDE = y$. What is the measure of $\angle BCD$ in terms of x and y?

(A) $90 + \dfrac{(x + y)}{2}$

(B) $180 - \dfrac{(x + y)}{2}$

(C) $360 - x - y$

(D) $2(x + y) - 90$

(E) $2(x + y) - 180$

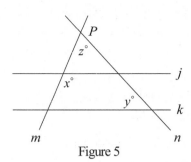

Figure 5

5. In Figure 5, lines j and k are parallel, and lines m and n intersect at point P. What is x in terms of y and z?

(A) $180 - y - z$

(B) $y + z$

(C) $y + z - 90$

(D) $180 - (\dfrac{y+z}{2})$

(E) $180 - y + z$

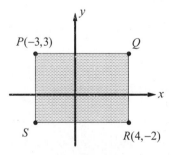

Figure 6

6. Figure 6 shows a rectangular region which contains all points (x, y). If a transformation T maps the points (x, y) in the rectangular region to the points $(x+1, 2y)$, what is the area of the rectangular region that consists of all points $(x+1, 2y)$?

(A) 35

(B) 48

(C) 56

(D) 70

(E) 105

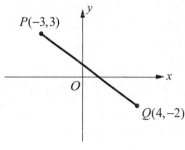

Figure 7

7. Segment PQ, shown in Figure 7, is reflected about the x-axis to form $\overline{P'Q'}$ (not shown). What is the slope of $\overline{P'Q'}$?

(A) $-\dfrac{5}{7}$

(B) $-\dfrac{3}{7}$

(C) 1

(D) $\dfrac{3}{7}$

(E) $\dfrac{5}{7}$

8. In the coordinate plane point $P(-3, 4)$ is rotated 90 degrees clockwise about the origin. What are the new coordinates of point P?

(A) $(4, -3)$

(B) $(-4, -3)$

(C) $(4, 3)$

(D) $(3, 4)$

(E) $(3, -4)$

9. What is the locus of points in a plane that are equidistant from the sides of a given angle?

    (A) a point

    (B) two points interior of the given angle

    (C) a triangle

    (D) an angle bisector of the given angle

    (E) a circle

10. Which of the following equations could represent all points in a plane that are less than 4 units from from the origin?

    (A) $x + y < 2$

    (B) $x + y < 4$

    (C) $x^2 + y^2 < 2$

    (D) $x^2 + y^2 < 4$

    (E) $x^2 + y^2 < 16$

11. What is the set of all points in a plane that are 2 cm from a line and 3 cm from a point on the line?

    (A) one point

    (B) two points

    (C) four points

    (D) one line

    (E) two lines

12. Given points $(0, 2)$ and $(4, 0)$, what is the locus of points equidistant from these two points?

    (A) a point

    (B) a line with slope of 2

    (C) a line with slope of -2

    (D) a line with undefined slope

    (E) a horizontal line

13. Point P is on line ℓ. Which of the following could be the set of points in space that are 5 cm from point P and located on a plane parallel to line ℓ?

    I. A point

    II. A circle

    III. No points

    (A) I only

    (B) II only

    (C) III only

    (D) I and II only

    (E) I, II and III

14. If T is the set of all points (x, y) mapped to the points $(3 - x, \frac{1}{2} y)$, which of the following is not true?

    (A) $T : (-3, 0) \rightarrow (6, 0)$

    (B) $T : (-2, 4) \rightarrow (5, 2)$

    (C) $T : (\frac{3}{2}, 0) \rightarrow (\frac{3}{2}, 0)$

    (D) $T : (2, -4) \rightarrow (1, 2)$

    (E) $T : (4, 6) \rightarrow (-1, 3)$

Answer Key

1. E	2. D	3. A	4. C	5. B
6. D	7. E	8. C	9. D	10. E
11. C	12. B	13. E	14. D	

Answers and Explanations

1. E

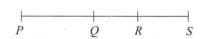

$PR = 3x + 5$, $RS = x + 8$, $PS = 3RS$

$PR + RS = PS$	Segment addition postulate
$PR + RS = 3RS$	Substitution: $PS = 3RS$
$PR = 2RS$	Subtraction
$3x + 5 = 2(x + 8)$	Substitution
$3x + 5 = 2x + 16$	
$x = 11$	

$PS = PR + RS = (3x + 5) + (x + 8)$
$= 4x + 13 = 4(11) + 13 = 57$

2. D

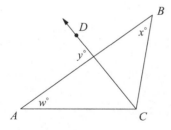

$m\angle ACB = 180 - (w + x)$

Since $\overrightarrow{CD}$ bisects $\angle ACB$,

$m\angle ACD = \dfrac{1}{2}[180 - (w + x)] = 90 - \dfrac{1}{2}(w + x)$.

$y = w + m\angle ACD$	Exterior angle theorem
$y = w + [90 - \dfrac{1}{2}(w + x)]$	Substitution
$y = 90 + \dfrac{1}{2}(w - x)$	Answer

3. A

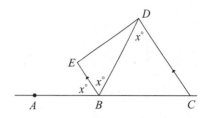

If $\overline{BE}$ bisects $\angle ABD$ and $m\angle ABE = x$, then $m\angle DBE = x$. Since $\overline{BE} \parallel \overline{CD}$, according to the Alternate interior angle theorem, the measure of $\angle BDC$ is also x.

4. C

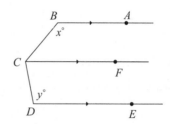

Since consecutive interior angles are supplementary, $m\angle BCF = 180 - x$ and $m\angle DCF = 180 - y$.

$m\angle BCD = m\angle BCF + m\angle DCF$
$= (180 - x) + (180 - y)$
$= 360 - x - y$

5. B

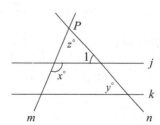

$m\angle 1 = y$	Corresponding angle postulate
$x = m\angle 1 + z$	Exterior angle theorem
$x = y + z$	Substitution

6. D

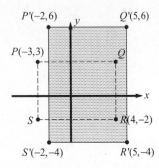

$T : (x, y) \rightarrow (x+1, 2y)$

$T : (-3, 3) \rightarrow (-3+1, 2 \cdot 3) = (-2, 6)$

$T : (4, 3) \rightarrow (4+1, 2 \cdot 3) = (5, 6)$

$T : (4, -2) \rightarrow (4+1, 2 \cdot -2) = (5, -4)$

$T : (-3, -2) \rightarrow (-3+1, 2 \cdot -2) = (-2, -4)$

length of the new rectangle $= 7$
width of the new rectangle $= 10$

The area of the rectangular region that consists of all points $(x+1, 2y)$ is $7 \cdot 10$, or 70.

7. E

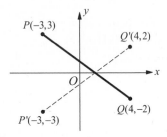

If points P and Q are reflected about the x-axis then the coordinates of P' will be $(-3, -3)$ and the coordinates of Q' will be $(4, -2)$.

Slope of $\overline{P'Q'} = \dfrac{2+3}{4+3} = \dfrac{5}{7}$

8. C

If point $P(x, y)$ is rotated $90°$ clockwise about the origin, $P(x, y) \rightarrow P'(y, -x)$.

$P(-3, 4) \rightarrow P'(4, 3)$

9. D

Make a sketch of an angle.

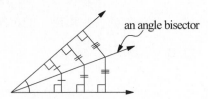

an angle bisector

The locus of all points in a plane that are equidistant from the sides of a given angle is an angle bisector of the given angle.

10. E

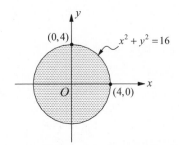

The locus of all points in a plane that are less than 4 units from the origin is all the points inside the circle whose center is the origin and radius is 4.

$x^2 + y^2 = 4^2$ represents the equation of circle whose center is the origin and radius is 4, and $x^2 + y^2 < 4^2$ represents all the points inside the circle.

11. C

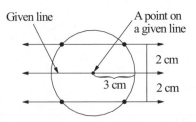

The locus of points in a plane that are 2 cm from a line are a pair of parallel lines, one on each side of the given line, and each located 2 cm from the given line.
The locus of points in a plane that are 3 cm from a point on the line is a circle with a radius of 3 cm. There are four points of intersection, that is, four points that fulfill both conditions.

12. B

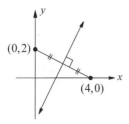

In a plane, the locus of points equidistant from two given points is the perpendicular bisector of the segment that joins the two points.

The slope of the segment joining the two points is

$$\frac{0-2}{4-0} = \frac{-2}{4} = -\frac{1}{2}.$$

Since the two lines are perpendicular, their slopes are negative reciprocals. Therefore the slope of the perpendicular bisector is 2.

The locus of points is a line with slope of 2.

13. E

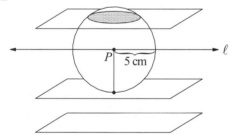

The set of points in space that are 5 cm from point P is a sphere with center P and radius of 5 cm.

A plane parallel to line ℓ could intersect a sphere at a circle, at a point, or not at all.

14. D

$$T : (x, y) \to (3 - x, \tfrac{1}{2}y)$$

(A) $T : (-3, 0) \to (3 - (-3), \tfrac{1}{2} \cdot 0) = (6, 0)$

(B) $T : (-2, 4) \to (3 - (-2), \tfrac{1}{2} \cdot 4) = (5, 2)$

(C) $T : (\tfrac{3}{2}, 0) \to (3 - \tfrac{3}{2}, \tfrac{1}{2} \cdot 0) = (\tfrac{3}{2}, 0)$

(D) $T : (2, -4) \to (3 - 2, \tfrac{1}{2} \cdot (-4)) = (1, -2) \neq (1, 2)$

(E) $T : (4, 6) \to (3 - 4, \tfrac{1}{2} \cdot 6) = (-1, 3)$

Choice (D) is correct.

CHAPTER 17
Triangles

17-1. Angles of a Triangle

The angle sum of a triangle is $180°$.

$m\angle A + m\angle B + m\angle C = 180^0$

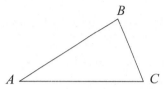

The acute angles of a right triangle are complementary.

The measure of an **exterior angle** of a triangle is equal to the sum of the measures of the two remote interior angles.

$m\angle BCD = m\angle A + m\angle B$

The measure of an exterior angle is greater than the measure of either of its corresponding remote interior angles.

$m\angle BCD > m\angle A$, $m\angle BCD > m\angle B$

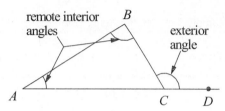

Example 1 □ Find the value of x and y in the figure at the right.

Solution □
$3x - 10 = x + 90$ Exterior angle theorem
$2x = 100$
$x = 50$ Answer

$x + y = 90$ The acute angles of a right triangle are complementary.
$50 + y = 90$
$y = 40$ Answer

17-2. Isosceles Triangles

If two sides of a triangle are congruent, then the angles opposite of those sides are congruent.

If $AB = BC$ then $m\angle C = m\angle A$.
The converse is also true.

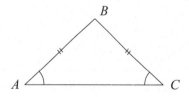

Example 2 □ In $\triangle ABC$ shown at the right, find the value of x.

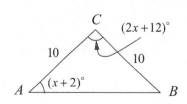

Solution □
$AC = BC \implies m\angle A = m\angle B$
$m\angle A + m\angle B + m\angle C = 180$
$(x + 2) + (x + 2) + (2x + 12) = 180$
$4x + 16 = 180$
$4x = 164$
$x = 41$ Answer

17-3. Pythagorean Theorem

In a right triangle, the sum of the squares of the lengths of the legs equals the square of the length of the hypotenuse.

A Pythagorean triple is a group of three whole numbers that satisfy the equation $a^2 + b^2 = c^2$.
Whole numbers such as 3, 4, 5 ($3^2 + 4^2 = 5^2$) and 5, 12, 13 ($5^2 + 12^2 = 13^2$) are Pythagorean triples.

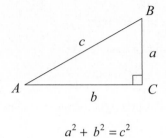

$$a^2 + b^2 = c^2$$

Example 3 ☐ In the figure at the right, find the value of x.

Solution ☐

$AB^2 = 6^2 + 3^2$	Pythagorean Theorem
$AB^2 = 45$	
$x^2 = AB^2 + 2^2$	Pythagorean Theorem
$x^2 = 45 + 4$	Substitution
$x = \sqrt{49} = 7$	Answer

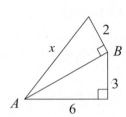

17-4. Special Right Triangles

In a **45°- 45°- 90° triangle**, the hypotenuse is $\sqrt{2}$ times as long as a leg.

In a **30°- 60°- 90° triangle,** the hypotenuse is twice as long as the shorter leg, and the longer leg is $\sqrt{3}$ times as long as the shorter leg.

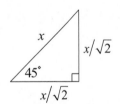
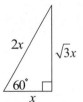
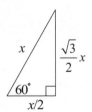

Example 4 ☐ In the figure at the right, find the length of $\overline{BC}$.

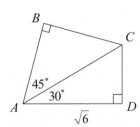

Solution ☐

$\sqrt{3} \cdot CD = AD$	30°- 60°- 90° triangle ratio
$\sqrt{3} \cdot CD = \sqrt{6}$	Substitution
$CD = \dfrac{\sqrt{6}}{\sqrt{3}} = \sqrt{2}$	
$AC = 2 \cdot CD = 2\sqrt{2}$	30°- 60°- 90° triangle ratio
$\sqrt{2} \cdot BC = AC$	45°- 45°- 90° triangle ratio
$\sqrt{2} \cdot BC = 2\sqrt{2}$	Substitution
$BC = 2$	Answer

17-5. Similar Triangles

AA Similarity

If two angles of one triangle are congruent to
two angles of another triangle, then the two
triangles are similar (denoted by the symbol ~).

If two triangles are similar, their corresponding
angles are congruent and their corresponding
sides are in proportion.

In the figure at the right , if $\angle A \cong \angle D$ and
$\angle B \cong \angle E$, then it follows that $\angle C \cong \angle F$.

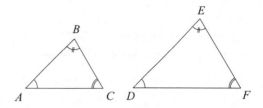

$\triangle ABC \sim \triangle DEF$, and $\dfrac{AB}{DE} = \dfrac{BC}{EF} = \dfrac{AC}{DF}$

Similarity in Right Triangles

If an altitude is drawn to the hypotenuse of a right triangle,
then the two triangles formed are similar to the original
triangle and to each other. In the figure at the right,

$\triangle CBD \sim \triangle ACD \sim \triangle ABC$

$\angle BCD \cong \ \angle A \ \ \cong \angle A$

$\angle B \ \ \ \cong \angle ACD \cong \angle B$

$\angle CDB \cong \angle ADC \cong \angle ACB.$

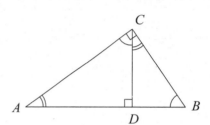

Example 5 □   a. In the figure below, find the values
             of x and y.

b. In the figure below, $\overline{AC} \perp \overline{BC}$ and
$\overline{CD} \perp \overline{AB}$. Find the length of $\overline{BD}$.

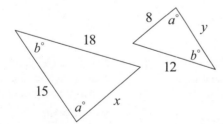

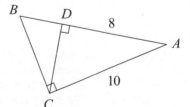

Solution   □   a. The two triangles are similar by *AA* similarity.

$$\frac{18}{12} = \frac{x}{8} \ \Rightarrow \ x = 12$$

$$\frac{18}{12} = \frac{15}{y} \ \Rightarrow \ y = 10$$

b. $\triangle ACD$ is a right triangle.

$AC^2 = AD^2 + DC^2 \ \Rightarrow \ 10^2 = 8^2 + DC^2 \ \Rightarrow \ DC = 6$

$\triangle ACD \sim \triangle CBD$ since $\angle A \cong \angle BCD$ and $\angle ADC \cong \angle CDB$.

$$\frac{BD}{DC} = \frac{DC}{AD} \ \Rightarrow \ \frac{BD}{6} = \frac{6}{8}$$

$BD = 4.5$

17-6. Ratios of Areas and Perimeters

Area of a triangle $= \frac{1}{2}b \cdot h$

(1) If two triangles are similar with corresponding sides in the ratio of $a:b$, then the ratio
   of their perimeters is $a:b$ and the ratio of their areas is $a^2:b^2$.

(2) If two triangles have equal heights, then the ratio of their areas is equal to the ratio of their bases.

(3) If two triangles have equal bases, then the ratio of their areas is equal to the ratio of their heights.

(1)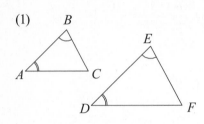

$\triangle ABC \sim \triangle DEF$

$$\frac{\text{Area of } \triangle ABC}{\text{Area of } \triangle DEF} = \frac{AB^2}{DE^2}$$

(2)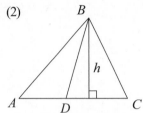

$\triangle ABD$ and $\triangle CBD$
have the same height.

$$\frac{\text{Area of } \triangle ABD}{\text{Area of } \triangle BCD} = \frac{AD}{DC}$$

(3)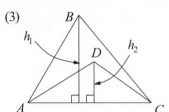

$\triangle ABC$ and $\triangle ADC$
have equal bases.

$$\frac{\text{Area of } \triangle ABC}{\text{Area of } \triangle ADC} = \frac{h_1}{h_2}$$

Example 6 □   In the figure at the right $\overline{BC} \parallel \overline{AE}$.
   a. Find the ratio of the areas of
      $\triangle ABE$ and $\triangle ACD$.
   b. Find the ratio of the areas of
      $\triangle ABE$ and $\triangle DFE$.

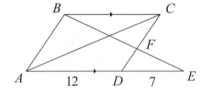

Solution   □   a. $\triangle ABE$ and $\triangle ACD$ have the
      same height, so the ratio of
      their areas is equal to the ratio
      of their bases.
      $$\frac{\text{Area of } \triangle ABE}{\text{Area of } \triangle ACD} = \frac{19}{12}$$

b. $\triangle ABE \sim \triangle DFE$, so the ratio of their
   areas is equal to the ratio of the squares
   of their corresponding sides.
   $$\frac{\text{Area of } \triangle ABE}{\text{Area of } \triangle DFE} = \frac{AE^2}{DE^2} = \frac{19^2}{7^2} = \frac{361}{49}$$

17-7. Proportional Parts

If a line parallel to one side of a triangle intersects the other two sides, then it divides those
sides proportionally.

In $\triangle ABC$, if $\overline{AC} \parallel \overline{DE}$ then it follows that

$\dfrac{BD}{DA} = \dfrac{BE}{EC}$, $\dfrac{DA}{BA} = \dfrac{EC}{BC}$, $\dfrac{BD}{DE} = \dfrac{BA}{AC}$, and $\dfrac{BE}{DE} = \dfrac{BC}{AC}$.

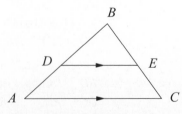

If D and E are the midpoints of $\overline{AB}$ and $\overline{BC}$,

respectively, then $\overline{DE} \parallel \overline{AC}$ and $DE = \dfrac{1}{2}AC$.

If a ray or a segment bisects an angle of a triangle, then it divides the opposite side into segments that have the same ratio as the ratio of the other two sides.

In $\triangle ABC$, if $\overline{BD}$ is the angle bisector of $\angle ABC$,

then $\dfrac{AD}{DC} = \dfrac{AB}{BC}$.

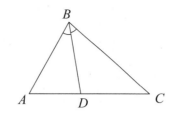

Example 7 □   a. Find the value of x in the figure below.

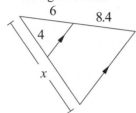

b. Find the length of $\overline{CD}$ in the figure below.

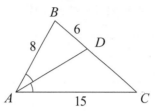

Solution   □   a. $\dfrac{4}{x} = \dfrac{6}{6+8.4}$

$\dfrac{4}{x} = \dfrac{6}{14.4}$

$6x = 4(14.4)$

$x = 9.6$ Answer

b. $\dfrac{6}{CD} = \dfrac{8}{15}$

$8 \cdot CD = 6 \cdot 15$

$8 \cdot CD = 90$

$CD = 11.25$ Answer

17-8. Inequalities for the Sides and Angles of a Triangle

In a triangle $a < b < c$ if and only if $m\angle A < m\angle B < m\angle C$.

The sum of the lengths of any two sides of a triangle is greater than the length of the third side.

$a < b+c$, $b < a+c$, and $c < a+b$.

Pythagorean Inequality

$c^2 > a^2 + b^2$ if and only if $\angle C$ is an obtuse angle.

$c^2 < a^2 + b^2$ if and only if $\angle C$ is an acute angle.

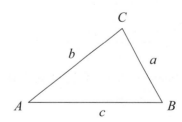

Example 8 □   In the triangle shown at the right, if x is an integer, what is one possible value of x?

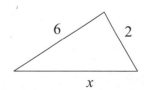

Solution   □ $6 - 2 < x < 6 + 2$

$4 < x < 8$

The possible values of x are 5, 6, and 7.

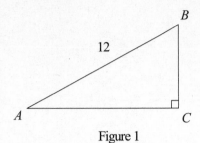

Figure 1

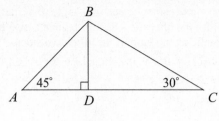

Figure 2

1. In the right triangle shown in Figure 1, if $AB = 12$ and $m\angle BAC = 30°$, what is the area of $\triangle ABC$?

 (A) 25.5

 (B) 31.2

 (C) 51

 (D) 56.5

 (E) 62.4

2. What is the area of a right triangle with an acute angle of $35°$ and a longer leg of length 10?

 (A) 20

 (B) 25

 (C) 30

 (D) 35

 (E) 40

3. In $\triangle PQR$, if $PQ = 11$, $QR = 14$, and $PR = 18$, which of the following is true?

 (A) $\angle Q$ is an acute angle.

 (B) $\angle Q$ is a right angle.

 (C) $\angle Q$ is an obtuse angle.

 (D) $m\angle P < m\angle R$

 (E) $m\angle Q < m\angle P$

4. In Figure 2, if $AB = 4$, what is the area of $\triangle ABC$?

 (A) 6

 (B) $2(2 + \sqrt{3})$

 (C) $2(\sqrt{2} + \sqrt{3})$

 (D) $4(1 + \sqrt{2})$

 (E) $4(1 + \sqrt{3})$

5. In $\triangle PQR$, $PQ = QR = 10$ and $PR = 12$. What is the area of $\triangle PQR$?

 (A) 48

 (B) 53

 (C) 60

 (D) 78

 (E) 96

6. What is the area of a triangle whose vertices are $(2, 7)$, $(10, 4)$, and $(2, 1)$?

 (A) 18

 (B) 20

 (C) 24

 (D) 29

 (E) 48

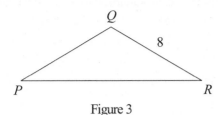

Figure 3

7. In the triangle shown in Figure 3, $PQ = QR = 8$. If $m\angle P = 30°$, what is the perimeter of $\triangle PQR$ to the nearest whole number?

(A) 24

(B) 25

(C) 27

(D) 28

(E) 30

8. In $\triangle PQR$, $m\angle Q = 72°$ and the length of side $\overline{QR}$ is 15. What is the length of the altitude from R to side $\overline{PQ}$?

(A) 14.3

(B) 11.6

(C) 9.5

(D) 7.9

(E) 4.6

9. What is the length of a diagonal of a square whose perimeter is 20?

(A) 6.3

(B) 7.1

(C) 8.2

(D) 8.7

(E) 9.4

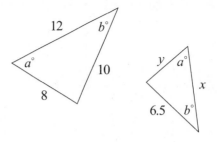

Figure 4

10. In Figure 4, what is the value of $x + y$?

(A) 10

(B) 11.5

(C) 13

(D) 14.5

(E) 16

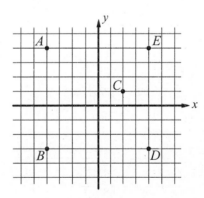

Figure 5

11. In Figure 5, triangles are to be formed using three of the five points shown on the xy-coordinates as vertices. Of the following triangles, which will have the least area?

(A) $\triangle ABC$

(B) $\triangle AEC$

(C) $\triangle CED$

(D) $\triangle BCD$

(E) $\triangle BED$

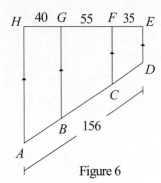

Figure 6

12. Figure 6 shows four parallel lines intersecting $\overline{AD}$ and $\overline{EH}$. If $AD = 156$, what is the length of $\overline{BC}$?

(A) 52

(B) 56

(C) 62

(D) 66

(E) 72

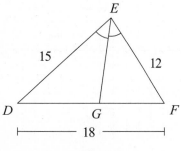

Figure 7

13. In Figure 7, $\overline{EG}$ bisects $\angle DEF$. If $DF = 18$, what is the length of $\overline{DG}$?

(A) 7

(B) 8

(C) 9

(D) 10

(E) 11

14. If an altitude of an equilateral triangle has length $3\sqrt{3}$, what is the perimeter of the triangle?

(A) 9

(B) 12

(C) 12.7

(D) 15.6

(E) 18

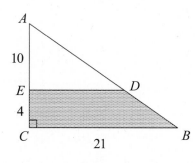

Figure 8

15. In Figure 8, $\triangle ABC$ has a right angle at C. If $\overline{BC} \parallel \overline{DE}$, what is the area of the shaded region?

(A) 64

(B) 72

(C) 82

(D) 88

(E) 98

Answer Key

1. B	2. D	3. C	4. E	5. A
6. C	7. E	8. A	9. B	10. C
11. C	12. D	13. D	14. E	15. B

Answers and Explanations

1. B

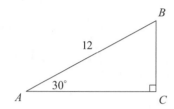

$AC = 12\cos 30° \approx 10.39$

$BC = 12\sin 30° = 6$

Area of $\triangle ABC = \dfrac{1}{2}(10.39)(6) = 31.17$

2. D

If one angle of a right triangle measures $35°$, then the other acute angle measures $55°$. Since $35° < 55°$, the longer leg is opposite of the $55°$ angle.

Sketch a right triangle.

Let $h =$ the length of the side opposite of the $35°$ angle.

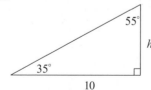

$\tan 35° = \dfrac{h}{10} \Rightarrow h = 10\tan 35° \approx 7$

Area of triangle $= \dfrac{1}{2}(10)(7) = 35$

3. C

Sketch triangle PQR.

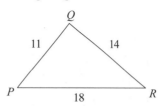

$18^2 > 11^2 + 14^2$. Then by the Pythagorean inequality, $\angle Q$ is an obtuse angle.

Choice (C) is correct.

4. E

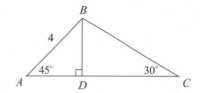

$AB = 4$

$AD = BD = 2\sqrt{2}$ 45°-45°-90° triangle ratio

$DC = BD \cdot \sqrt{3}$ 30°-60°-90° triangle ratio

$\quad = 2\sqrt{2} \cdot \sqrt{3}$

$\quad = 2\sqrt{6}$

Area of $\triangle ABC = \dfrac{1}{2} AC \cdot BD$

$= \dfrac{1}{2}(2\sqrt{2} + 2\sqrt{6})(2\sqrt{2}) = (\sqrt{2} + \sqrt{6})(2\sqrt{2})$

$= 4 + 2\sqrt{12} = 4 + 4\sqrt{3} = 4(1 + \sqrt{3})$

5. A

Draw triangle PQR and segment QS, which is perpendicular to $\overline{PR}$.

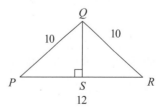

$PS = SR = 6$ since $\triangle PQS \cong \triangle RQS$.

$PQ^2 = PS^2 + QS^2 \Rightarrow 10^2 = 6^2 + QS^2$

$\Rightarrow QS^2 = 100 - 36 = 64 \Rightarrow QS = 8$

Area of $\triangle PQR = \dfrac{1}{2}(12)(8) = 48$

6. C

Make a drawing.

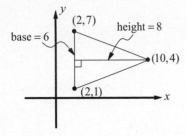

The drawing shows that the base of the triangle is 6, and the height is 8.

Area of the triangle $= \dfrac{1}{2}(6)(8) = 24$

7. E

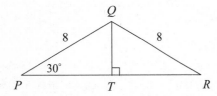

Draw an altitude $\overline{QT}$ that is perpendicular to $\overline{PR}$.

$QT = 4$	30°-60°-90° triangle ratio
$PT = 4\sqrt{3}$	30°-60°-90° triangle ratio
$PT = RT$	$\triangle PQT \cong \triangle RQT$
$PR = PT + TR$	
$\quad = 4\sqrt{3} + 4\sqrt{3}$	
$\quad = 8\sqrt{3}$	

Perimeter of $\triangle PQR$

$= 8 + 8 + 8\sqrt{3} = 16 + 8\sqrt{3} \approx 29.86$

8. A

Sketch triangle PQR and draw an altitude from R to side $\overline{PQ}$.

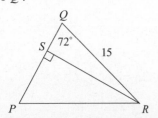

Use the sine ratio.

$$\sin 72° = \frac{RS}{QR} = \frac{RS}{15}$$

$$RS = 15 \sin 72° \approx 14.3$$

9. B

Draw a square.

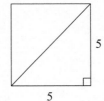

If the perimeter of the square is 20, the length of each side is 5.

By the $45°$-$45°$-$90°$ triangle ratio, the diagonal of the square has length $5\sqrt{2}$, or 7.07.

10. C

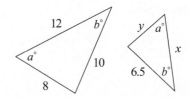

The two triangles are similar by AA similarity, so their corresponding sides are in proportion.

Set up a proportion.

$$\frac{10}{6.5} = \frac{12}{x} \implies x = 7.8$$

$$\frac{10}{6.5} = \frac{8}{y} \implies y = 5.2$$

$$x + y = 7.8 + 5.2 = 13$$

11. C

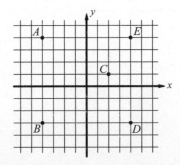

(A) Area of $\triangle ABC = \dfrac{1}{2}(7)(6) = 21$

(B) Area of $\triangle AEC = \dfrac{1}{2}(8)(3) = 12$

(C) Area of $\triangle CED = \dfrac{1}{2}(7)(2) = 7$

(D) Area of $\triangle BCD = \dfrac{1}{2}(8)(4) = 16$

(E) Area of $\triangle BED = \dfrac{1}{2}(8)(7) = 28$

$\triangle CED$ has the least area.

12. D

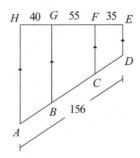

The ratio $EF : FG : GH = 35 : 55 : 40 = 7 : 11 : 8$.
Since $\overline{DE} \parallel \overline{CF} \parallel \overline{BG} \parallel \overline{AH}$, the ratio
$CD : BC : AB$ is also $7 : 11 : 8$.
Let $CD = 7x$, $BC = 11x$, and $AB = 8x$.
$AD = AB + BC + CD$
$156 = 8x + 11x + 7x$
$156 = 26x$
$6 = x$
$BC = 11 \cdot 6 = 66$

13. D

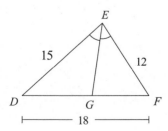

Let $DG = x$, then $FG = 18 - x$.
Since $\overline{EG}$ bisects $\angle DEF$, $\dfrac{ED}{DG} = \dfrac{EF}{FG}$.

$\dfrac{15}{x} = \dfrac{12}{18 - x} \;\Rightarrow\; 15(18 - x) = 12x$
$\Rightarrow\; 270 - 15x = 12x \;\Rightarrow\; 270 = 27x$
$\Rightarrow\; x = 10$

14. E

Draw an equilateral triangle ABC.

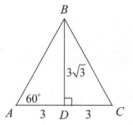

If the altitude $\overline{BD}$ measures $3\sqrt{3}$, then by the
$30°\text{-}60°\text{-}90°$ triangle ratio $AD = DC = 3$
$\Rightarrow\; AC = 6$.

Perimeter of the triangle $= 3 \cdot 6 = 18$

15. B

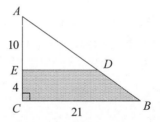

Since $\overline{BC} \parallel \overline{DE}$, $\dfrac{AE}{ED} = \dfrac{AC}{CB}$.

$\dfrac{10}{ED} = \dfrac{14}{21} \;\Rightarrow\; 14ED = 10 \cdot 21$
$\Rightarrow\; ED = 15$

Area of the shaded region

$=$ Area of $\triangle ABC -$ Area of $\triangle ADE$

$= \dfrac{1}{2}(21)(14) - \dfrac{1}{2}(15)(10) = 72$

CHAPTER 18
Polygons

18-1. Parallelograms

A **parallelogram** is a quadrilateral in which the opposite sides are parallel to each other.

Properties of a Parallelogram

Opposite sides are congruent.

Opposite angles are congruent.

Consecutive angles are supplementary.

The diagonals bisect each other.

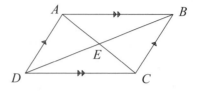

In $\square ABCD$ above, $\overline{AB} \parallel \overline{CD}$ and $\overline{AD} \parallel \overline{BC}$.

The area of a parallelogram equals the product of a base and the height to the base.
$A = b \cdot h$

Example 1 □   Find the area of parallelogram $ABCD$, shown at the right.

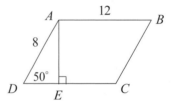

Solution □   Find the height of the parallelogram by using the sine ratio.

$$\sin 50° = \frac{AE}{AD} = \frac{AE}{8}$$

$$AE = 8\sin 50° \approx 6.13$$

Area of $\square ABCD = b \cdot h = 12 \times 6.13 = 73.6$ Answer

18-2. Special Parallelograms

A **rhombus** is a parallelogram with four sides of equal measure.

The diagonals of a rhombus are perpendicular to each other, and each diagonal of a rhombus bisects a pair of opposite angles.

The area of rhombus equals half the product of its diagonals.

$$A = \frac{1}{2} d_1 \cdot d_2$$

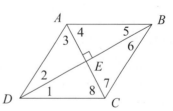

In rhombus $ABCD$, $AB = BC = CD = DA$.
$\overline{AC} \perp \overline{BD}$, $m\angle 1 = m\angle 2 = m\angle 5 = m\angle 6$,
and $m\angle 3 = m\angle 4 = m\angle 7 = m\angle 8$
$\triangle ABE \cong \triangle CBE \cong \triangle CDE \cong \triangle ADE$

A **rectangle** is a quadrilateral with four right angles.

The diagonals of a rectangle are congruent and bisect each other. The diagonals divide the rectangle into four triangles of equal area.

The area of a rectangle equals the product of its length and height.

$$A = \ell \cdot w$$

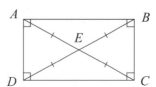

In the rectangle $ABCD$, $AE = DE = BE = CE$.
Area of $\triangle ABE = $ Area of $\triangle BCE = $
Area of $\triangle CDE = $ Area of $\triangle ADE$

If a quadrilateral is both a rhombus and a rectangle it is a **square**.

A square has four right angles and four congruent sides.

The area of a square is the square of the length of a side.

$A = s^2$

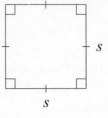

If the perimeter of a rectangle is known, the maximum area occurs when the length and width are equal in measure. This shape is a square.

Example 2 □ Find the area of rhombus *ABCD*, shown at the right.

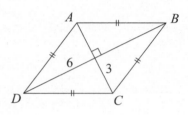

Solution □ Since *ABCD* is a rhombus, and the length of the diagonal is known, use the formula $A = \frac{1}{2} d_1 \cdot d_2$.

$d_1 = 6 + 6 = 12$ and $d_2 = 3 + 3 = 6$

$A = \frac{1}{2}(12)(6) = 36$ Answer

18-3. Trapezoids

A **trapezoid** is a quadrilateral with exactly one pair of parallel sides.

The **median** of a trapezoid is parallel to the bases, and its measure is one-half the sum of the measures of the bases.

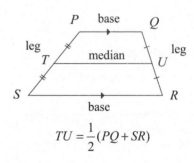

The area of a trapezoid equals half the product of the height and the sum of the bases.

$A = \frac{1}{2} h(b_1 + b_2)$

$TU = \frac{1}{2}(PQ + SR)$

If the legs of a trapezoid are congruent, then the trapezoid is an **isosceles trapezoid**.

The diagonals of an isosceles trapezoid are congruent. Both pairs of base angles of an isosceles trapezoid are congruent.

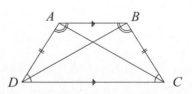

In isosceles trapezoid *ABCD*, $\overline{AC} \cong \overline{BD}$.
$\angle ADC \cong \angle BCD$ and $\angle DAB \cong CBA$

Example 3 □ Find the area of trapezoid *TRAP*, shown at the right.

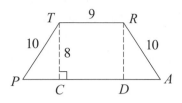

Solution □ $10^2 = PC^2 + 8^2 \implies PC^2 = 36$
$\implies PC = 6$
In the isosceles trapezoid $PC = AD$.
$PA = PC + CD + DA = 6 + 9 + 6 = 21$
Area of trapezoid *TRAP*
$= \frac{1}{2}h(b_1 + b_2) = \frac{1}{2} \cdot 8(21 + 9) = 120$

■

18-4. Regular Polygons

A **regular polygon** is a convex polygon with all sides congruent and all angles congruent.
A circle can be circumscribed about any regular polygon.

The **radius of a regular polygon** is the distance from the center to a vertex.
A **central angle of a regular polygon** is an angle formed by two radii drawn
to consecutive vertices.

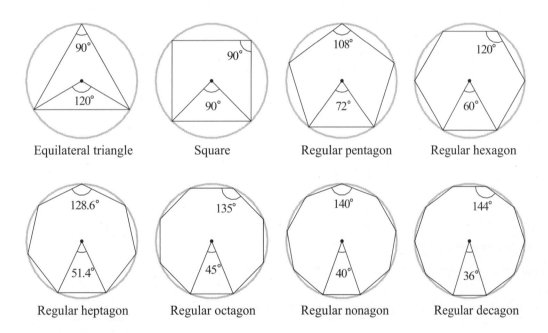

| Equilateral triangle | Square | Regular pentagon | Regular hexagon |

| Regular heptagon | Regular octagon | Regular nonagon | Regular decagon |

Interior Angle Sum Theorem

The sum of the measures of the interior angles of an *n*-sided polygon is $(n-2)180$.

The measure of each angle of a regular *n*-sided polygon is $\dfrac{(n-2)180}{n}$.

The measure of a central angle of a regular *n*-sided polygon is $\dfrac{360}{n}$.

Exterior Angle Sum Theorem

The sum of the measures of the exterior angles of any convex polygon is 360.

Example 4 □   An equilateral triangle is inscribed in a circle with radius 6. Find the height of the triangle.

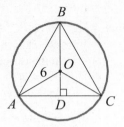

Solution □   a. $m\angle AOC = \dfrac{360}{3} = 120$

$\Rightarrow m\angle AOD = 60$

$\Rightarrow \triangle AOD$ is a 30°-60°-90° triangle.

$\Rightarrow OD = 3$

$AO = BO = 6$ (All radii of a circle are $\cong$.)

$BD = BO + OD = 6 + 3 = 9$

18-5. Ratios of Areas and Perimeters

If two polygons are similar with corresponding sides in the ratio $a:b$, then

1) the ratio of their perimeters is $a:b$ and

2) the ratio of their areas is $a^2 : b^2$.

Example 5 □   Two regular pentagons have sides of 3 and 8 respectively. Find the ratio of their perimeters and the ratio of their areas.

Solution □   Two regular pentagons are similar.

The ratio of perimeters $= \dfrac{3}{8}$ Answer

The ratio of areas $= \dfrac{3^2}{8^2} = \dfrac{9}{64}$ Answer

18-6. Area Addition Postulate

The area of a region is the sum of the areas of its non-overlapping parts.

Example 6 □   Find the area of the figure at the right.

Solution □   Triangle ABC is a 45°-45°-90° triangle.

Therefore $AC = BC = 4$, and $AB = 4\sqrt{2}$.

Then the radius of the semicircle $= 2\sqrt{2}$.

Area of the figure

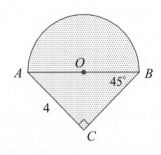

$= \dfrac{1}{2}\pi(2\sqrt{2})^2 + \dfrac{1}{2}(4)(4)$

$= 4\pi + 8$ Answer

1. If a square has diagonal 6, then its area is

   (A) $6\sqrt{2}$

   (B) 12

   (C) $9\sqrt{2}$

   (D) 18

   (E) 24

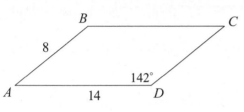

Figure 1

2. What is the area of parallelogram $ABCD$ in Figure 1?

   (A) 39

   (B) 42

   (C) 48

   (D) 56

   (E) 69

3. What is the measure of one of the smaller angles of a parallelogram in the xy-plane that has vertices with coordinates $(-1,1)$, $(0,4)$, $(5,4)$, and $(4,1)$?

   (A) 56.3°

   (B) 61.6°

   (C) 66.0°

   (D) 71.6°

   (E) 78.5°

4. If points $(-2,3)$, $(0,-1)$, $(4,1)$, and $(2,k)$ are the vertices of a square, then $k =$

   (A) 2

   (B) 3

   (C) 4

   (D) 5

   (E) 6

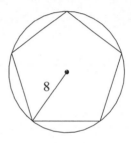

Figure 2

5. Figure 2 shows a regular pentagon whose radius is 8. What is the perimeter of the pentagon to the nearest whole number?

   (A) 40

   (B) 47

   (C) 53

   (D) 60

   (E) 67

6. If a regular hexagon has perimeter 24, then its area is

   (A) $12\sqrt{2}$

   (B) $24\sqrt{2}$

   (C) $12\sqrt{3}$

   (D) $24\sqrt{3}$

   (E) $12\sqrt{6}$

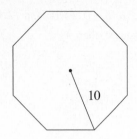

Figure 3

7. Figure 3 shows a regular octagon whose radius is 10. What is the area of the octagon to the nearest whole number?

(A) 283

(B) 317

(C) 355

(D) 387

(E) 416

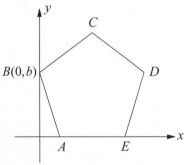

Figure 4

8. In Figure 4, a regular pentagon *ABCDE* with side of length 8 touches the *y*-axis at point *B*. What is the value of *b*?

(A) 6.6

(B) 7.0

(C) 7.6

(D) 8.1

(E) 8.6

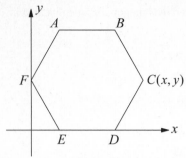

Figure 5

9. In Figure 5, a regular hexagon *ABCDEF* with side of length 4 intersects the *y*-axis at point *F*. If $C(x, y)$ is a vertex of the hexagon, what is the value of $x + y$?

(A) 9.98

(B) 11.46

(C) 12.70

(D) 13.29

(E) 13.87

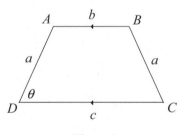

Figure 6

10. What is the area of isosceles trapezoid *ABCD* in Figure 6?

(A) $\dfrac{\cos\theta}{2a}(b+c)$

(B) $\dfrac{\sin\theta}{2a}(b+c)$

(C) $\dfrac{1}{2}a\cos\theta(b+c)$

(D) $\dfrac{1}{2}a\sin\theta(b+c)$

(E) $\dfrac{1}{2}a\tan\theta(b+c)$

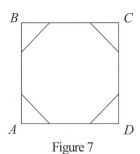

Figure 7

11. Figure 7 shows a regular octagon with four of its sides on the sides of square *ABCD*. If the area of square *ABCD* is 4, what is the length of a side of the octagon?

   (A) $\dfrac{\sqrt{2}}{2}$

   (B) $2(\sqrt{2}-1)$

   (C) 1.2

   (D) $\dfrac{4}{3}$

   (E) $\sqrt{2}-1$

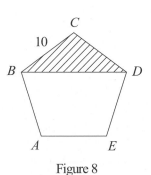

Figure 8

12. Figure 8 shows a regular pentagon with side of length 10. What is the area of the shaded region?

   (A) 36.7

   (B) 42.5

   (C) 47.8

   (D) 58.5

   (E) 68.0

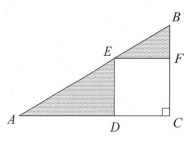

Figure 9

13. Figure 9 shows a square inscribed in a right triangle, with two of its sides on the legs of the triangle. If the area of square *CDEF* is 36 and $m\angle BAC = 30°$, what is the area of the shaded region?

   (A) $12\sqrt{2}$

   (B) $24\sqrt{2}$

   (C) $12\sqrt{3}$

   (D) $24\sqrt{3}$

   (E) $48\sqrt{3}$

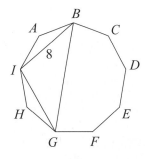

Figure 10

14. Figure 10 shows a regular nonagon *ABCDEFGHI* where the length of $\overline{BI}$ is 8. What is the length of $\overline{BG}$?

   (A) 10.4

   (B) 11.2

   (C) 12.3

   (D) 13.1

   (E) 13.9

Answer Key

1. D	2. E	3. D	4. D	5. B
6. D	7. A	8. C	9. B	10. D
11. B	12. C	13. D	14. C	

Answers and Explanations

1. D

If a square has diagonal 6, then by the $45°$-$45°$-$90°$
triangle ratio the length of each side is $\dfrac{6}{\sqrt{2}}$, or $3\sqrt{2}$.

Area of the square $= 3\sqrt{2} \cdot 3\sqrt{2} = 18$

2. E

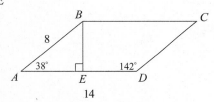

Draw $\overline{BE}$, which is $\perp \overline{AD}$.
$m\angle A = 38°$, since consecutive angles of
a parallelogram are supplementary.

$\sin 38° = \dfrac{BE}{8} \implies BE = 8 \cdot \sin 38° \approx 4.925$

Area of the parallelogram
$= AD \cdot BE = (14)(4.925) = 68.95$

3. D

Sketch a parallelogram in the xy-plane.

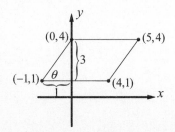

Use the tangent ratio to find the angle θ.

$\tan\theta = \dfrac{3}{1} = 3 \implies \theta = \tan^{-1}(3) \approx 71.6°$

4. D

Sketch a square in the xy-plane.

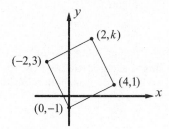

Use the slope formula.
The slope of the segment containing $(0,-1)$ and

$(4,1)$ is $\dfrac{1-(-1)}{4-0}$, or $\dfrac{1}{2}$.

The slope of the segment containing $(-2,3)$ and

$(2,k)$ is $\dfrac{k-3}{2-(-2)}$, or $\dfrac{k-3}{4}$.

Since opposite sides of a square are parallel
to each other, their slopes should be equal.

Therefore $\dfrac{k-3}{4} = \dfrac{1}{2} \implies 2(k-3) = 4 \implies k = 5$

5. B

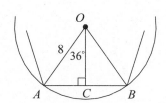

The measure of central angle AOB is $\dfrac{360°}{5}$, or $72°$.

$m\angle AOC = \dfrac{1}{2}m\angle AOB = 36$

$\sin 36° = \dfrac{AC}{OA} = \dfrac{AC}{8} \implies AC = 8 \cdot \sin 36° \approx 4.7$

$\implies AB = 2AC = 9.4$

Perimeter of the pentagon $= 5(9.4) = 47$

6. D

A regular hexagon comprises six equilateral triangles.

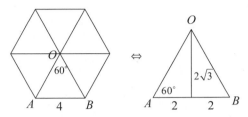

The measure of central angle AOB is $\dfrac{360°}{6}$, or $60°$.

Use the $30°$-$60°$-$90°$ triangle ratio to find the altitude of equilateral triangle AOB.

Since the perimeter of the regular hexagon is 24, the length of each side is $24 \div 6$, or 4.

The altitude is $2\sqrt{3}$.

Then the area of $\Delta AOB = \dfrac{1}{2}(4)(2\sqrt{3}) = 4\sqrt{3}$ and

the area of the regular hexagon $= 6 \cdot 4\sqrt{3} = 24\sqrt{3}$.

7. A

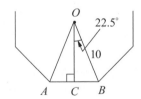

$m\angle AOB = \dfrac{360}{8} = 45$

$m\angle BOC = \dfrac{1}{2}m\angle AOB = 22.5$

$\sin 22.5° = \dfrac{BC}{OB} = \dfrac{BC}{10} \Rightarrow BC = 10\sin 22.5° \approx 3.83$

$\cos 22.5° = \dfrac{OC}{OB} = \dfrac{OC}{10} \Rightarrow OC = 10\cos 22.5° \approx 9.24$

Area of $\Delta AOB = \dfrac{1}{2}AB \cdot OC = \dfrac{1}{2}(2 \cdot 3.83)(9.24)$
≈ 35.4

Area of the octagon $= 8(35.4) = 283.2$

8. C

The measure of each angle of a regular n-sided polygon is $\dfrac{(n-2)180}{n}$.

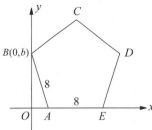

$m\angle BAE = \dfrac{(5-2)180}{5} = 108$

$m\angle BAO = 180 - 108 = 72$

$\sin 72° = \dfrac{OB}{8} \Rightarrow OB = 8\sin 72° \approx 7.6$

9. B

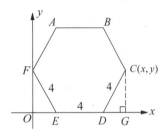

$m\angle FED = \dfrac{(6-2)180}{6} = 120$

$m\angle FEO = 180 - 120 = 60$

$\cos 60° = \dfrac{OE}{4} \Rightarrow OE = 4\cos 60° = 2$

Draw a segment $CG \perp$ to the x-axis.

$m\angle CDG = 60°$, so $DG = 4\cos 60° = 2$.

$OG = OE + ED + DG = 2 + 4 + 2 = 8$
$\Rightarrow x = 8$

$CG = 4\sin 60° \approx 3.46 \Rightarrow y \approx 3.46$

$x + y = 8 + 3.46 = 11.46$

10. D

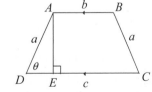

Draw a segment $AE \perp$ to $\overline{CD}$.

$\sin \theta = \dfrac{AE}{a} \Rightarrow AE = a\sin \theta$

Area of isosceles trapezoid $ABCD$

$= \dfrac{1}{2}h(b_1 + b_2) = \dfrac{1}{2}a\sin\theta(b+c)$

11. B

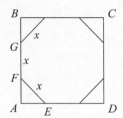

Let $x =$ the length of the side of the octagon. If the area of the square $ABCD$ is 4, then the length of each side of square is 2.

$$m\angle FED = \frac{(8-2)180}{8} = 135$$

$$m\angle FEA = 180 - 135 = 45$$

By the $45°$-$45°$-$90°$ triangle ratio,

$$AE = AF = \frac{\sqrt{2}}{2}x \text{ and } GB = \frac{\sqrt{2}}{2}x.$$

$$AB = AF + FG + GB$$

$$2 = \frac{\sqrt{2}}{2}x + x + \frac{\sqrt{2}}{2}x \implies 2 = \sqrt{2}x + x$$

$$\implies 2 = x(\sqrt{2}+1) \implies x = \frac{2}{\sqrt{2}+1}$$

$$\implies x = \frac{2(\sqrt{2}-1)}{(\sqrt{2}+1)(\sqrt{2}-1)} \implies x = 2(\sqrt{2}-1)$$

12. C

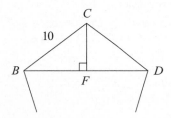

$$m\angle BCD = \frac{(5-2)180}{5} = 108$$

$$m\angle BCF = \frac{1}{2}m\angle BCD = 54$$

$$\cos 54° = \frac{CF}{BC} = \frac{CF}{10} \implies CF = 10\cos 54° \approx 5.9$$

$$\sin 54° = \frac{BF}{BC} = \frac{BF}{10} \implies BF = 10\sin 54° \approx 8.1$$

$$BD = 2BF = 16.2$$

Area of the shaded region

$$= \frac{1}{2}(16.2)(5.9) = 47.8$$

13. D

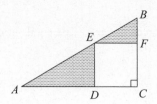

$CD = DE = EF = FC = 6$, since the area of square $CDEF$ is 36.
$m\angle BEF = 30$, since $m\angle BAC = 30$ and $CD \parallel EF$.

$$AD = \sqrt{3} \cdot DE = 6\sqrt{3} \qquad 30°\text{-}60°\text{-}90° \text{ triangle ratio}$$

$$BF = \frac{EF}{\sqrt{3}} = \frac{6}{\sqrt{3}} = 2\sqrt{3} \qquad 30°\text{-}60°\text{-}90° \text{ triangle ratio}$$

Area of the shaded region

$$= \frac{1}{2}AD \cdot DE + \frac{1}{2}EF \cdot BF$$

$$= \frac{1}{2}[(6\sqrt{3})(6) + (6)(2\sqrt{3})]$$

$$= \frac{1}{2}[36\sqrt{3} + 12\sqrt{3})]$$

$$= 24\sqrt{3}$$

14. C

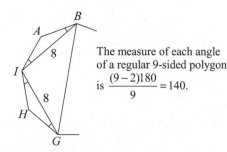

The measure of each angle of a regular 9-sided polygon is $\frac{(9-2)180}{9} = 140$.

Therefore $m\angle A = m\angle AIH = m\angle H = 140$.
$AI = AB$ since the polygon is regular.

$$m\angle AIB = \frac{1}{2}(180-140) = 20$$

$$m\angle HIG = \frac{1}{2}(180-140) = 20$$

$$m\angle BIG = m\angle AIH - (m\angle AIB + m\angle HIG)$$

$$= 140 - (20 + 20) = 100$$

Use the Law of cosines to find the length of $\overline{BG}$.

$$BG^2 = 8^2 + 8^2 - 2(8)(8)\cos 100° \approx 150.2$$

$$\implies BG \approx 12.3$$

CHAPTER 19
Circles

19-1. Circles

In a circle, **all radii are equal in measure.**

The measure of an arc, not to be confused with the length of an arc, is defined as the measure of its central angle.

In circle O, $\angle AOD$ is a central angle and $\overset{\frown}{AD}$ is an arc.

A **minor arc**, such as $\overset{\frown}{AB}$ and $\overset{\frown}{AD}$, is named by its endpoints: $\overset{\frown}{AD}$ is read "arc AD." The measure of a minor arc is always less than 180. We use three letters to name a **major arc**: $\overset{\frown}{ABC}$ is read "arc ABC."

$\overset{\frown}{DAB}$ and $\overset{\frown}{BCD}$ are **semicircles**.

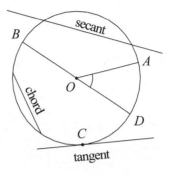

Example 1 □ In circle O shown at the right, $\overline{PS}$ is a diameter and $\overline{OQ} \parallel \overline{SR}$. If $m\angle POQ = 50$, what is the measure of $\overset{\frown}{RS}$?

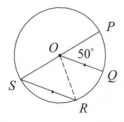

Solution □ $m\angle OSR = m\angle POQ = 50$ Corresponding angle postulate

Draw $\overline{OR}$.
$OS = OR$ All radii of a circle are equal in measure.
$m\angle OSR = m\angle ORS = 50$ Isosceles triangle theorem
$m\angle OSR + m\angle ORS + m\angle ROS = 180$ The angle sum in a triangle is 180.
$50 + 50 + m\angle ROS = 180$ Substitution
$m\angle ROS = 80$ Simplify.
$m\overset{\frown}{RS} = 80$ $m\angle ROS = m\overset{\frown}{RS}$

19-2. Arc Lengths and Areas of Sectors

A **sector** of a circle is a region bounded by two radii and the arc determined by the two radii.

In circle O, $m\angle AOB = x$, and r is the radius.

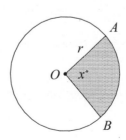

Length of $\overset{\frown}{AB} = 2\pi r \cdot \dfrac{x}{360}$

Area of sector $AOB = \pi r^2 \cdot \dfrac{x}{360}$.

Example 2 □ Find the area and perimeter of the shaded region in the figure shown at the right.

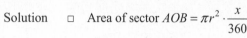

Solution   □   Area of sector $AOB = \pi r^2 \cdot \dfrac{x}{360}$

$$= \pi(6)^2 \cdot \frac{90}{360} = 9\pi$$

Area of $\triangle AOB = \dfrac{1}{2} \cdot 6 \cdot 6 = 18$

Area of shaded region
= area of sector AOB − area of $\triangle AOB$
$= 9\pi - 18$ Answer

Length of arc $\overset{\frown}{AB}$

$$= 2\pi r \cdot \frac{x}{360} = 2\pi(6) \cdot \frac{90}{360} = 3\pi$$

$AB = 6\sqrt{2}$ 45°-45°-90° triangle ratio

Perimeter of shaded region
$= 3\pi + 6\sqrt{2}$ Answer   ■

19-3. Distance Traveled by a Wheel

The distance traveled by a wheel $= 2\pi r \times$ number of revolutions

Example 3 □ A car is traveling at a constant speed of 50 miles per hour. If the radius of the tire is 1 foot, what is the number of revolutions the tire makes in 30 minutes? (1 mile $= 5,280$ ft)

Solution   □   The distance traveled in 30 minutes is 25 miles.
The distance traveled by a wheel $= 2\pi r \times$ number of revolutions
25 miles $= 2\pi(1 \text{ ft}) \cdot$ number of revolutions

Number of revolutions $= \dfrac{25 \text{ miles}}{2\pi \text{ ft}} = \dfrac{25 \cdot (5280 \text{ ft})}{2\pi \text{ ft}} \approx 21,008$ Answer   ■

19-4. Chords and Tangents

In a circle, **congruent chords have congruent arcs**.
If $AB = CD$ then $\overset{\frown}{AB} = \overset{\frown}{CD}$.

In a circle, **congruent chords are equidistant from the center**.
If $AB = CD$ then $OP = OQ$.

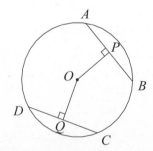

In a circle, **the longer the chord, the closer it is to the center**.
If $AB > CD$ then $OP < OQ$.

In a circle, **if a diameter is perpendicular to a chord, then it bisects the chord.**

In circle O, $\overline{CD}$ is a diameter and $\overline{AB}$ is a chord.

$\overline{CD} \perp \overline{AB}$ and $AE = BE$.

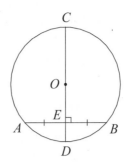

If a line is tangent to a circle, then it is perpendicular to the radius drawn to the point of tangency.

In circle O, $\overline{PA}$ and $\overline{PB}$ are tangents.

$\overline{PA} \perp \overline{OA}$ and $\overline{PB} \perp \overline{OB}$.

Tangents to a circle from the same exterior point are congruent.

$\overline{PA} \cong \overline{PB}$.

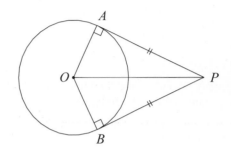

Example 4 □   In the figure shown at the right, $\overline{AB} \perp \overline{OC}$ and $\overline{PB}$ is tangent to circle O. If $OC = 3$, $AB = 8$, and $BP = 12$ what is the length of $\overline{OP}$?

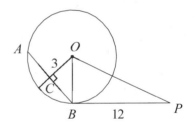

Solution   □   Since $\overline{AB} \perp \overline{OC}$, OC bisects $\overline{AB}$.
Therefore $BC = 4$.
$OB^2 = OC^2 + BC^2$
$OB^2 = 3^2 + 4^2$
$OB = 5$
Since $\overline{PB}$ is tangent to circle O, $\overline{OB} \perp \overline{PB}$.
$OP^2 = OB^2 + PB^2$
$OP^2 = 5^2 + 12^2 = 169$
$OP = \sqrt{169} = 13$ Answer

19-5. Angles and Segments of a Circle

The measure of an inscribed angle is equal to one-half the measure of its intercepted arc.

$\angle ABC$ is an inscribed angle and $\overset{\frown}{AC}$ is its intercepted arc.

$m\angle ABC = \dfrac{1}{2} m\overset{\frown}{AC}$

$m\angle ABC = \dfrac{1}{2} m\angle AOC$

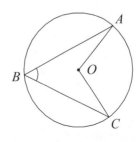

An angle inscribed in a semicircle is a right angle.

If $\overarc{DAB}$ is a semicircle then $\angle A$ is a right angle.

Conversely, if $\angle A$ is a right angle then $\overarc{DAB}$ is a semicircle and $\overline{BD}$ is a diameter of circle O.

If a rectangle is inscribed in a circle, then the diagonal of the rectangle is a diameter of the circle.

$\overline{BD}$ is also a diagonal of rectangle $ABCD$, and a diameter of the circle.

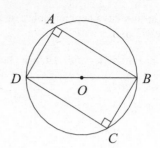

If a quadrilateral is inscribed in a circle, then its opposite angles are supplementary.

Quadrilateral $ABCD$ is inscribed in circle O.
$m\angle A + m\angle C = 180$
$m\angle B + m\angle D = 180$

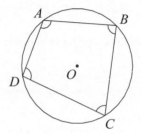

Example 5   □   In the figure shown at the right, what is the length of $\overline{PQ}$?

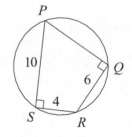

Solution   □   Since $\overline{PS} \perp \overline{RS}$ and $\overline{PQ} \perp \overline{RQ}$,
$\overline{PR}$ is a diameter of the circle.

$PR^2 = PS^2 + RS^2$ Pythagorean theorem

$PR^2 = 10^2 + 4^2 = 116$

$PR^2 = PQ^2 + RQ^2$ Pythagorean theorem

$116 = PQ^2 + 6^2$ Substitution

$PQ^2 = 80$

$PQ = \sqrt{80} = 4\sqrt{5}$ Answer

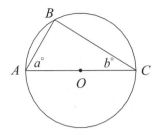

Figure 1

1. In Figure 1, points A, B, and C lie on a circle and O is the center of the circle. What is the value of $a+b$?

    (A) 70

    (B) 80

    (C) 90

    (D) 110

    (E) It cannot be determined.

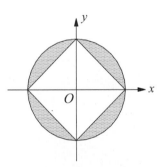

Figure 2

2. In Figure 2, a square is inscribed in the circle whose equation is $x^2 + y^2 = 9$. What is the area of the shaded region?

    (A) 10.3

    (B) 15.5

    (C) 43.8

    (D) 75.9

    (E) 92.5

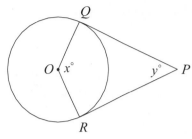

Figure 3

3. In Figure 3, $\overline{PQ}$ and $\overline{PR}$ are tangent to a circle with center O. Which of the following equations is true of the angles x and y?

    (A) $\frac{1}{2}x - y = 90$

    (B) $\frac{1}{2}x + y = 180$

    (C) $x - y = 180$

    (D) $x + y = 180$

    (E) It cannot be determined.

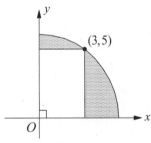

Figure 4

4. Figure 4 shows a point $(3,5)$ lying on a circle and a rectangle inscribed in the quarter circle. What is the area of the shaded region?

    (A) 9.7

    (B) 10.8

    (C) 11.7

    (D) 13.0

    (E) 14.2

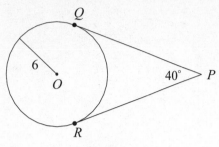

Figure 5

5. In Figure 5, $\overline{PQ}$ and $\overline{PR}$ are tangent to a circle of radius 6. What is the length of the segment QR (not shown)?

(A) 9.8

(B) 11.3

(C) 12.9

(D) 14.2

(E) 15.6

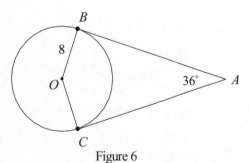

Figure 6

6. In Figure 6, $\overline{AB}$ and $\overline{AC}$ are tangent to a circle of radius 8. What is the length of the segment AB?

(A) 8.4

(B) 11.0

(C) 13.6

(D) 24.6

(E) 25.9

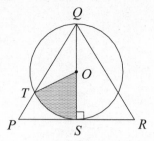

Figure 7

7. In Figure 7, $\triangle PQR$ is equilateral, with side length of 4. If $\overline{PR}$ is tangent to the circle and $\overline{OT}$ is a radius, what is the area of sector OTS?

(A) $\dfrac{\pi}{2}$

(B) $\dfrac{2\pi}{3}$

(C) $\dfrac{5\pi}{6}$

(D) π

(E) $\dfrac{4\pi}{3}$

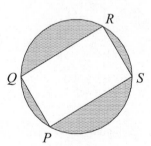

Figure 8

8. Rectangle $PQRS$ is inscribed in a circle as shown in Figure 8. If the length of side is $\overline{PQ}$ is 6 and the length of side $\overline{QR}$ is 10, what is the area of the shaded region?

(A) 26.6

(B) 30.3

(C) 36.3

(D) 42.7

(E) 46.8

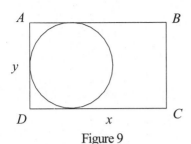

Figure 9

Note: Figure not drawn to scale.

9. Figure 9 shows a rectangle and a circle inscribed in the rectangle. If the ratio of the area of the circle to the area of the rectangle is 5 to 8, what is the value of $\frac{y}{x}$?

(A) $\dfrac{2\pi}{5}$

(B) $\dfrac{5}{2\pi}$

(C) $\dfrac{3\pi}{5}$

(D) $\dfrac{5}{3\pi}$

(E) $\dfrac{4\pi}{5}$

10. A regular hexagon is inscribed in a circle. If the radius of the circle is 6, what is the area of the hexagon?

(A) 96

(B) $54\sqrt{3}$

(C) 108

(D) $64\sqrt{3}$

(E) $72\sqrt{3}$

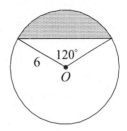

Figure 10

11. Figure 10 shows circle O whose radius is 6. What is the perimeter of the shaded region?

(A) $3\sqrt{2} + 2\pi$

(B) $6\sqrt{2} + 2\pi$

(C) $3\sqrt{3} + 4\pi$

(D) $6\sqrt{3} + 4\pi$

(E) $6\sqrt{3} + 6\pi$

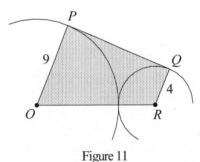

Figure 11

12. In Figure 11, circles O and P, with radii 9 and 4, are tangent to each other. If $\overline{PQ}$ is a common external tangent, what is the area of the shaded region?

(A) 68

(B) 78

(C) 84

(D) 90

(E) 98

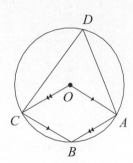

Figure 12

13. In Figure 12, $OABC$ is a parallelogram and $ABCD$ is a quadrilateral inscribed in a circle with center O. If $m\angle OAB = 46°$, what is the degree measure of $\angle CDA$?

   (A) 44

   (B) 46

   (C) 54

   (D) 64

   (E) 67

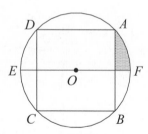

Figure 13

14. In Figure 13, a square is inscribed in a circle of diameter 4. If diameter EF is parallel to the side AD, what is the perimeter of the shaded region?

   (A) $\sqrt{2} + \dfrac{\pi}{2}$

   (B) $\sqrt{2} + \pi$

   (C) $2 + \dfrac{\pi}{2}$

   (D) $2 + \pi$

   (E) $2\sqrt{2} + \pi$

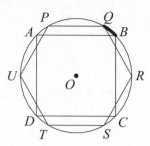

Figure 14

15. In Figure 14, a regular hexagon $PQRSTU$ and a square $ABCD$ are inscribed in a circle with radius 6. If $PQ \parallel AB$, what is the length of the arc QB?

   (A) $\dfrac{\pi}{6}$ (B) $\dfrac{\pi}{3}$ (C) $\dfrac{3\pi}{8}$

   (D) $\dfrac{\pi}{2}$ (E) $\dfrac{5\pi}{8}$

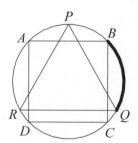

Figure 15

16. In Figure 15, an equilateral triangle PQR and a square $ABCD$ are inscribed in a circle with radius 4. If $\overline{AB} \parallel \overline{QR}$, what is the length of the arc QB?

   (A) π (B) $\dfrac{4\pi}{3}$ (C) $\dfrac{5\pi}{3}$

   (D) 2π (E) $\dfrac{7\pi}{3}$

Answer Key

1. C	2. A	3. D	4. C	5. B
6. D	7. A	8. E	9. B	10. B
11. D	12. B	13. E	14. C	15. D
16. C				

Answers and Explanations

1. C

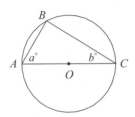

An angle inscribed in a semicircle is a right angle.
$m\angle B = 90 \implies a + b = 90$

2. A

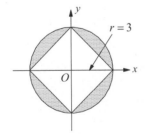

Since the equation of the circle is $x^2 + y^2 = 9$,
the radius of the circle is 3.
Area of the circle $= \pi(3)^2 = 9\pi$
Diagonal of the square = Diameter of the circle = 6
Length of the edge of the square
$= \dfrac{6}{\sqrt{2}} = \dfrac{6 \cdot \sqrt{2}}{\sqrt{2} \cdot \sqrt{2}} = 3\sqrt{2}$
Area of the square $= 3\sqrt{2} \cdot 3\sqrt{2} = 18$
Area of the shaded region
= Area of circle − Area of square
$= 9\pi - 18 \approx 10.3$

3. D

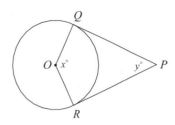

If a line is tangent to a circle, then it is ⊥ to the radius drawn to the point of tangency. Therefore $m\angle PQO = 90$ and $m\angle PRO = 90$.

The sum of the angles of a quadrilateral is $360°$.
$m\angle PQO + m\angle PRO + x + y = 360$
$\implies 90 + 90 + x + y = 360$
$\implies x + y = 180$

4. C

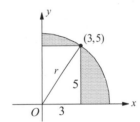

Let $r =$ the radius of the quarter circle. Then
$r^2 = 3^2 + 5^2 = 34$
Area of the quarter circle
$= \dfrac{1}{4}\pi r^2 = \dfrac{1}{4}\pi \cdot 34 = \dfrac{17\pi}{2}$
Area of the rectangle $= 3 \cdot 5 = 15$
Area of the shaded region
= Area of the quarter circle − Area of the rectangle
$= \dfrac{17\pi}{2} - 15 \approx 11.7$

5. B

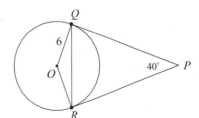

In a circle all radii are $\cong$. So $OQ = OR = 6$.

If a line is tangent to a circle, then it is ⊥ to the radius drawn to the point of tangency.

Therefore $m\angle PQO = m\angle PRO = 90$.

The sum of the angles of a quadrilateral is $360°$.

$m\angle QOR + m\angle P + m\angle PQO + m\angle PRO = 360$

$m\angle QOR + 40 + 90 + 90 = 360 \qquad m\angle P = 40$

$m\angle QOR + 40 = 180$

$m\angle QOR = 140$

Use the Law of cosines.

$QR^2 = OQ^2 + OR^2 - 2 \cdot OQ \cdot OR \cdot \cos 140°$

$QR^2 = 6^2 + 6^2 - 2 \cdot 6 \cdot 6 \cdot \cos 140°$

$QR^2 \approx 127$

$QR = \sqrt{127} \approx 11.3$

6. D

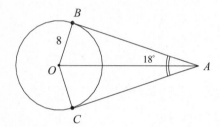

$\overline{AB} \perp \overline{OB}$, $\overline{AC} \perp \overline{OC}$ Tangents are $\perp$ to radii.

$AB = AC$ Tangents from a point are $\cong$.

$OB = OC$ In a circle all radii are $\cong$.

By SAS postulate $\triangle AOB \cong \triangle AOC$.
Therefore $m\angle BAO = m\angle CAO = 18$.

$\tan 18° = \dfrac{8}{AB} \implies AB = \dfrac{8}{\tan 18°} \approx 24.6$

7. A

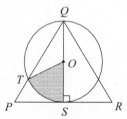

$\triangle PQR$ is an equilateral with side length of 4.
Therefore $PQ = 4$, $PS = 2$, $m\angle P = 60$, and
$m\angle PQS = 30$.

$QS = PS \cdot \sqrt{3} = 2\sqrt{3}$

Therefore the radius of circle O is $\sqrt{3}$.
Since $OQ = OT$, $m\angle PQS = m\angle OTQ = 30$.

By the Exterior angle theorem,
$m\angle TOS = m\angle PQS + m\angle OTQ$

$m\angle TOS = 30 + 30 = 60$

Area of sector $TOS = \pi r^2 \times \dfrac{m\angle TOS}{360}$

$= \pi(\sqrt{3})^2 \times \dfrac{60}{360}$

$= \dfrac{\pi}{2}$

8. E

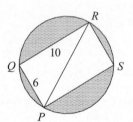

If a rectangle is inscribed in a circle, the diagonal
of the rectangle is the diameter of the circle.

$PR^2 = 6^2 + 10^2 = 136$

$PR = \sqrt{136} = \sqrt{4}\sqrt{34} = 2\sqrt{34}$

Therefore the radius of the circle is $\sqrt{34}$.

Area of the shaded region
= Area of circle − Area of rectangle

$= \pi(\sqrt{34})^2 - 6 \cdot 10$

$= 34\pi - 60$

≈ 46.8

9. B

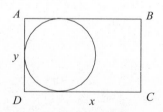

Radius of the circle $= \dfrac{1}{2}AD = \dfrac{1}{2}y$

Area of the circle $= \pi r^2 = \pi (\frac{1}{2} y)^2 = \dfrac{\pi y^2}{4}$

Area of the rectangle $= xy$

$$\dfrac{\text{Area of circle}}{\text{Area of rectangle}} = \dfrac{5}{8}$$

$\Rightarrow \dfrac{\frac{\pi y^2}{4}}{xy} = \dfrac{5}{8} \Rightarrow \dfrac{\pi y^2}{4xy} = \dfrac{5}{8}$

$\Rightarrow \dfrac{\pi y}{4x} = \dfrac{5}{8} \Rightarrow \dfrac{y}{x} = \dfrac{5}{8} \cdot \dfrac{4}{\pi} = \dfrac{5}{2\pi}$

10. B

Sketch a circle and an inscribed hexagon.

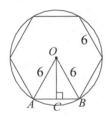

A regular hexagon consists of 6 equilateral $\triangle$ s.
$\triangle AOB$ is equilateral and $\triangle AOC$ is a $30°$-$60°$-$90°$ triangle.

Therefore $AC = \dfrac{1}{2}(6) = 3$ and $OC = 3\sqrt{3}$.

Area of $\triangle AOB = \dfrac{1}{2}(6)(3\sqrt{3}) = 9\sqrt{3}$

Area of the regular hexagon
$= 6 \cdot 9\sqrt{3} = 54\sqrt{3}$

11. D

Draw a segment OB which is $\perp$ to AC.

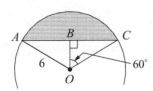

$\triangle OBC$ is a $30°$-$60°$-$90°$ triangle. Therefore
$OB = 3$ and $BC = 3\sqrt{3}$.

$AC = 2BC = 6\sqrt{3}$

Length of $\overparen{AC}$
$= 2\pi r \times \dfrac{\text{central angle of the sector}}{360}$
$= 2\pi(6) \times \dfrac{120}{360} = 4\pi$

Perimeter of the shaded region
$= 6\sqrt{3} + 4\pi$

12. B

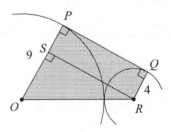

Since $\overline{PQ}$ is tangent to the circles O and R,
$\overline{OP} \perp \overline{PQ}$ and $\overline{RQ} \perp \overline{PQ}$.

From point R draw a perpendicular line to $\overline{OP}$
and let S be the point of intersection. In rectangle
$PQRS$, $PQ = SR$ and $SP = RQ = 4$.

$OS = OP - SP = 9 - 4 = 5$
$OR = $ length of the radius of circle O
$\quad\quad + $ length of the radius of circle R
$\quad\quad = 9 + 4 = 13$

In $\triangle ORS$, $OR^2 = OS^2 + SR^2$.
$13^2 = 5^2 + SR^2 \Rightarrow SR^2 = 144$
$\Rightarrow SR = 12 \Rightarrow PQ = 12$

Area of the shaded region (which is a trapezoid)
$= \dfrac{1}{2}(OP + RQ) \cdot PQ$
$= \dfrac{1}{2}(9 + 4) \cdot 12$
$= 78$

13. E

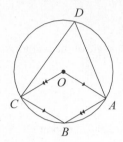

Given $m\angle OAB = 46$.

Since consecutive interior angles of a parallelogram are supplementary $m\angle AOC + m\angle OAB = 180$.

$m\angle AOC + 46 = 180$

$m\angle AOC = 134$

The measure of an inscribed angle $= \frac{1}{2}$ the measure of its intercepted arc, so $m\angle CDA = \frac{1}{2} m\angle AOC$.

$m\angle CDA = \frac{1}{2}(134) = 67$

14. C

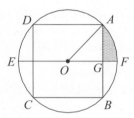

Diameter of the circle $= 4 \implies OA = 2$

Since $\overline{EF} \parallel \overline{AD}$, $m\angle AOG = 45$.

$AG = OG = \sqrt{2}$ by the $45°$-$45°$-$90°$ triangle ratio.

$GF = OF - OG = 2 - \sqrt{2}$

Length of $\overparen{AF} = 2\pi(2) \times \dfrac{45}{360} = \dfrac{\pi}{2}$

Perimeter of the shaded region

$= AG + GF + \text{length of } \overparen{AF}$

$= \sqrt{2} + (2 - \sqrt{2}) + \dfrac{\pi}{2}$

$= 2 + \dfrac{\pi}{2}$

15. D

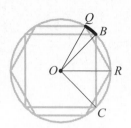

Draw $\overline{OQ}$, $\overline{OB}$, $\overline{OR}$, and $\overline{OC}$.

Q and R are subsequent vertices of the regular hexagon, so $m\overparen{QR} = m\angle QOR = \dfrac{1}{6} \cdot 360 = 60$.

Since B and C are subsequent vertices of the square, $m\angle BOC = \dfrac{1}{4} \cdot 360 = 90$.

$m\overparen{BR} = m\angle BOR = \dfrac{1}{2} m\angle BOC = \dfrac{1}{2} \cdot 90 = 45$

$m\overparen{BQ} = m\overparen{QR} - m\overparen{BR} = 60 - 45 = 15$

Length of the arc BQ

$= 2\pi r \times \dfrac{m\overparen{BQ}}{360} = 2\pi(6) \times \dfrac{15}{360} = \dfrac{1}{2}\pi$

16. C

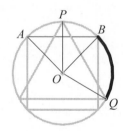

Draw $\overline{OA}$, $\overline{OP}$, $\overline{OB}$, and $\overline{OQ}$.

Points P and Q are vertices of the equilateral triangle, so $m\overparen{PQ} = m\angle POQ = \dfrac{1}{3} \cdot 360 = 120$.

Since A and B are subsequent vertices of the square, $m\angle BOA = \dfrac{1}{4} \cdot 360 = 90$.

$m\overparen{PB} = m\angle POB = \dfrac{1}{2} m\angle BOA = \dfrac{1}{2}(90) = 45$

$m\overparen{BQ} = m\overparen{PQ} - m\overparen{PB} = 120 - 45 = 75$

Length of the arc BQ

$= 2\pi r \times \dfrac{m\overparen{BQ}}{360} = 2\pi(4) \times \dfrac{75}{360} = \dfrac{5}{3}\pi$

CHAPTER 20
Three-dimensional Geometry

20-1. Prisms

A **prism** is a polyhedron (a space figure whose faces are polygons) with two congruent and parallel faces. These two faces are called the **bases** of the prism.

Volume of a prism = Base area × Height

Lateral area = Perimeter of base × Height

Total surface area = Base area + Lateral area

A **cube** is a prism in which all the faces are squares.

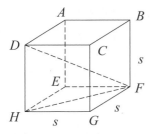

Volume of a cube $= s^3$

Total surface area $= 6s^2$

Length of diagonal $\overline{DF} = \sqrt{s^2 + s^2 + s^2} = \sqrt{3}s$

A rectangular solid is a prism with a rectangular base and rectangular lateral faces.

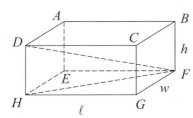

Volume of a rectangular solid = Base area × Height = $\ell \cdot w \cdot h$

Total surface area $= 2(\ell w + wh + \ell h)$

Length of diagonal $\overline{DF} = \sqrt{\ell^2 + w^2 + h^2}$

A **net** is a two-dimensional figure that can be folded into a three-dimensional figure.

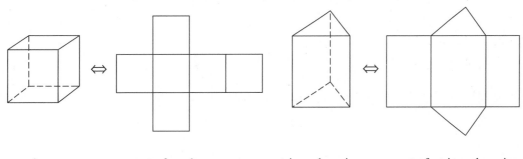

cube   net of a cube   triangular prism   net of a triangular prism

Example 1 □   In the figure at the right, what is the
length of the diagonal $\overline{AE}$?

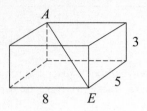

Solution □ $AE = \sqrt{\ell^2 + w^2 + h^2}$

$= \sqrt{8^2 + 5^2 + 3^2} = \sqrt{98}$

$= 7\sqrt{2}$ Answer

20-2. Cylinders

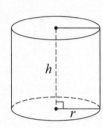

Volume of a cylinder $=$ Base area $\times$ Height $= \pi r^2 h$

Total surface area $= 2\pi rh + 2\pi r^2$

Example 2 □   A cylinder with height 10 has a total surface area of 150π cm^2.
What is the volume of the cube?

Solution □   Total surface area $= 2\pi rh + 2\pi r^2$

$150\pi = 2\pi r(10) + 2\pi r^2$ Total surface area is 150π cm^2.

$150\pi = 20\pi r + 2\pi r^2$ Simplify.

$r^2 + 10r - 75 = 0$ Divide both sides by 2π and write
the equation in standard form.

$(r+15)(r-5) = 0$ Factor.

$r = -15$ or $r = 5$ Solve for r.

Since r is positive, $r = 5$.
Volume $= \pi r^2 h = \pi(5^2) \cdot 10$

$= 250\pi$ cm^3 Answer

20-3. Pyramids and Cones

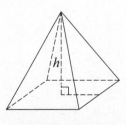

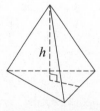

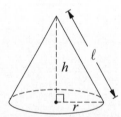

Square Pyramid   Triangular Pyramid   Circular Cone

Volume of a pyramid $= \frac{1}{3}Bh$, where B is the area of the base and h is the height of the pyramid.

Volume of a cone $= \frac{1}{3}\pi r^2 h$, where πr^2 is the area of the base and h is the height of the cone.

Total surface area of a cone $= \pi r^2 + \pi r \ell$, where $\ell = \sqrt{r^2 + h^2}$.

Example 3 □ In the rectangular prism shown at the right, A, B, C, and D are vertices of the prism. What is the volume of the pyramid formed by these vertices?

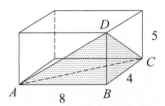

Solution   □ In pyramid $ABCD$, we can use triangle ABC as the base of the pyramid and $\overline{BD}$ as the altitude to the base.

Volume of the pyramid

$$= \frac{1}{3}Bh = \frac{1}{3}(\frac{1}{2} \cdot 8 \cdot 4) \cdot 5 = \frac{80}{3} \qquad \text{Answer}$$

20-4. Spheres

Volume of a sphere $= \frac{4}{3}\pi r^3$

Surface area $= 4\pi r^2$

A plane can intersect a sphere at a point or in a circle. When a plane intersects a sphere so that it contains the center of the sphere, the intersection is called a **great circle**.

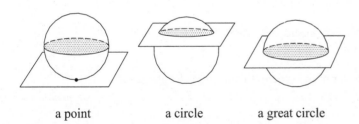

a point   a circle   a great circle

Example 4 □ A plane passes through a sphere 2 inches from the center of the sphere. If the volume of the sphere is 36π in^3 , what is the area of the intersected circle?

Solution   □ Volume $= \frac{4}{3}\pi r^3 = 36\pi \implies r = 3$

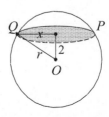

Let $x =$ the radius of circle P.

$OQ^2 = OP^2 + PQ^2$ Pythagorean theorem

$3^2 = 2^2 + x^2$ Substitution

$x^2 = 5$

Area of intersected circle

$= \pi x^2 = 5\pi$ Answer

20-5. Inscribed Solids

 a.

 b.

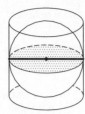 c.

 d.

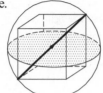 e.

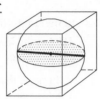 f.

a. If a cube is inscribed in a cylinder, then the diagonal of a face of the cube is equal to the diameter of the cylinder.

b. If a cylinder is inscribed in a cube, then the diameter of the cylinder is equal to the length of the edge of the cube.

c. If a sphere is inscribed in a cylinder, the sphere and the cylinder have the same diameter.

d. If a cylinder is inscribed in a sphere, the diameter of the sphere is equal to the cylinder's diagonal $(= \sqrt{(\text{diameter of cylinder})^2 + (\text{height of cylinder})^2})$.

e. If a cube or a rectangular prism is inscribed in a sphere, the diagonal of the cube or the rectangular prism is equal to the diameter of the sphere.

f. If a sphere is inscribed in a cube, the diameter of the sphere is equal to the length of the edge of the cube.

Example 5 □   A cube is inscribed in a cylinder with radius 6.
What is the volume of the cube?

Solution   □   When a cube is inscribed in a cylinder,
the diagonal of a face of the cube is equal
to the diameter of the cylinder.
The diagonal of the face of the cube
$= 2r = 2(6) = 12$

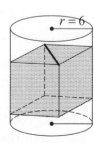

Let $x =$ the length of the edge of cube.
By the Pythagorean theorem,
$x^2 + x^2 = 12^2 \implies x = 6\sqrt{2}$.

Volume of the cube
$= x^3 = (6\sqrt{2})^3 = 432\sqrt{2}$ Answer

20-6. Ratios of Surface Areas and Volumes

If two solids are similar with corresponding sides in the ratio of $a : b$, then their surface areas have a ratio of $a^2 : b^2$, and their volumes have a ratio of $a^3 : b^3$.

Example 6 □   A diagonal of a smaller cube is $2\sqrt{3}$ and a diagonal of a larger cube is $5\sqrt{3}$. If the volume of the smaller cube is 12 cubic units, what is the volume of the larger cube?

Solution   □   The ratio of diagonals $= \dfrac{2\sqrt{3}}{5\sqrt{3}} = \dfrac{2}{5}. \Rightarrow$ The ratio of volumes $= \dfrac{2^3}{5^3} = \dfrac{8}{125}.$

$$\frac{\text{volume of smaller cube}}{\text{volume of larger cube}} = \frac{8}{125} \Rightarrow \frac{12}{\text{volume of larger cube}} = \frac{8}{125}$$

Volume of the larger cube $= \dfrac{12 \cdot 125}{8} = 187.5$ cubic units   Answer

20-7. Solids Generated by Rotation

By rotating a plane figure around an axis, a space figure is formed. On the SAT, there are usually three types of solids produced by the rotation of a plane figure around an axis:

1) A cone is formed by rotating a triangle in space around an axis.

2) A cylinder is formed by rotating a rectangle in space around an axis.

3) A sphere is formed by rotating a semicircle in space around an axis.

Solids can be generated by rotating a plane figure around a horizontal axis (or x-axis).

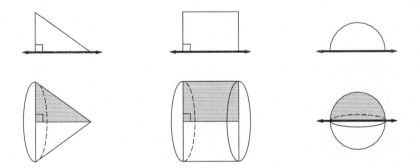

Solids can be generated by rotating a plane figure around a vertical axis (or y-axis).

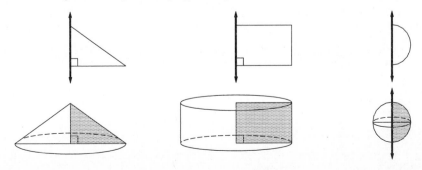

Example 7 □ A triangle is formed by the line $y = -\dfrac{1}{2}x + 2$, x-axis, and y-axis.

Find the volume of the space figure generated by rotating the triangle around the x-axis.

Solution □ If the triangle is rotated around the x-axis, a cone of radius 2 and height 4 will be generated.

Volume of the cone $= \dfrac{1}{3}\pi r^2 h$

$= \dfrac{1}{3}\pi(2)^2(4) = \dfrac{16}{3}\pi$ Answer

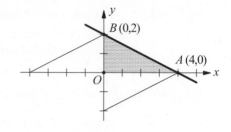

20-8. Coordinates in Space $\boxed{L2}$

In three-dimensional space, three mutually perpendicular number lines are placed so that they intersect at zero, called the **origin**. A point in space is represented by an **ordered triple** of real numbers (x, y, z).

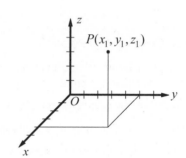

The Distance Formula

The distance between two points $P(x_1, y_1, z_1)$ and $Q(x_2, y_2, z_2)$

in space is $d = \sqrt{(x_2 - x_1)^2 + (y_2 - y_1)^2 + (z_2 - z_1)^2}$.

The Midpoint Formula

For a segment $\overline{PQ}$ with endpoints $P(x_1, y_1, z_1)$ and $Q(x_2, y_2, z_2)$, the coordinates of

the midpoint M are $(\dfrac{x_1 + x_2}{2}, \dfrac{y_1 + y_2}{2}, \dfrac{z_1 + z_2}{2})$.

Example 8 □ Find the distance and the midpoint of the line segment between the points $P(2, 5, 7)$ and $Q(10, 3, 3)$.

Solution □ $d = \sqrt{(10-2)^2 + (3-5)^2 + (3-7)^2}$

$= \sqrt{64 + 4 + 16}$

$= \sqrt{84} = 2\sqrt{21}$ Answer

The coordinates of the midpoint of the line segment $\overline{PQ}$ are

$(\dfrac{2+10}{2}, \dfrac{5+3}{2}, \dfrac{7+3}{2}) = (6, 4, 5)$ Answer

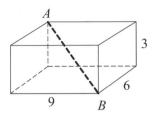

Figure 1

1. In Figure 1, what is the length of $\overline{AB}$?

    (A) 9.7

    (B) 10.3

    (C) 11.2

    (D) 12.4

    (E) 13.6

2. A cylinder with height of 6 is inscribed in a sphere with radius 5. What is the volume of the cylinder?

    (A) 76π

    (B) 82π

    (C) 88π

    (D) 96π

    (E) 108π

3. The radius of the base of a right circular cone is 10 and the radius of a parallel cross section is 6. If the distance between the base and the cross section is 5, what is the height of the cone?

    (A) 6

    (B) 7

    (C) 8.5

    (D) 10

    (E) 12.5

4. A right circular cylinder has radius 4 and height 6. If P and Q are two points on its surface, what is the maximum straight-line distance between P and Q?

    (A) 7.2

    (B) 8.9

    (C) 10

    (D) 11.5

    (E) 12

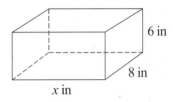

Figure 2

5. In Figure 2, if the total surface area of the rectangular prism is 432 in^2 , what is the value of x?

    (A) 11

    (B) 12

    (C) 13

    (D) 14

    (E) 15

6. A triangle is formed by the line $y = -3x + 6$, the x-axis, and the y-axis. What is the volume of the space figure generated by rotating the triangle around the y-axis?

    (A) 6π

    (B) 8π

    (C) 12π

    (D) 16π

    (E) 24π

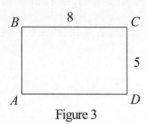

Figure 3

7. Rectangle $ABCD$ in Figure 3 is rotated about side $\overline{AD}$, and it generates a space figure of volume s. When the same rectangle is rotated about side $\overline{AB}$, it generates a space figure of volume t. What is the value of $\dfrac{s}{t}$?

(A) $\dfrac{5}{8}$

(B) $\dfrac{8}{5}$

(C) $\dfrac{25}{64}$

(D) $\dfrac{64}{25}$

(E) $\dfrac{125}{512}$

8. The radius of a cylinder is r and the height is h. If the radius is increased by 50% and the height is decreased by 50%, which of the following is true of the volume of the new cylinder?

(A) The volume is decreased by 12.5%.

(B) The volume is decreased by 25%.

(C) The volume is unchanged.

(D) The volume is increased by 12.5%.

(E) The volume is increased by 25%.

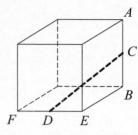

Figure 4

9. Figure 4 shows a cube with edge of length 6. If C is the midpoint of segment AB and D is the midpoint of segment EF, what is the length of CD?

(A) $3\sqrt{2}$

(B) $3\sqrt{3}$

(C) $4\sqrt{3}$

(D) $3\sqrt{6}$

(E) $6\sqrt{3}$

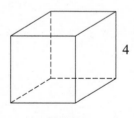

Figure 5

10. Figure 5 shows a cube with edge of length 4. What is the length of the segment from the center of the cube to one of its corners?

(A) $2\sqrt{2}$

(B) $2\sqrt{3}$

(C) $4\sqrt{2}$

(D) $4\sqrt{3}$

(E) $3\sqrt{6}$

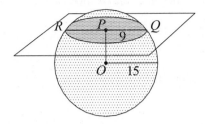

Figure 6

11. In Figure 6, a plane intersects a sphere in a circle that has a radius of 9. If the radius of the sphere is 15, what is the length of $\overline{OP}$?

(A) 10

(B) $8\sqrt{2}$

(C) $3\sqrt{13}$

(D) 12

(E) $6\sqrt{6}$

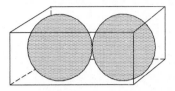

Figure 8

13. Figure 8 shows 2 identical spheres inscribed in a rectangular prism. If the volume of each sphere is 36π in^2, what is the volume of the rectangular prism in cubic inches?

(A) 216

(B) 324

(C) 432

(D) 648

(E) 864

14. What is the distance between the points $P(3,9,14)$ and $Q(7,18,2)$? $\boxed{L2}$

(A) 10.2

(B) 11.6

(C) 12.0

(D) 13.9

(E) 15.5

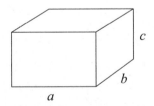

Figure 7

12. In Figure 7, the areas of two of the faces are 10 and 35. If the dimensions a, b, and c are integers, what is the volume of the rectangular prism?

(A) 70

(B) 75

(C) 80

(D) 90

(E) 105

Answer Key

1. C	2. D	3. E	4. C	5. B
6. B	7. A	8. D	9. D	10. B
11. D	12. A	13. C	14. E	

Answers and Explanations

1. C

$$AB = \sqrt{\ell^2 + w^2 + h^2}$$
$$= \sqrt{9^2 + 6^2 + 3^2} = \sqrt{126}$$
$$\approx 11.2$$

2. D

If a cylinder is inscribed in a sphere, the diameter of the sphere is equal to the cylinder's diagonal.

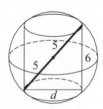

Let $d =$ the diameter of the cylinder.
$$10^2 = d^2 + 6^2 \Rightarrow d^2 = 64$$
$$\Rightarrow d = 8 \Rightarrow r = 4$$

Volume of the cylinder
$$= \pi r^2 h = \pi (4)^2 \cdot 6$$
$$= 96\pi$$

3. E

Draw a cone and a cross section.

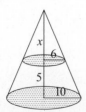

Let $x =$ the height of the smaller cone.
$$\frac{x}{6} = \frac{x+5}{10} \Rightarrow 10x = 6(x+5)$$
$$\Rightarrow 10x = 6x + 30 \Rightarrow 4x = 30 \Rightarrow x = 7.5$$

Height of the cone $= 7.5 + 5 = 12.5$

4. C

The maximum straight-line distance between P and Q is the diagonal of the cylinder.

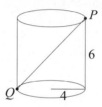

The diameter of the cylinder is 8.
$$PQ^2 = 6^2 + 8^2 = 100$$
$$PQ = 10$$

5. B

Total surface area of the rectangular prism
$$= 2(\ell w + wh + \ell h) = 2(8x + 48 + 6x) = 28x + 96$$

Therefore $28x + 96 = 432 \Rightarrow 28x = 336$

$$\Rightarrow x = 12$$

6. B

Draw the line $y = -3x + 6$ on the xy-coordinates.

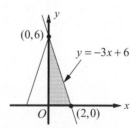

The x-intercept of the line is 2, and the y-intercept of the line is 6.
The cone generated by rotating the triangle around the y-axis has radius 2 and height 6.

Volume of the cone

$$= \frac{1}{3}\pi r^2 h$$

$$= \frac{1}{3}\pi(2)^2(6)$$

$$= 8\pi$$

7. A

If rectangle $ABCD$ is rotated about side $\overline{AD}$, a cylinder of radius 5 and height 8 is generated.

Volume $s = \pi(5)^2 \cdot 8 = 200\pi$

If rectangle $ABCD$ is rotated about side $\overline{AB}$, a cylinder of radius 8 and height 5 is generated.

Volume $t = \pi(8)^2 \cdot 5 = 320\pi$

$$\frac{s}{t} = \frac{200\pi}{320\pi} = \frac{5}{8}$$

8. D

The radius of a cylinder is r and the height is h.

The radius of the new cylinder is $r + 0.5r$, or $1.5r$. The height of the new cylinder is $h - 0.5h$, or $0.5h$.

Volume of the new cylinder

$$= \pi(1.5r)^2(0.5h)$$

$$= 1.125\pi r^2 h$$

Therefore the volume of the new cylinder is increased by 12.5%.

9. D

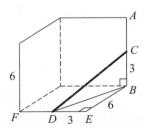

$DE = 3$ and $BC = 3$ since C and D are midpoints of the edges of the cube.

$$DB^2 = DE^2 + BE^2$$
$$DB^2 = 3^2 + 6^2 = 45$$

$$CD^2 = DB^2 + BC^2$$
$$CD^2 = 45 + 3^2 = 54$$
$$CD = \sqrt{54} = \sqrt{9}\sqrt{6} = 3\sqrt{6}$$

10. B

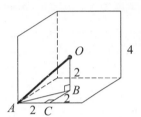

Let point O be the center of the cube. Let OB be the distance from the center to the base and OA be the distance from the center to one of the corners. Draw a segment BC which is $\perp$ to the edge of the cube. Then $OB = AC = BC = 2$.

$$AB^2 = AC^2 + BC^2$$
$$AB^2 = 2^2 + 2^2 = 8$$

$$OA^2 = OB^2 + AB^2$$
$$OA^2 = 2^2 + 8 = 12$$
$$OA = \sqrt{12} = 2\sqrt{3}$$

11. D

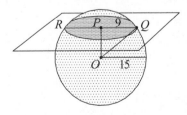

Draw $\overline{OQ}$.

$OQ = 15$ since $\overline{OQ}$ is a radius of the sphere.

$$OQ^2 = OP^2 + PQ^2$$

$$15^2 = OP^2 + 9^2 \;\Rightarrow\; OP^2 = 144 \;\Rightarrow\; OP = 12$$

12. A

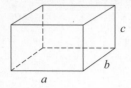

The dimensions a, b, and c are integers.
Let $ab = 10$ and $bc = 35$.

$a \cdot b = 1 \cdot 10$ or $a \cdot b = 2 \cdot 5$
$b \cdot c = 1 \cdot 35$ or $b \cdot c = 5 \cdot 7$

We can conclude that $a = 2$, $b = 5$, and $c = 7$.

Volume of the rectangular prism
$= 2 \cdot 5 \cdot 7 = 70$

13. C

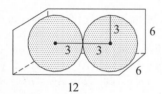

The volume of each sphere is given as 36π in^2.

Volume of a sphere $= \dfrac{4}{3}\pi r^3$

$\dfrac{4}{3}\pi r^3 = 36\pi \;\Rightarrow\; r = 3$

Therefore the length of the rectangular prism is 12, width is 6, and height is 6.

Volume of the rectangular prism
$= 12 \cdot 6 \cdot 6 = 432$

14. E $\boxed{L2}$

$P(3, 9, 14)$ and $Q(7, 18, 2)$

$d = \sqrt{(x_2 - x_1)^2 + (y_2 - y_1)^2 + (z_2 - z_1)^2}$

$ = \sqrt{(7-3)^2 + (18-9)^2 + (2-14)^2}$

$ = \sqrt{16 + 81 + 144}$

$ = \sqrt{241}$

$ \approx 15.5$

Part B

PRACTICE TESTS

Math Level 1

Test Form A
Mathematics Level 1

Answer Sheet

1 Ⓐ Ⓑ Ⓒ Ⓓ Ⓔ   21 Ⓐ Ⓑ Ⓒ Ⓓ Ⓔ   41 Ⓐ Ⓑ Ⓒ Ⓓ Ⓔ
2 Ⓐ Ⓑ Ⓒ Ⓓ Ⓔ   22 Ⓐ Ⓑ Ⓒ Ⓓ Ⓔ   42 Ⓐ Ⓑ Ⓒ Ⓓ Ⓔ
3 Ⓐ Ⓑ Ⓒ Ⓓ Ⓔ   23 Ⓐ Ⓑ Ⓒ Ⓓ Ⓔ   43 Ⓐ Ⓑ Ⓒ Ⓓ Ⓔ
4 Ⓐ Ⓑ Ⓒ Ⓓ Ⓔ   24 Ⓐ Ⓑ Ⓒ Ⓓ Ⓔ   44 Ⓐ Ⓑ Ⓒ Ⓓ Ⓔ
5 Ⓐ Ⓑ Ⓒ Ⓓ Ⓔ   25 Ⓐ Ⓑ Ⓒ Ⓓ Ⓔ   45 Ⓐ Ⓑ Ⓒ Ⓓ Ⓔ
6 Ⓐ Ⓑ Ⓒ Ⓓ Ⓔ   26 Ⓐ Ⓑ Ⓒ Ⓓ Ⓔ   46 Ⓐ Ⓑ Ⓒ Ⓓ Ⓔ
7 Ⓐ Ⓑ Ⓒ Ⓓ Ⓔ   27 Ⓐ Ⓑ Ⓒ Ⓓ Ⓔ   47 Ⓐ Ⓑ Ⓒ Ⓓ Ⓔ
8 Ⓐ Ⓑ Ⓒ Ⓓ Ⓔ   28 Ⓐ Ⓑ Ⓒ Ⓓ Ⓔ   48 Ⓐ Ⓑ Ⓒ Ⓓ Ⓔ
9 Ⓐ Ⓑ Ⓒ Ⓓ Ⓔ   29 Ⓐ Ⓑ Ⓒ Ⓓ Ⓔ   49 Ⓐ Ⓑ Ⓒ Ⓓ Ⓔ
10 Ⓐ Ⓑ Ⓒ Ⓓ Ⓔ   30 Ⓐ Ⓑ Ⓒ Ⓓ Ⓔ   50 Ⓐ Ⓑ Ⓒ Ⓓ Ⓔ
11 Ⓐ Ⓑ Ⓒ Ⓓ Ⓔ   31 Ⓐ Ⓑ Ⓒ Ⓓ Ⓔ
12 Ⓐ Ⓑ Ⓒ Ⓓ Ⓔ   32 Ⓐ Ⓑ Ⓒ Ⓓ Ⓔ
13 Ⓐ Ⓑ Ⓒ Ⓓ Ⓔ   33 Ⓐ Ⓑ Ⓒ Ⓓ Ⓔ
14 Ⓐ Ⓑ Ⓒ Ⓓ Ⓔ   34 Ⓐ Ⓑ Ⓒ Ⓓ Ⓔ
15 Ⓐ Ⓑ Ⓒ Ⓓ Ⓔ   35 Ⓐ Ⓑ Ⓒ Ⓓ Ⓔ
16 Ⓐ Ⓑ Ⓒ Ⓓ Ⓔ   36 Ⓐ Ⓑ Ⓒ Ⓓ Ⓔ
17 Ⓐ Ⓑ Ⓒ Ⓓ Ⓔ   37 Ⓐ Ⓑ Ⓒ Ⓓ Ⓔ
18 Ⓐ Ⓑ Ⓒ Ⓓ Ⓔ   38 Ⓐ Ⓑ Ⓒ Ⓓ Ⓔ
19 Ⓐ Ⓑ Ⓒ Ⓓ Ⓔ   39 Ⓐ Ⓑ Ⓒ Ⓓ Ⓔ
20 Ⓐ Ⓑ Ⓒ Ⓓ Ⓔ   40 Ⓐ Ⓑ Ⓒ Ⓓ Ⓔ

Reference Information

The following information is for your reference in answering some of the questions on this test.

Volume of a right circular cone with radius r and height h: $V = \dfrac{1}{3}\pi r^2 h$

Lateral area of a right circular cone with base circumference C and slant height ℓ: $S = \dfrac{1}{2}C\ell$

Volume of a sphere with radius r: $V = \dfrac{4}{3}\pi r^3$

Surface area of a sphere with radius r: $S = 4\pi r^2$

Volume of a pyramid with base area B and height h: $V = \dfrac{1}{3}Bh$

Test Form A
SAT Subject Test in Mathematics Level 1

50 Questions   1 hour

For each of the following problems, decide which is the BEST of the choices given. If the exact numerical value is not one of the choices, select the choice that best approximates this value. Then fill in the corresponding circle on the answer sheet.

Notes: (1) A calculator will be necessary for answering some of the questions on this test. For each question you will have to decide whether or not you should use a calculator. Programmable calculators and calculators that can display graphs are permitted.

(2) The only angle measure used on the Math Level 1 Test is degree measure. Make sure your calculator is in the degree mode.

(3) Figures that accompany problems on this test are intended to provide information useful in solving the problems. They are drawn as accurately as possible EXCEPT when it is stated in a specific problem that the figure is not drawn to scale. All figures lie in a plane unless otherwise indicated.

(4) Unless otherwise specified, the domain of any function f is assumed to be the set of all real numbers x for which $f(x)$ is a real number.

(5) Reference information that may be useful in answering the questions on this test can be found on the page preceding Question 1.

1. If $x = \dfrac{1}{2}$, then $(x+1)(1-x) =$

(A) $-\dfrac{3}{2}$ (B) $-\dfrac{1}{2}$ (C) $\dfrac{1}{2}$ (D) $\dfrac{3}{4}$ (E) $\dfrac{3}{2}$

2. In Figure 1, if $AB = 6x - 3$ and $BC = \dfrac{2}{3} AB$, what is the length of AC in terms of x?

(A) $8x - 4$

(B) $9x - 6$

(C) $10x - 5$

(D) $10x - 8$

(E) $12x - 9$

Figure 1

3. If the product of two consecutive odd integers equals 9 times the smaller integer, what is the sum of the two integers?

(A) 12   (B) 13   (C) 14   (D) 15   (E) 16

4. At the office supply store Tommy and Jane each bought binders and storage boxes. Tommy paid $29.75 for three binders and one storage box, while Jane paid $32.50 for two binders and two storage boxes. What is the price of one of the binders?

   (A) $5.95

   (B) $6.75

   (C) $7.95

   (D) $8.25

   (E) $9.50

5. $a^{n-2} \cdot a \cdot a^{1-n} =$

   (A) $-a$ (B) $\dfrac{1}{a}$ (C) 0 (D) a (E) 1

6. What is the value of m if $5x + my = 6$ passes through the point $(3, -3)$?

   (A) -2 (B) 1 (C) 3 (D) 4 (E) 6

7. What is the area of the triangle shown in Figure 2?

   (A) 9

   (B) $4\sqrt{2}$

   (C) 4.5

   (D) $3\sqrt{2}$

   (E) 4

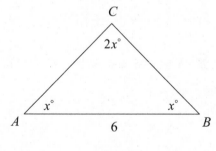

Figure 2

8. Which of the following describes the solution set of $|x - 2| < 4$?

   (A) All the points less than 2 units from 4.

   (B) All the points more than 2 units from 4.

   (C) All the points less than 4 units from 2.

   (D) All the points more than 4 units from 2.

   (E) All the points 4 units from 2.

9. If $\sqrt[3]{12-x} = -2.7$, then $x =$

   (A) −7.683

   (B) 4.71

   (C) 22.184

   (D) 31.683

   (E) 216.125

10. Figure 3 shows the results of a survey about people's reasons for giving flowers. If 480 people gave flowers for romance, how many people gave flowers for congratulation?

   (A) 68

   (B) 84

   (C) 98

   (D) 114

   (E) 128

Giving Flowers

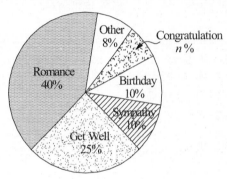

Figure 3

11. What is the area of a triangle whose vertices are $(3,1)$, $(0,\sqrt{15})$, and $(-5,1)$?

   (A) 8.9

   (B) 9.4

   (C) 10.2

   (D) 11.5

   (E) 18.8

12. If the line $y = 2$ and the circle with center $(-4,5)$ and radius 5 intersect on the xy-plane, what are the x-coordinates of the points of intersection?

   (A) −8 and 0

   (B) −4 and 4

   (C) −0.42 and −9.58

   (D) −1.92 and 6.08

   (E) −3.42 and 4.58

13. Which of the following is the reciprocal of $\sqrt{3} - \sqrt{2}$?

(A) $\dfrac{\sqrt{6}}{2}$

(B) $\sqrt{6}$

(C) $\dfrac{\sqrt{3} + \sqrt{2}}{2}$

(D) $\dfrac{\sqrt{3} - \sqrt{2}}{2}$

(E) $\sqrt{3} + \sqrt{2}$

14. Figure 4 shows the five exterior angles of a pentagon. What is the sum of the measures of the five marked angles?

(A) 300°

(B) 360°

(C) 420°

(D) 480°

(E) 540°

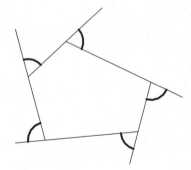

Figure 4

$$\begin{bmatrix} 2x + 3y = 7 \\ -mx = ny - 14 \end{bmatrix}$$

15. If the system of equations shown above has infinitely many solutions, what is the value of $m + n$?

(A) 5   (B) 7   (C) 10   (D) 14   (E) 21

16. For all positive integers a, b, and c, let $\{a, b, c\}$ be defined as

$\{a, b, c\} = \dfrac{a^b}{b^c}$. If $\{6, 2, c\} = 9$, then $c =$

(A) $\dfrac{1}{2}$ (B) 2   (C) 3   (D) 4   (E) 6

17. If $f(x) = x^3 + 8$ and $g(x) = 2x - 3$, then $f(g(\frac{1}{2})) =$

    (A) 0   (B) 2   (C) 4   (D) 6   (E) 8

18. In Figure 5, if $\triangle ABC$ is reflected across the line $x = 3$ (not shown), what will be the coordinates of the reflection of point A?

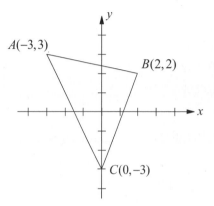

Figure 5

    (A) $(3,3)$

    (B) $(6,3)$

    (C) $(8,3)$

    (D) $(9,3)$

    (E) $(11,3)$

19. If $f(x) = 1 - \sqrt{x+2}$, which of the following values is *not* included in the range of f?

    (A) −3   (B) −1   (C) 0   (D) 1   (E) 2

20. If $4(n-4)^{-1} = (n+4)$ and $n > 0$, then $n =$

    (A) 0   (B) 3.2   (C) $2\sqrt{5}$ (D) 6.5   (E) 8

21. Which of the following equations has the same solution(s) as $|-x+1| = 2$?

    (A) $x+1 = 0$

    (B) $-x+3 = 0$

    (C) $(x-3)^2 = 4$

    (D) $x^2 - 2x - 3 = 0$

    (E) $x^2 + 2x - 3 = 0$

22. In Figure 6, points A, B, and C lie on a circle with center O. Which of the following must be true?

    I. $m\angle 1 + m\angle 4 = 90$

    II. $m\angle 3 < m\angle 1 < m\angle 2$

    III. $m\angle 1 = \dfrac{1}{2} m\angle AOC$

    (A) I only

    (B) II only

    (C) III only

    (D) I and III only

    (E) I, II, and III

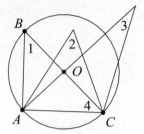

Figure 6

23. For $ab \neq 0$, $\dfrac{a^3 b}{-ab^{-1}} \cdot \dfrac{2}{a} =$

    (A) $-\dfrac{2a}{b^2}$

    (B) $\dfrac{2a}{b^2}$

    (C) $-2ab^2$

    (D) $2ab^2$

    (E) $-2a$

24. Which of the following could be the equation of the parabola shown in Figure 7?

    (A) $x^2 = y - 2$

    (B) $x^2 = y + 2$

    (C) $y^2 = x - 2$

    (D) $y^2 = x + 2$

    (E) $y^2 = -x - 2$

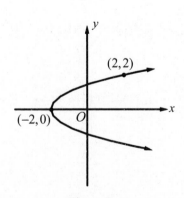

Figure 7

25. What is the length of the line segment on the line $y = 2x + 5$ whose endpoints have x-coordinates -2 and 3?

    (A) 5

    (B) $5\sqrt{2}$

    (C) $5\sqrt{5}$

    (D) 12

    (E) 15

26. In Figure 8, if $\overline{PR} \parallel \overline{ST}$, what is the perimeter of the shaded region?

    (A) 28

    (B) 32.5

    (C) 36

    (D) 38.5

    (E) 42

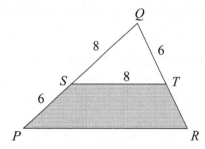

Note: Figure not drawn to scale.

Figure 8

27. Which of the following quadratic equations has two roots whose sum is 3 and product is $\dfrac{7}{4}$?

    (A) $3x^2 - 9x + 21 = 0$

    (B) $4x^2 - 12x + 7 = 0$

    (C) $2x^2 - 6x + 7 = 0$

    (D) $2x^2 - 3x + 7 = 0$

    (E) $x^2 - 6x + 14 = 0$

28. The function f is defined as $f(x) = x - [x]$, where $[x]$ is the greatest integer less than or equal to x. What is the value of $\dfrac{f(-1.2)}{f(2.4)}$?

    (A) 2   (B) $\dfrac{1}{2}$ (C) 0   (D) $-\dfrac{1}{2}$ (E) -2

29. Given: 1) If A is a circle, then B is an ellipse.

       2) B is not an ellipse.

Which of the following must be true?

(A) A is a circle.

(B) B is not a circle.

(C) A is not a circle.

(D) B is a circle.

(E) A is an ellipse.

30. Figure 9 shows the graph of $y = g(x)$. If $g(-1) = k$, what is the value of $g(k)$?

(A) −1   (B) 1   (C) 2   (D) 4   (E) 5

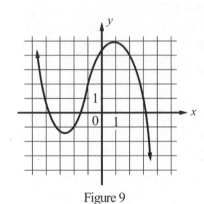

Figure 9

31. In a biology class 20 students took a test and their average (arithmetic mean) score was 82. If the average score for 12 of the students was 78, what was the average score for the remaining 8 students?

(A) 84   (B) 85   (C) 86   (D) 88   (E) 90

32. Figure 10 shows a rectangular prism whose total surface area is 220. What is the volume of the rectangular prism?

(A) 200

(B) 240

(C) 280

(D) 320

(E) 360

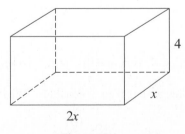

Figure 10

33. If $7^x = 14$, what does 2^x equal?

(A) 0.86 (B) 1.41 (C) 1.92 (D) 2.24 (E) 2.56

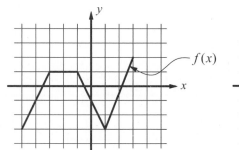 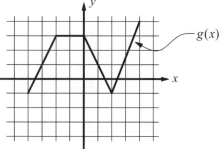

Figure 11

34. In Figure 11, the graphs of f and g are shown. If the function g is defined as $g(x) = f(x-a) + c$, what is the value of ac?

(A) −3   (B) −2   (C) −1   (D) 1   (E) 2

35. If $x^3 - 3x^2 + 5x - 6 = (x-2)p(x)$, where $p(x)$ is a polynomial, then $p(x) =$

(A) $x^2 + 3x - 4$

(B) $x^2 - x + 3$

(C) $x^2 + 4x - 3$

(D) $x^2 - 3x + 6$

(E) $x^2 + 4x + 3$

36. If $0° < \theta < 90°$ and $\cos\theta = \dfrac{2}{3}$, then $\tan\theta =$

(A) $\dfrac{1}{3}$ (B) $\dfrac{1}{2}$ (C) $\dfrac{\sqrt{5}}{2}$ (D) $\sqrt{5}$ (E) 5

37. Which of the following shaded regions could be the

graph of $\begin{cases} -x+y \geq 2 \\ x+2y \leq 2 \end{cases}$?

(A)
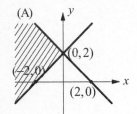

(B)
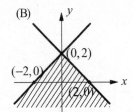

(C)
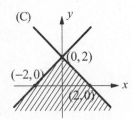

(D)
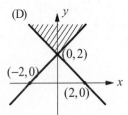

(E)
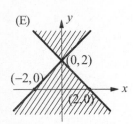

38. Figure 12 shows a rectangular prism with edges of lengths
6, 8, and 10. If points B and D are midpoints of two of the
edges, which of the following is true?

(A) $m\angle ADF < m\angle ABF < m\angle ACF$

(B) $m\angle ADF < m\angle ACF < m\angle ABF$

(C) $m\angle ACF < m\angle ABF < m\angle ADF$

(D) $m\angle ACF < m\angle ADF < m\angle ABF$

(E) $m\angle ABF < m\angle ACF < m\angle ADF$

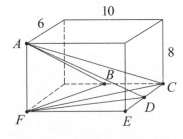

Figure 12

39. If the first three terms of an arithmetic sequence are $x+1$, $2x-1$, and $x+7$, then what is the value of the fourth term?

    (A) 13   (B) 15   (C) 18   (D) 23   (E) 28

40. $2 - \sin^2(3x) - \cos^2(3x) =$

    (A) –2   (B) –1   (C) 0   (D) 1   (E) 3

41. Figure 13 shows a regular octagon with sides of length 2. What is the area of the shaded region?

    (A) $4(\sqrt{2}+1)$

    (B) $4(\sqrt{3}+1)$

    (C) $6(\sqrt{3}+1)$

    (D) $8(\sqrt{2}-1)$

    (E) $8(\sqrt{2}+1)$

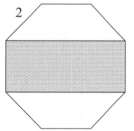

2

Figure 13

42. Two walls are separated by a hallway which is 8 feet wide. An electrician places the foot of a ladder against the base of a wall and the top of the ladder against the other wall.

    If the angle between the floor and the ladder is $63°$, how far up the opposite wall will the top of the ladder reach?

    (A) 11.6

    (B) 13.9

    (C) 15.7

    (D) 17.6

    (E) 21.5

43. If $\log_b 7 = 3$, then $b =$

    (A) 1.29   (B) 1.44   (C) 1.91   (D) 2.16   (E) 2.38

44. If $i^2 = -1$, which of the following equations is equivalent

to $2a + bi = \dfrac{16}{2a - bi}$, for all real numbers a and b?

(A) $\dfrac{a^2}{4} - \dfrac{b^2}{16} = 1$

(B) $\dfrac{a^2}{4} + \dfrac{b^2}{16} = 1$

(C) $\dfrac{a^2}{16} - \dfrac{b^2}{4} = 1$

(D) $\dfrac{a^2}{16} + \dfrac{b^2}{4} = 1$

(E) $4a^2 + b^2 = 0$

45. In Figure 14, circles O and P, with radii 25 and 9, are
tangent to each other. If $\overline{PQ}$ is a common external
tangent, what is the perimeter of the shaded region?

(A) 84

(B) 98

(C) 102

(D) 114

(E) 135

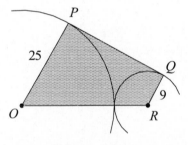

Note: Figure not drawn to scale.

Figure 14

46. If $f(x) = \dfrac{|3x|}{x}$, for $x \neq 0$, which of the following must be true?

I. $f(1) = f(3)$

II. $f(-1) = f(-3)$

III. $f(-1) = f(1)$

(A) None

(B) I only

(C) II only

(D) I and II only

(E) I, II, and III

47. A triangular region is formed by the lines $y = \dfrac{2}{3}x$, $x = 6$,

and the x-axis. If the triangular region is rotated around the x-axis, what is the volume of the space figure generated?

(A) 18π

(B) 21π

(C) 24π

(D) 27π

(E) 32π

48. Figure 15 is the graph of $y = f(x)$. Which of the following is the graph of $y = |f(x)|$?

Figure 15

(A)

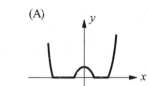

(B)

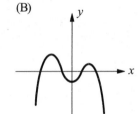

(C)

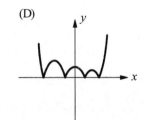

(D)

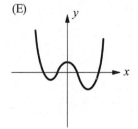

(E)

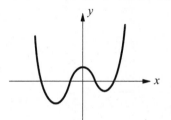

49. If two dice are rolled, what is the probability that the dice show the same number?

(A) $\dfrac{1}{6}$ (B) $\dfrac{3}{12}$ (C) $\dfrac{1}{3}$ (D) $\dfrac{5}{12}$ (E) $\dfrac{1}{2}$

50. In Figure 16, a regular pentagon *PQRST* and an equilateral triangle *PUV* are inscribed in a circle with radius 6. What is the length of the arc *QU*?

(A) 1.4π

(B) 1.6π

(C) 1.8π

(D) 2.0π

(E) 2.4π

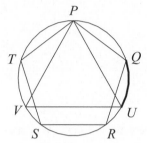

Figure 16

STOP

IF YOU FINISH BEFORE TIME IS CALLED, YOU MAY CHECK YOUR WORK ON THIS TEST ONLY.
DO NOT TURN TO ANY OTHER TEST IN THIS BOOK.

Answer Key

1. D	2. C	3. E	4. B	5. E
6. C	7. A	8. C	9. D	10. B
11. D	12. A	13. E	14. B	15. C
16. B	17. A	18. D	19. E	20. C
21. D	22. E	23. C	24. D	25. C
26. B	27. B	28. A	29. C	30. D
31. D	32. A	33. E	34. E	35. B
36. C	37. A	38. D	39. B	40. D
41. A	42. C	43. C	44. B	45. B
46. D	47. E	48. D	49. A	50. B

Answers and Explanations

1. D

$$x = \frac{1}{2}$$

$$(\frac{1}{2}+1)(1-\frac{1}{2}) = (\frac{3}{2})(\frac{1}{2}) = \frac{3}{4}$$

2. C

A   B   C

$AB = 6x - 3$ and $BC = \frac{2}{3}AB$

$AC = AB + BC$

$\quad = AB + \frac{2}{3}AB = \frac{5}{3}AB$

$\quad = \frac{5}{3}(6x - 3)$

$\quad = 10x - 5$

3. E

Let x be an odd integer, then $x + 2$ is the larger of the two consecutive odd integers.

The product of two consecutive odd integers   Nine times the smaller integer

$$\overbrace{x(x+2)} \;=\; \overbrace{9x}$$

$x^2 + 2x = 9x \;\Rightarrow\; x^2 - 7x = 0 \;\Rightarrow\; x(x-7) = 0$
$\Rightarrow\; x = 0$ or $x = 7$

Since x is an odd integer, $x = 7$. The larger integer is 9.

The sum of the two integers is $7 + 9$, or 16.

4. B

Let $x =$ the cost of one binder
and $y =$ the cost of one storage box.

$3x + y = 29.75$ Tommy paid $29.75 for three binders and one storage box.

$2x + 2y = 32.50$ Jane paid $32.50 for two binders and two storage boxes.

Multiply both sides of the first equation by -2.

$\quad -2(3x + y) = -2(29.75)$
$\Rightarrow\; -6x - 2y = -59.50$
$\underline{+\; |2x + 2y = 32.50} \quad$ Add the second equation.
$\quad -4x \qquad = -27$

$\qquad x = 6.75$

5. E

$$a^{n-2} \cdot a \cdot a^{1-n} = a^{(n-2)+1+(1-n)} = a^0 = 1$$

6. C

$5x + my = 6$

The line passes through the point $(3, -3)$.
Substitute $x = 3$ and $y = -3$ into the equation.

$5(3) + m(-3) = 6$
$\Rightarrow\; 15 - 3m = 6$
$\Rightarrow\; m = 3$

7. A

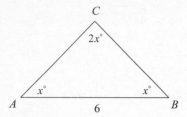

Since the angle sum in a triangle is 180,
$x + x + 2x = 180 \Rightarrow 4x = 180 \Rightarrow x = 45$.

Therefore $\triangle ABC$ is a $45°$-$45°$-$90°$ triangle. In a $45°$-$45°$-$90°$ triangle the hypotenuse is $\sqrt{2}$ times as long as a leg.

$$AC \cdot \sqrt{2} = AB \Rightarrow AC \cdot \sqrt{2} = 6 \Rightarrow AC = \frac{6}{\sqrt{2}}$$

Area of $\triangle ABC$

$= \frac{1}{2}(AC)(BC)$

$= \frac{1}{2}(\frac{6}{\sqrt{2}})(\frac{6}{\sqrt{2}})$ $AC = BC = \frac{6}{\sqrt{2}}$

$= 9$

8. C

$|x - 2| < 4$
$\Rightarrow -4 < x - 2 < 4$
$\Rightarrow -2 < x < 6$

2 is the midpoint of -2 and 6. The line graph shows that the solutions are all the points less than 4 units from 2.

9. D

$\sqrt[3]{12 - x} = -2.7$
$(\sqrt[3]{12 - x})^3 = (-2.7)^3$
$12 - x = -19.683$
$x = 31.683$

10. B

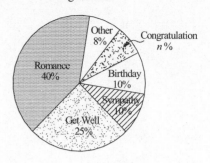

$n\% + 8\% + 40\% + 25\% + 10\% + 10\% = 100\%$
$\Rightarrow n = 7$

Let $x = $ the total number of people.

$0.4x = 480$ 480 people gave flowers for romantic reasons.

$x = 1,200$

The number of people who gave flowers for congratulation $= 1,200 \times 0.07 = 84$.

11. D

Draw a triangle whose vertices are $(3,1)$, $(0, \sqrt{15})$, and $(-5,1)$ on the xy-plane.

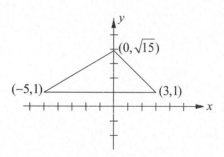

Area of the triangle
$= \frac{1}{2}(8)(\sqrt{15} - 1) \approx 11.5$

12. A

The equation of the circle with center $(-4, 5)$ and radius 5 is $(x+4)^2 + (y-5)^2 = 5^2$. Since the circle intersects the line $y = 2$, substitute $y = 2$ into the equation of the circle.

$(x+4)^2 + (2-5)^2 = 5^2$

$$(x+4)^2 = 16$$
$$\Rightarrow x+4 = \pm\sqrt{16}$$
$$\Rightarrow x = 0 \text{ or } x = -8$$

13. E

The reciprocal of $\sqrt{3}-\sqrt{2}$ is $\dfrac{1}{\sqrt{3}-\sqrt{2}}$.

$$\dfrac{1}{\sqrt{3}-\sqrt{2}}$$
$$= \dfrac{(\sqrt{3}+\sqrt{2})}{(\sqrt{3}-\sqrt{2})(\sqrt{3}+\sqrt{2})}$$
$$= \dfrac{(\sqrt{3}+\sqrt{2})}{3+\sqrt{6}-\sqrt{6}-2}$$
$$= \sqrt{3}+\sqrt{2}$$

14. B

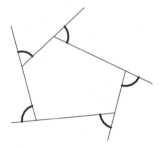

The sum of the measures of the exterior angles of any convex polygon is $360°$.

15. C

$$\begin{bmatrix} 2x+3y = 7 \\ -mx = ny-14 \end{bmatrix}$$

A system of two equations has infinitely many solutions if the two graphs are the same line, i.e. the two lines have the same slope and the same y-intercept.

Subtract ny from both sides of the second equation.

$$-mx - ny = -14$$

Multiply the first equation by -2 to make the constant the same for both equations.

$$-4x - 6y = -14$$

From the two equations we can conclude that $m = 4$ and $n = 6$.

$$m + n = 4 + 6 = 10$$

16. B

$$\{a,b,c\} = \dfrac{a^b}{b^c}$$

$$\{6,2,c\} = \dfrac{6^2}{2^c} \qquad a = 6 \text{ and } b = 2$$

$$\{6,2,c\} = 9 \qquad \text{Given}$$

$$\dfrac{6^2}{2^c} = 9 \qquad \text{Substitution}$$

$$36 = 9 \cdot 2^c \qquad \text{Multiply by } 2^c \text{ on both sides.}$$

$$2^c = 4 \qquad \text{Divide by 9 on both sides.}$$

$$c = 2 \qquad \text{Answer}$$

17. A

$$f(x) = x^3 + 8 \text{ and } g(x) = 2x - 3$$

$$g(\tfrac{1}{2}) = 2(\tfrac{1}{2}) - 3 = -2$$

$$f(g(\tfrac{1}{2})) = f(-2) = (-2)^3 + 8 = 0$$

18. D

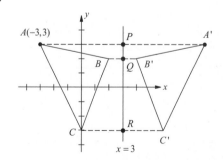

In the figure above, point A is reflected across the line $x = 3$ to create an image of A' .

$AP = 6$ and $AP = A'P$.

Therefore $A'P = 6$ and the coordinates of the reflection of point A are $(9,3)$.

19. E

The range of f is the set of all possible y-values as x varies throughout the domain.

Use a graphing calculator to find a graph of the function $f(x) = 1 - \sqrt{x+2}$.

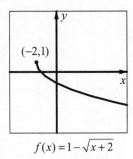

$$f(x) = 1 - \sqrt{x+2}$$

From the graph we read that the range of f is the set of all y-values such that $y \le 1$. In other words, the range of f is the interval $(-\infty, 1]$.

20. C

$$4(n-4)^{-1} = (n+4)$$
$$\Rightarrow \ 4 \cdot \frac{1}{(n-4)} = (n+4)$$
$$\Rightarrow \ 4 = (n+4)(n-4) \ \Rightarrow \ 4 = n^2 - 16$$
$$\Rightarrow \ n^2 = 20$$
$$\Rightarrow \ n = \pm\sqrt{20} = \pm 2\sqrt{5}$$
Since $n > 0$, $n = 2\sqrt{5}$.

21. D

$$|-x+1| = 2$$
$$\Rightarrow \ -x+1 = 2 \ \text{or} \ -x+1 = -2$$
$$\Rightarrow \ x = -1 \ \text{or} \ x = 3$$
Since the equation has two solutions, discard answer choices (A) and (B).

(C) $(x-3)^2 = 4 \ \Rightarrow \ x-3 = \pm\sqrt{4} = \pm 2$
  $x = 5 \ \text{or} \ x = 1$
(D) $x^2 - 2x - 3 = 0 \ \Rightarrow \ (x+1)(x-3) = 0$
  $x = -1 \ \text{or} \ x = 3$

Choice (D) is correct.

22. E

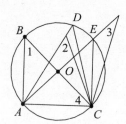

$m\angle BAC = 90$ — An angle inscribed in a semicircle is a right angle

$m\angle 1 + m\angle 4 = 90$ — The acute angles of a right $\triangle$ are complementary.

Roman numeral I is true.

Since the measure of an inscribed angle equals one-half the measure of its intercepted arc, inscribed angles intercepting the same arc must be congruent.

$m\angle 1 = m\angle ADC = m\angle AEC$
$m\angle 2 > m\angle ADC$ — Exterior angle theorem
$m\angle 3 < m\angle AEC$ — Exterior angle theorem
$m\angle 3 < m\angle 1 < m\angle 2$

Roman numeral II is true.

$m\angle 1 = \dfrac{1}{2} m\angle AOC$ — The measure of an inscribed angle is one-half the measure of its intercepted arc.

Roman numeral III is true.

23. C

$$\frac{a^3 b}{-ab^{-1}} \cdot \frac{2}{a} = \frac{a^3 b}{-a \cdot \dfrac{1}{b}} \cdot \frac{2}{a} = \frac{a^3 b}{\dfrac{-a}{b}} \cdot \frac{2}{a}$$

$$= a^3 b \cdot \frac{b}{-a} \cdot \frac{2}{a} = \frac{2a^3 b^2}{-a^2} = -2ab^2$$

24. D

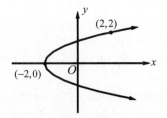

The vertex of the parabola is $(-2, 0)$ and the graph opens to the right.

Therefore the standard equation of the parabola is $x = a(y-0)^2 - 2$ or $x + 2 = ay^2$.

Since the graph passes through a point $(2,2)$, we can substitute $x = 2$ and $y = 2$ into the equation of the parabola.

$(2) + 2 = a(2)^2 \Rightarrow a = 1$

The standard equation of the parabola is

$x + 2 = y^2$.

Choice (D) is correct.

25. C

$y = 2x + 5$
If $x = -2$, $y = 2(-2) + 5 = 1$
If $x = 3$, $y = 2(3) + 5 = 11$

The length of the line segment with endpoints $(-2,1)$ and $(3,11)$ is

$d = \sqrt{(3+2)^2 + (11-1)^2}$

$= \sqrt{25 + 100}$

$= \sqrt{125}$

$= 5\sqrt{5}$

26. B

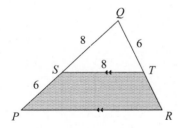

$\dfrac{QS}{ST} = \dfrac{QP}{PR} \Rightarrow \dfrac{8}{8} = \dfrac{14}{PR} \Rightarrow PR = 14$

$\dfrac{QS}{SP} = \dfrac{QT}{TR} \Rightarrow \dfrac{8}{6} = \dfrac{6}{TR} \Rightarrow TR = 4.5$

Perimeter of the shaded region
$= ST + TR + PR + SP$

$= 8 + 4.5 + 14 + 6$

$= 32.5$

27. B

If $ax^2 + bx + c = 0$, the sum of the roots $= -\dfrac{b}{a}$

and the product of the roots $= \dfrac{c}{a}$.

Test each answer choice.

(A) $3x^2 - 9x + 21 = 0$

Sum of the roots $= -\dfrac{b}{a} = -\dfrac{-9}{3} = 3$

Product of the roots $= \dfrac{c}{a} = \dfrac{21}{3} = 7$

(B) $4x^2 - 12x + 7 = 0$

Sum of the roots $= -\dfrac{b}{a} = -\dfrac{-12}{4} = 3$

Product of the roots $= \dfrac{c}{a} = \dfrac{7}{4}$

Choice (B) is correct.

28. A

$[x]$ is the greatest integer less than or equal to x.
$[-1.2] = -2$, since the greatest integer less than or equal to -1.2 is -2.
$[2.4] = 2$, since the greatest integer less than or equal to 2.4 is 2.

f is defined as $f(x) = x - [x]$

$\dfrac{f(-1.2)}{f(2.4)} = \dfrac{-1.2 - [-1.2]}{2.4 - [2.4]} = \dfrac{-1.2 - (-2)}{2.4 - (2)}$

$= \dfrac{0.8}{0.4} = 2$

29. C

Statement: If p, then q.
Contrapositive: If not q, then not p.

A statement and its contrapositive are logically equivalent.

Given: 1) If A is a circle, then B is an ellipse.
　　　　2) B is not an ellipse.

We can conclude that A is not a circle.

30. D

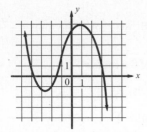

$g(-1) = k$

The graph of $y = g(x)$ shows $g(-1) = 2$.

So $k = 2$, and $g(k) = g(2) = 4$.

31. D

If the average score of 20 students in a biology class is 82, then the sum of scores is $20 \cdot 82$, or 1640. If the average score for 12 students is 78, then the sum of those scores is $12 \cdot 78$, or 936. The sum of the scores for the remaining 8 students is $1640 - 936$, or 704.

The average score of the remaining 8 students

$= \dfrac{704}{8} = 88$.

32. A

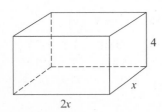

Total surface area of the rectangular prism
$= 2(\ell \cdot w + w \cdot h + l \cdot h)$

$= 2(2x \cdot x + x \cdot 4 + 2x \cdot 4)$

$= 2(2x^2 + 12x) = 4x^2 + 24x$

Total surface of the rectangular prism is 220.
$4x^2 + 24x = 220 \ \Rightarrow \ 4x^2 + 24x - 220 = 0$
$\Rightarrow \ 4(x^2 + 6x - 55) = 0 \ \Rightarrow \ 4(x-5)(x+11) = 0$
$\Rightarrow \ x = 5 \ \text{or} \ x = -11$

Since the length cannot be negative, $x = 5$.
Volume $= 2x \cdot x \cdot 4 = 2(5) \cdot (5) \cdot 4 = 200$

33. E

$7^x = 14$

$\log 7^x = \log 14$ Take log on both sides.

$x \cdot \log 7 = \log 14$ $\log_b M^p = p \cdot \log_b M$

$x = \dfrac{\log 14}{\log 7} \approx 1.356$

$2^x = 2^{1.356} \approx 2.56$

34. E

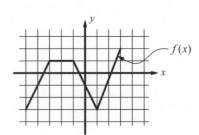

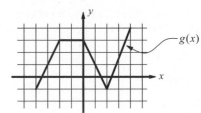

The graph of g is the graph of f moved 1 unit to the right and 2 units up.

Therefore $g(x) = f(x-1) + 2$.

$g(x) = f(x-a) + c \ \Rightarrow \ a = 1 \ \text{and} \ c = 2$
$ac = 2$

35. B

$x^3 - 3x^2 + 5x - 6 = (x-2)p(x)$

Divide.

$$
\begin{array}{r}
x^2 - x + 3 \\
x-2 \overline{\smash{\big)}\ x^3 - 3x^2 + 5x - 6} \\
\underline{x^3 - 2x^2} \\
-x^2 + 5x \\
\underline{-x^2 + 2x} \\
3x - 6 \\
\underline{3x - 6} \\
0
\end{array}
$$

36. C

$\cos \theta = \dfrac{2}{3}$. Draw a right triangle whose acute

angle is θ, length of the hypotenuse is 3, and
length of the side adjacent to θ is 2.

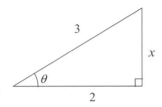

Use the Pythagorean theorem to find the length
of the opposite side.

$2^2 + x^2 = 3^2 \ \Rightarrow \ x = \sqrt{3^2 - 2^2} = \sqrt{5}$

$\tan \theta = \dfrac{\text{opposite side}}{\text{adjacent side}} = \dfrac{\sqrt{5}}{2}$

37. A

$\begin{cases} -x + y \ge 2 \\ x + 2y \le 2 \end{cases}$

Change the equations into slope-intercept form

and graph the lines $y = x + 2$ and $y = -\dfrac{1}{2}x + 1$.

Test an ordered pair that is not on the boundary
and see if it satisfies the given inequality.

The origin is a convenient point to use.

$\begin{cases} -0 + 0 \ge 2 & \text{Not true} \\ 0 + 2(0) \le 2 & \text{True} \end{cases}$

If $(0,0)$ does not satisfy both inequalities, the
point $(0,0)$ should not be in the shaded region.
Discard answer choices (B), (C), and (E).

Test another ordered pair that is not on the
boundary, such as $(-3,0)$.

$\begin{cases} -(-3) + 0 \ge 2 & \text{True} \\ (-3) + 2(0) \le 2 & \text{True} \end{cases}$

$(-3,0)$ satisfies both pairs of inequalities, so the
point $(-3,0)$ should be in the shaded region.

Choice (A) is correct.

38. D

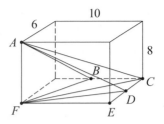

Use the tangent ratio to compare the measures
of the angles.

$\tan \angle ABF = \dfrac{AF}{BF}$

$\tan \angle ACF = \dfrac{AF}{CF}$

$\tan \angle ADF = \dfrac{AF}{DF}$

In the rectangular prism,

$BF < DF < CF \ \Rightarrow \ \dfrac{AF}{CF} < \dfrac{AF}{DF} < \dfrac{AF}{BF}$

$\Rightarrow \ \tan \angle ACF < \tan \angle ADF < \tan \angle ABF$

If $0° \le \theta < 90°$, the tangent ratio increases as
the measure of the angle increases. Therefore,
$m\angle ACF < m\angle ADF < m\angle ABF$.

39. B

In an arithmetic sequence, the difference
between successive terms is always the same.

The difference between the 2nd and 1st term   The difference between the 3rd and 2nd term

So, $\overbrace{(2x-1) - (x+1)} = \overbrace{(x+7) - (2x-1)}$

$\Rightarrow \ x - 2 = -x + 8 \ \Rightarrow \ 2x = 10 \ \Rightarrow \ x = 5$

Substitute $x = 5$ into the first three terms of the
sequence. The sequence is
$5+1$, $2(5)-1$, $5+7 \ldots$, or 6, 9, 12, . . .

The difference between successive terms is 3,
and therefore the value of the fourth term is 15.

40. D

$2 - \sin^2(3x) - \cos^2(3x)$

$= 2 - [\sin^2(3x) + \cos^2(3x)] \qquad \text{Factor.}$

$= 2 - 1 \qquad\qquad\qquad\qquad \sin^2 \theta + \cos^2 \theta = 1$

$= 1$

41. A

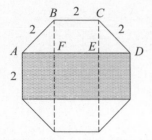

Each interior angle of a regular octagon

$$= \frac{(n-2)180^\circ}{n} = \frac{(8-2)180^\circ}{8} = 135^\circ$$

$$m\angle ABF = m\angle ABC - m\angle CBF$$

$$= 135^\circ - 90^\circ$$

$$= 45^\circ$$

$\triangle ABF$ and $\triangle DCE$ are $45^\circ\text{-}45^\circ\text{-}90^\circ$ triangles, and the ratio of the hypotenuse to a leg is $\sqrt{2}:1$. Therefore $AF = DE = \sqrt{2}$.

$$AD = AF + FE + ED$$

$$= \sqrt{2} + 2 + \sqrt{2}$$

$$= 2\sqrt{2} + 2$$

Area of the shaded region

$$= 2(2\sqrt{2} + 2)$$

$$= 4(\sqrt{2} + 1)$$

42. C

Draw a diagram.

In the figure above, h is the height from the floor to the top of the ladder.

Use the tangent ratio.

$$\tan 63^\circ = \frac{h}{8}$$

$$\Rightarrow h = 8 \cdot \tan 63^\circ \approx 15.7$$

43. C

$$\log_b 7 = 3$$

$$b^3 = 7 \qquad \text{Definition of log}$$

$$(b^3)^{\frac{1}{3}} = (7)^{\frac{1}{3}} \qquad \text{Take the cube root on both sides.}$$

$$b = (7)^{\frac{1}{3}} \approx 1.91$$

44. B

$$2a + bi = \frac{16}{2a - bi}$$

$$\Rightarrow (2a + bi)(2a - bi) = 16$$

$$\Rightarrow 4a^2 - 2abi + 2abi - b^2 i^2 = 16$$

$$\Rightarrow 4a^2 - 2abi + 2abi - b^2(-1) = 16$$

$$\Rightarrow 4a^2 + b^2 = 16$$

$$\Rightarrow \frac{a^2}{4} + \frac{b^2}{16} = 1$$

45. B

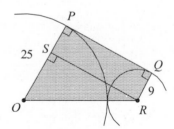

Since $\overline{PQ}$ is tangent to the circles O and R, $\overline{OP} \perp \overline{PQ}$ and $\overline{RQ} \perp \overline{PQ}$.

OP = radius of circle O = 25

QR = radius of circle R = 9

OR = radius of circle O + radius of circle R
= 25 + 9 = 34

Now to find the length of $\overline{PQ}$, from R draw a perpendicular line to $\overline{OP}$ and let S be the point of intersection. In rectangle $PQRS$, $PQ = SR$ and $SP = RQ$.

$OS = OP - SP = 25 - 9 = 16$

In $\triangle ORS$, $OR^2 = OS^2 + SR^2$.

$$34^2 = 16^2 + SR^2 \Rightarrow SR^2 = 900$$

$$\Rightarrow SR = 30 \Rightarrow PQ = 30$$

Perimeter of the shaded region
$$= OP + PQ + QR + OR$$
$$= 25 + 30 + 9 + 34 = 98$$

46. D

$f(x) = \dfrac{|3x|}{x}$, for $x \neq 0$

1) If $x > 0$, then $3x$ is positive so $|3x| = 3x$ and

$f(x) = \dfrac{|3x|}{x} = \dfrac{3x}{x} = 3$.

2) If $x < 0$, then $3x$ is negative so $|3x| = -3x$ and

$f(x) = \dfrac{|3x|}{x} = \dfrac{-3x}{x} = -3$.

   I. $f(1) = 3$ and $f(3) = 3$
      Therefore $f(1) = f(3)$

   II. $f(-1) = -3$ and $f(-3) = -3$
      Therefore $f(-1) = f(-3)$

   III. $f(-1) = -3$ and $f(1) = 3$
      Therefore $f(-1) \neq f(1)$

Roman numerals I and II are true.

47. E

Draw the graphs of $y = \dfrac{2}{3}x$ and $x = 6$ on the

xy-plane.

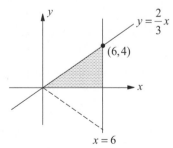

To find the point of intersection, substitute $x = 6$

into the equation $y = \dfrac{2}{3}x \Rightarrow y = \dfrac{2}{3}(6) = 4$.

So $(6,4)$ is the point of intersection.
The space figure generated by rotating the triangular region around the x-axis is a cone whose radius is 4 and height is 6.

Volume of the cone $= \dfrac{1}{3}\pi(4)^2(6) = 32\pi$

48. D

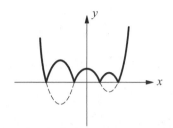

Reflect the portion of the graph of $y = f(x)$ lying below the x-axis over the x-axis.
That is the graph of $y = |f(x)|$.
Choice (D) is correct.

49. A

If two dice are rolled there are $6 \cdot 6$, or 36, possible outcomes. Of these there are 6 possible outcomes in which the dice show the same number:
$(1,1)$, $(2,2)$, $(3,3)$, $(4,4)$, $(5,5)$, and $(6,6)$.

$P(\text{showing the same number}) = \dfrac{6}{36} = \dfrac{1}{6}$

50. B

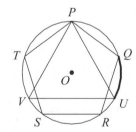

In the figure above, $m\overset{\frown}{PQU} = \dfrac{360}{3} = 120$ and

$m\overset{\frown}{PQ} = \dfrac{360}{5} = 72$.

$m\overset{\frown}{QU} = m\overset{\frown}{PQU} - m\overset{\frown}{PQ} = 120 - 72 = 48$

Length of $\overset{\frown}{QU} = 2\pi r \cdot \dfrac{m\overset{\frown}{QU}}{360} = 2\pi(6) \cdot \dfrac{48}{360}$

$\qquad\qquad = 1.6\pi$

Test Form B
Mathematics Level 1

Answer Sheet

1 Ⓐ Ⓑ Ⓒ Ⓓ Ⓔ	21 Ⓐ Ⓑ Ⓒ Ⓓ Ⓔ	41 Ⓐ Ⓑ Ⓒ Ⓓ Ⓔ
2 Ⓐ Ⓑ Ⓒ Ⓓ Ⓔ	22 Ⓐ Ⓑ Ⓒ Ⓓ Ⓔ	42 Ⓐ Ⓑ Ⓒ Ⓓ Ⓔ
3 Ⓐ Ⓑ Ⓒ Ⓓ Ⓔ	23 Ⓐ Ⓑ Ⓒ Ⓓ Ⓔ	43 Ⓐ Ⓑ Ⓒ Ⓓ Ⓔ
4 Ⓐ Ⓑ Ⓒ Ⓓ Ⓔ	24 Ⓐ Ⓑ Ⓒ Ⓓ Ⓔ	44 Ⓐ Ⓑ Ⓒ Ⓓ Ⓔ
5 Ⓐ Ⓑ Ⓒ Ⓓ Ⓔ	25 Ⓐ Ⓑ Ⓒ Ⓓ Ⓔ	45 Ⓐ Ⓑ Ⓒ Ⓓ Ⓔ
6 Ⓐ Ⓑ Ⓒ Ⓓ Ⓔ	26 Ⓐ Ⓑ Ⓒ Ⓓ Ⓔ	46 Ⓐ Ⓑ Ⓒ Ⓓ Ⓔ
7 Ⓐ Ⓑ Ⓒ Ⓓ Ⓔ	27 Ⓐ Ⓑ Ⓒ Ⓓ Ⓔ	47 Ⓐ Ⓑ Ⓒ Ⓓ Ⓔ
8 Ⓐ Ⓑ Ⓒ Ⓓ Ⓔ	28 Ⓐ Ⓑ Ⓒ Ⓓ Ⓔ	48 Ⓐ Ⓑ Ⓒ Ⓓ Ⓔ
9 Ⓐ Ⓑ Ⓒ Ⓓ Ⓔ	29 Ⓐ Ⓑ Ⓒ Ⓓ Ⓔ	49 Ⓐ Ⓑ Ⓒ Ⓓ Ⓔ
10 Ⓐ Ⓑ Ⓒ Ⓓ Ⓔ	30 Ⓐ Ⓑ Ⓒ Ⓓ Ⓔ	50 Ⓐ Ⓑ Ⓒ Ⓓ Ⓔ
11 Ⓐ Ⓑ Ⓒ Ⓓ Ⓔ	31 Ⓐ Ⓑ Ⓒ Ⓓ Ⓔ	
12 Ⓐ Ⓑ Ⓒ Ⓓ Ⓔ	32 Ⓐ Ⓑ Ⓒ Ⓓ Ⓔ	
13 Ⓐ Ⓑ Ⓒ Ⓓ Ⓔ	33 Ⓐ Ⓑ Ⓒ Ⓓ Ⓔ	
14 Ⓐ Ⓑ Ⓒ Ⓓ Ⓔ	34 Ⓐ Ⓑ Ⓒ Ⓓ Ⓔ	
15 Ⓐ Ⓑ Ⓒ Ⓓ Ⓔ	35 Ⓐ Ⓑ Ⓒ Ⓓ Ⓔ	
16 Ⓐ Ⓑ Ⓒ Ⓓ Ⓔ	36 Ⓐ Ⓑ Ⓒ Ⓓ Ⓔ	
17 Ⓐ Ⓑ Ⓒ Ⓓ Ⓔ	37 Ⓐ Ⓑ Ⓒ Ⓓ Ⓔ	
18 Ⓐ Ⓑ Ⓒ Ⓓ Ⓔ	38 Ⓐ Ⓑ Ⓒ Ⓓ Ⓔ	
19 Ⓐ Ⓑ Ⓒ Ⓓ Ⓔ	39 Ⓐ Ⓑ Ⓒ Ⓓ Ⓔ	
20 Ⓐ Ⓑ Ⓒ Ⓓ Ⓔ	40 Ⓐ Ⓑ Ⓒ Ⓓ Ⓔ	

Reference Information

The following information is for your reference in answering some of the questions on this test.

Volume of a right circular cone with radius r and height h: $V = \frac{1}{3}\pi r^2 h$

Lateral area of a right circular cone with base circumference C and slant height ℓ: $S = \frac{1}{2}C\ell$

Volume of a sphere with radius r: $V = \frac{4}{3}\pi r^3$

Surface area of a sphere with radius r: $S = 4\pi r^2$

Volume of a pyramid with base area B and height h: $V = \frac{1}{3}Bh$

Test Form B
SAT Subject Test in Mathematics Level 1

50 Questions   1 hour

For each of the following problems, decide which is the BEST of the choices given. If the exact numerical value is not one of the choices, select the choice that best approximates this value. Then fill in the corresponding circle on the answer sheet.

Notes: (1) A calculator will be necessary for answering some of the questions on this test. For each question you will have to decide whether or not you should use a calculator. Programmable calculators and calculators that can display graphs are permitted.

(2) The only angle measure used on the Math Level 1 Test is degree measure. Make sure your calculator is in the degree mode.

(3) Figures that accompany problems on this test are intended to provide information useful in solving the problems. They are drawn as accurately as possible EXCEPT when it is stated in a specific problem that the figure is not drawn to scale. All figures lie in a plane unless otherwise indicated.

(4) Unless otherwise specified, the domain of any function f is assumed to be the set of all real numbers x for which $f(x)$ is a real number.

(5) Reference information that may be useful in answering the questions on this test can be found on the page preceding Question 1.

USE THIS SPACE SCRATCHWORK.

1. If $\dfrac{1}{x-1} = 2$, then $x =$

(A) $\dfrac{3}{2}$ (B) 2   (C) $\dfrac{5}{2}$ (D) 3   (E) $\dfrac{7}{2}$

2. One half of a number n is increased by 12. If the cube root of that result equals 3, what is the value of n?

(A) 15   (B) 18   (C) 22   (D) 30   (E) 38

3. If $p \cdot q = 18$ and $q \cdot r = 26$, where p, q and r are positive integers greater than 1, then $p \cdot r =$

(A) 18

(B) 26

(C) 42

(D) 52

(E) 117

4. If m is the largest prime factor of 84 and n is the largest prime
   factor of 165, then $m+n =$

   (A) 12   (B) 14   (C) 18   (D) 26   (E) 30

5. The height of an object t seconds after it is thrown upward with
   initial velocity v is given by the formula $h = -16t^2 + vt$. If $v = 80$,
   what is the height of the object after 3.5 seconds?

   (A) 55   (B) 64   (C) 84   (D) 96   (E) 108

6. Chen has 32 quarters and dimes, of which d are dimes.
   What is the total value of the coins in dollars?

   (A) $8 + 0.1d$

   (B) $32 - 0.15d$

   (C) $8 + 0.25d$

   (D) $32 + 0.1d$

   (E) $8 - 0.15d$

7. $\sqrt{\sqrt[3]{6}} =$

   (A) 2.363

   (B) 1.348

   (C) 20.544

   (D) 26.125

   (E) 27.456

8. For all values of x, let x ▲ be defined as x ▲ $= \sqrt{2x-1}$
   and $\boxed{x}$ be defined as $\boxed{x} = x^2 + 2$. If 3 ▲ $= m$, then $\boxed{m} =$

   (A) $\sqrt{5} + 2$ (B) 5   (C) $\sqrt{10}$ (D) 7   (E) $m+2$

9. The average (arithmetic mean) of a, b, and c is 71, and the average of b and c is 57. What is the value of a?

(A) 92

(B) 99

(C) 108

(D) 121

(E) 132

10. In Figure 1, if rectangle $ABCD$ is reflected across $\overline{CD}$, what will be the coordinates of the reflection of point B?

(A) $(3,-5)$

(B) $(3,-4)$

(C) $(3,-2)$

(D) $(6,1)$

(E) $(6,3)$

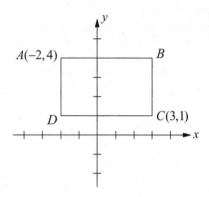

Figure 1

11. The measure of an angle is 32 less than three times its supplement. What is the measure of the angle?

(A) 45   (B) 53   (C) 75   (D) 105   (E) 127

12. Which of the following is equivalent to $\{x: \ -1 < x < 7\}$?

(A) $\{x: \ |x+3| > 4\}$

(B) $\{x: \ |x+3| < 4\}$

(C) $\{x: \ |x-3| > 4\}$

(D) $\{x: \ |x-3| < 4\}$

(E) $\{x: \ |x+1| < 7\}$

13. $(-2a^2b)^3(2ab^2)^{-2} =$

(A) $-2a^4b$

(B) $\dfrac{-2a^4}{b}$

(C) $-32a^4b$

(D) $\dfrac{-2a}{b}$

(E) $\dfrac{-32a^3}{b}$

14. In Figure 2, what is the area of $\triangle ACD$?

(A) 4.5

(B) 5.7

(C) 6.9

(D) 8.3

(E) 9

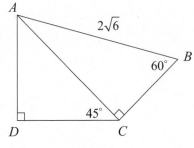

Figure 2

15. Which of the following is the equation of a line that passes through $(-2, 4)$ and is parallel to $6x - 3y = 10$?

(A) $y = -2x + 8$

(B) $y = 2x + 8$

(C) $y = -2x - 8$

(D) $y = 2x + 10$

(E) $y = 2x - 10$

16. What is the remainder when $x^4 - 5x^3 + 4x - 3$ is divided by $x + 1$?

(A) −3   (B) −2   (C) −1   (D) 0   (E) 1

17. If $f(-2x+1) = -6x+2$ for all real numbers x,
    then $f(x) =$

    (A) $-4x+1$

    (B) $3x-1$

    (C) $3x+1$

    (D) $-3x+1$

    (E) $-3x-1$

18. If $2x-3y+z = 11$ and $x-2y = 2$, what is the
    value of $y+z$?

    (A) 7

    (B) 5

    (C) 4

    (D) 1

    (E) It cannot be determined from the information
        given.

19. In Figure 3, the length of each of the five line segments
    is equal to 10. What is the area of quadrilateral $ABCD$?

    (A) 43.3

    (B) 70.7

    (C) 78.6

    (D) 82.4

    (E) 86.6

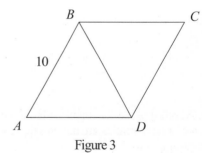

Figure 3

20. What is the length of the line segment on the line $y = \sqrt{3}x - 2$
    whose endpoints have x-coordinates 0 and 6?

    (A) 6

    (B) $3\sqrt{3}$

    (C) $4\sqrt{3}$

    (D) $6\sqrt{3}$

    (E) 12

21. For $x(x+3)(2x-1) \neq 0$, $\dfrac{2x^2+5x-3}{(x+3)} \times (\dfrac{2x-1}{x})^{-1} =$

    (A) $\dfrac{x}{2x-1}$

    (B) $\dfrac{(2x-1)^2}{x}$

    (C) $\dfrac{1}{x}$

    (D) x

    (E) $\dfrac{x}{x+3}$

22. In Figure 4, the grid consists of unit squares. What is the value of $\sin \angle FGH$?

    (A) 0.53

    (B) 0.64

    (C) 0.72

    (D) 0.77

    (E) 0.81

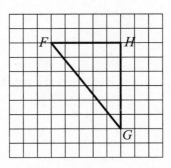

Figure 4

23. An indirect proof of the statement "If laser printers are on sale, then inkjet printers are not on sale" could begin with the assumption:

    (A) Laser printers are on sale.

    (B) Laser printers are not on sale.

    (C) Inkjet printers are on sale.

    (D) Inkjet printers are not on sale.

    (E) Both laser printers and inkjet printers are on sale.

24. If $\dfrac{1}{2}$ and -4 are both zeros of the polynomial $p(x)$,
then which of the following could be a factor of $p(x)$?

   (A) $2x^2 + 7x - 4$

   (B) $2x^2 - 7x + 4$

   (C) $2x^2 - 7x - 2$

   (D) $2x^2 - 7x + 2$

   (E) $x^2 - 2$

25. What is the area of parallelogram $ABCD$ in Figure 5?

   (A) 20

   (B) 23.1

   (C) 28.3

   (D) 32.6

   (E) 40

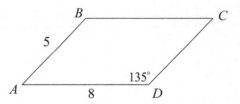

Figure 5

26. $1 - (\sin x - \cos x)^2 =$

   (A) -1

   (B) 0

   (C) 2

   (D) $2\sin x \cos x$

   (E) $-2\sin x \cos x$

27. The scatter plot in Figure 6 shows the relationship
between the distance d from home to school and
the time t it takes to get to school. Which of the
following equations best represents the relation
between the time and the distance?

   (A) $t = -d + 22$

   (B) $t = d + 10$

   (C) $t = 2d$

   (D) $t = 2d + 5$

   (E) $t = 3.5d$

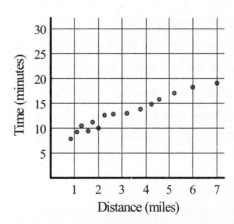

Figure 6

28. Which of the following is a graph of a function?

(A)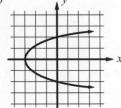

(B)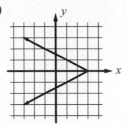

(C)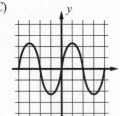

(D)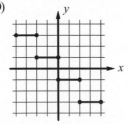

(E)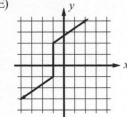

29. If $f(x) = x$ and $g(x) = \dfrac{x^2 + 2x}{x + 2}$, how are the graphs of f and g are related?

    (A) They are exactly the same.

    (B) They are the same except when $x = -2$.

    (C) They are the same except when $x = 2$.

    (D) They intersect at one point.

    (E) They do not intersect.

30. If $f(x) = -2x - 7$ and $f(g(-1)) = 5$, which of the
    following could be $g(x)$?

    (A) $-3x - 1$

    (B) $3x - 1$

    (C) $-4x + 2$

    (D) $4x - 2$

    (E) $5x - 2$

31. The electrical resistance in ohms of a wire varies directly as
    its length. If a wire 120 cm long has a resistance of 8 ohms,
    what is the resistance of the wire when it is 270 cm long?

    (A) 12 ohms

    (B) 14 ohms

    (C) 16 ohms

    (D) 18 ohms

    (E) 22 ohms

32. In Figure 7, R is a point on the circle with center O and
    $\overline{PQ}$ and $\overline{PS}$ are tangent to the circle. If r is the measure
    of $\angle QRS$ and p is the measure of $\angle P$, which of the
    following is true?

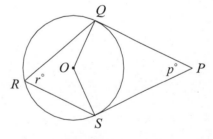

Figure 7

    (A) $r + p = 180$

    (B) $2r + p = 180$

    (C) $r + 2p = 180$

    (D) $2r - p = 90$

    (E) $r - p = 90$

33. If $i^2 = -1$, which of the following is equal to $(3 + i)(1 - i)$?

    (A) $2 - 2i$

    (B) $4 - 2i$

    (C) $4 + 2i$

    (D) $3 + 2i$

    (E) $3 - 2i$

34. If $f(x) = \dfrac{2x-5}{3}$, then the inverse function of f, f^{-1}, is

(A) $\dfrac{3x+5}{2}$

(B) $\dfrac{3x-5}{2}$

(C) $\dfrac{-3x+5}{2}$

(D) $\dfrac{-3x-5}{2}$

(E) $\dfrac{-2x+5}{3}$

35. In Figure 8, $ABCD$ and $PQRS$ are two congruent rectangles each with sides of lengths $2x$ and x. Two congruent circles are inscribed in rectangle $ABCD$ and eight congruent circles are inscribed in rectangle $PQRS$. What is the ratio of the area of the shaded region in rectangle $ABCD$ to the area of the shaded region in rectangle $PQRS$?

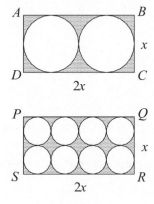

Figure 8

(A) $\dfrac{1}{2}$ (B) $\dfrac{4}{5}$ (C) 1   (D) $\dfrac{5}{4}$ (E) 2

36. A parabola whose equation is $x + y^2 = 3$ and a line whose equation is $x + 2y = 0$ intersect on the xy-plane. What are the y-coordinates of the points of intersection?

(A) 3 and -1

(B) 2 and -1

(C) $\dfrac{3}{4}$ and 1

(D) $-\dfrac{3}{4}$ and 1

(E) $\dfrac{3}{4}$ and -1

37. Which of the following could be the equation of the circle shown in Figure 9?

(A) $x^2 + y^2 - 4x - 6y - 12 = 0$

(B) $x^2 + y^2 - 4x + 6y - 24 = 0$

(C) $x^2 + y^2 - 4x + 6y - 12 = 0$

(D) $x^2 + y^2 + 4x - 6y - 24 = 0$

(E) $x^2 + y^2 + 4x + 6y - 12 = 0$

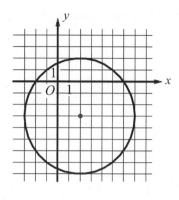

Figure 9

38. If $8^a = 5^b$, what is the value of $\dfrac{a}{b}$?

(A) 0.63   (B) 0.77   (C) 1. 29   (D) 1.60   (E) 3.08

39. If the 1st term of an arithmetic sequence is -11 and the 7th term is 7, what is the 99th term of the sequence?

(A) 195

(B) 206

(C) 217

(D) 250

(E) 283

40. In right triangle ABC in Figure 10, $(\tan A + \tan B)\sin A =$

(A) $\dfrac{b}{c}$ (B) $\dfrac{c}{b}$ (C) $\dfrac{a}{c}$ (D) $\dfrac{c}{a}$ (E) $\dfrac{b}{a}$

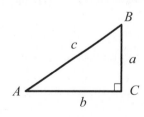

Figure 10

41. Which of the following shaded regions could be the graph of ?

(A)
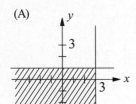

(B)
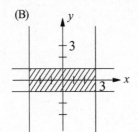

(C)
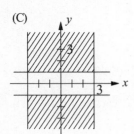

(D)
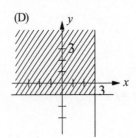

(E)
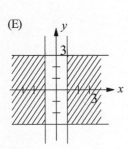

42. The areas of two of the faces of a rectangular prism are 12 and 21. If the dimensions of the rectangular prism are integers, what is the volume of the rectangular prism?

(A) 60   (B) 68   (C) 72   (D) 84   (E) 98

43. If $\log_3 a = k$, then what does $\log_3 9a$ equal?

(A) $2k$

(B) $3k$

(C) $2 + k$

(D) $3 + k$

(E) $9 + k$

44. A bag contains r red balls, b blue balls, and g green balls. If a ball is picked at random from the bag, the probability that the ball is red is $\dfrac{3}{8}$. What is the value of $\dfrac{b+g}{r}$?

(A) $\dfrac{8}{3}$ (B) 2   (C) $\dfrac{5}{3}$ (D) $\dfrac{8}{5}$ (E) $\dfrac{6}{5}$

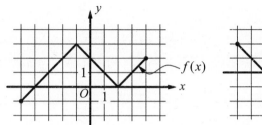 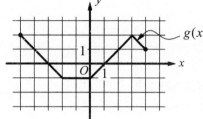

Figure 11

45. In Figure 11, the graphs of f and g are shown. What is the value of $\dfrac{g(f(-2))}{f(g(-2))}$?

(A) $-\dfrac{1}{2}$ (B) $\dfrac{1}{3}$ (C) 1   (D) $\dfrac{3}{2}$ (E) 2

46. In Figure 12, what is the area of the shaded region?

(A) $\dfrac{\pi-2}{4}$

(B) $\dfrac{\pi-2}{2}$

(C) $\dfrac{\pi-1}{2}$

(D) $\dfrac{\pi+1}{8}$

(E) $\dfrac{\pi+1}{4}$

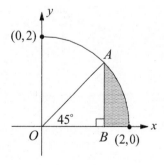

Figure 12

47. In Figure 13, a regular nonagon is inscribed in a circle whose radius is 12. What is the length of $\overline{CD}$?

(A) 17.0

(B) 18.6

(C) 20.8

(D) 22.3

(E) 25.1

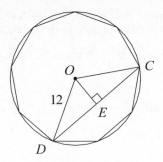

Figure 13

48. The graph of $y = f(x)$ is shown in Figure 14. Which of the following graphs could be the graph of $y = -f(x)$?

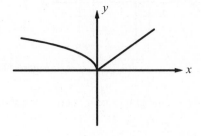

Figure 14

(A)
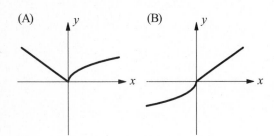

(B)

(C)
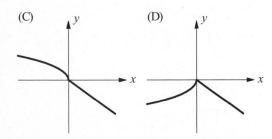

(D)

(E)
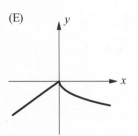

49. In Figure 15, the cube has edge length 4. If *C* is the midpoint of segment *AB*, what is the length of $\overline{CD}$?

(A) 6

(B) $4\sqrt{2}$

(C) $4\sqrt{3}$

(D) 8

(E) $6\sqrt{2}$

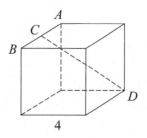

Figure 15

50. In Figure 16, two semicircles with diameters 6 and 8 are rotated about side $\overline{AC}$ to generate spheres. What is the ratio of the volume of the smaller sphere to the volume of the larger sphere?

(A) $\dfrac{3}{4}$

(B) $\dfrac{9}{16}$

(C) $\dfrac{21}{32}$

(D) $\dfrac{45}{64}$

(E) $\dfrac{27}{64}$

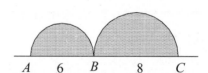

Figure 16

STOP

IF YOU FINISH BEFORE TIME IS CALLED, YOU MAY CHECK YOUR WORK ON THIS TEST ONLY.
DO NOT TURN TO ANY OTHER TEST IN THIS BOOK.

Answer Key

1. A	2. D	3. E	4. C	5. C
6. E	7. B	8. D	9. B	10. C
11. E	12. D	13. B	14. A	15. B
16. C	17. B	18. A	19. E	20. E
21. D	22. B	23. C	24. A	25. C
26. D	27. D	28. C	29. B	30. D
31. D	32. B	33. B	34. A	35. C
36. A	37. C	38. B	39. E	40. B
41. C	42. D	43. C	44. C	45. B
46. B	47. C	48. D	49. A	50. E

Answers and Explanations

1. A

$$\frac{1}{x-1} = 2$$

$$\Rightarrow 1 = 2(x-1) \Rightarrow 1 = 2x - 2$$

$$\Rightarrow x = \frac{3}{2}$$

2. D

one half of   is increased
a number   by 12

$$\overbrace{\frac{1}{2}n} \qquad \overbrace{+12}$$

$$\sqrt[3]{\frac{1}{2}n + 12} = 3$$

$$\frac{1}{2}n + 12 = 3^3 \Rightarrow \frac{1}{2}n = 15$$

$$\Rightarrow n = 30$$

3. E

$$pq = 18 \text{ and } qr = 26$$

$$18 = 2 \cdot 9 \text{ or } 3 \cdot 6$$

$$26 = 2 \cdot 13$$

We can conclude that $q = 2$, $p = 9$, and $r = 13$.

$$pr = 9 \cdot 13 = 117$$

4. C

Find the prime factorizations of 84 and 165.

$$84 = 2^2 \cdot 3 \cdot 7$$

$$165 = 3 \cdot 5 \cdot 11$$

Therefore $m = 7$ and $n = 11$.

$$m + n = 7 + 11 = 18$$

5. C

$$h = -16t^2 + vt$$

$$h = -16(3.5)^2 + (80)(3.5) \qquad v = 80 \text{ and } t = 3.5$$

$$= 84$$

6. E

If $d =$ the number of dimes, then

$32 - d =$ the number of quarters.

Total value in dollars

$$= 0.1d + 0.25(32 - d) \qquad \text{dime} = 0.1 \text{ dollars}$$

$$= 8 - 0.15d \qquad \text{quarter} = 0.25 \text{ dollars}$$

7. B

$$\sqrt{\sqrt[3]{6}} = ((6^{\frac{1}{3}}))^{\frac{1}{2}} = 6^{\frac{1}{6}} \approx 1.348$$

8. D

$$x \,\blacktriangle = \sqrt{2x - 1} \qquad \text{Defined Operation}$$

$$3 \,\blacktriangle = \sqrt{2 \cdot 3 - 1} = \sqrt{5} \qquad x = 3$$

Since $3 \,\blacktriangle = m$, $m = \sqrt{5}$.

$$\boxed{x} = x^2 + 2 \qquad \text{Defined Operation}$$

$$\boxed{m} = m^2 + 2$$

$$\boxed{\sqrt{5}} = (\sqrt{5})^2 + 2 \qquad m = \sqrt{5}$$

$$= 7 \qquad \text{Answer}$$

9. B

The average (arithmetic mean) of a, b, and c is 71.

$$\Rightarrow \frac{a+b+c}{3} = 71 \Rightarrow a+b+c = 213$$

The average of b and c is 57.

$$\Rightarrow \frac{b+c}{2} = 57 \Rightarrow b+c = 114$$

$a+b+c = 213$
$a+114 = 213 \qquad\qquad b+c = 114$
$a = 99$

10. C

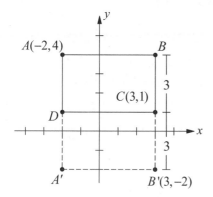

$BC = B'C = 3$, since point B' is the reflection of B across $\overline{CD}$. The coordinates of point B' are $(3,-2)$.

11. E

Let $x =$ the measure of an angle, then $180 - x =$ the measure of its supplement.

$$\underbrace{x}_{\text{The measure of an angle}} = \underbrace{3(180-x)}_{\text{3 times its supplement}} \underbrace{-32}_{\text{32 less than}}$$

$x = 540 - 3x - 32$
$4x = 508$
$x = 127$

12. D

Test each answer choice.

(A) $|x+3| > 4 \Rightarrow x+3 > 4$ or $x+3 < -4$

(B) $|x+3| < 4 \Rightarrow -4 < x+3 < 4$
$\qquad\qquad\qquad\qquad \Rightarrow -7 < x < 1$

(C) $|x-3| > 4 \Rightarrow x-3 > 4$ or $x-3 < -4$

(D) $|x-3| < 4 \Rightarrow -4 < x-3 < 4$
$\qquad\qquad\qquad\qquad \Rightarrow -1 < x < 7$

Choice (D) is correct.

13. B

$$(-2a^2b)^3(2ab^2)^{-2}$$

$$= (-2)^3 a^6 b^3 \cdot \frac{1}{(2ab^2)^2}$$

$$= -8a^6 b^3 \cdot \frac{1}{4a^2 b^4}$$

$$= -\frac{2a^4}{b}$$

14. A

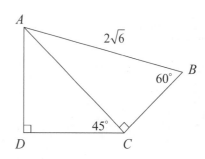

$\triangle ABC$ is a $30°$-$60°$-$90°$.

$$BC = \frac{1}{2} AB = \sqrt{6}$$

$$AC = BC \cdot \sqrt{3} = \sqrt{6} \cdot \sqrt{3} = \sqrt{18} = 3\sqrt{2}$$

$\triangle ACD$ is a $45°$-$45°$-$90°$.

$AC = CD \cdot \sqrt{2}$

$$\Rightarrow 3\sqrt{2} = CD \cdot \sqrt{2} \Rightarrow CD = 3$$

Area of $\triangle ACD = \frac{1}{2}(3)(3) = 4.5$

15. B

$6x - 3y = 10$

$$y = 2x - \frac{10}{3} \qquad\qquad \text{Slope-intercept form}$$

$$y = 2x + b$$ Slope-intercept form of the line parallel to $y = 2x - \dfrac{10}{3}$.

$$4 = 2(-2) + b$$ Substitute $x = -2$ and $y = 4$, since the line passes through $(-2, 4)$.

$$b = 8$$ Solve for b.

$$y = 2x + 8$$

16. C

Use the remainder theorem.

If $f(x)$ is divided by $x + 1$, the remainder is $f(-1)$.

$$f(x) = x^4 - 5x^3 + 4x - 3$$

$$f(-1) = (-1)^4 - 5(-1)^3 + 4(-1) - 3 = -1$$

17. B

$$f(-2x + 1) = -6x + 2$$

Test each answer choice.

(A) If $f(x) = -4x + 1$, then

$$f(-2x + 1) = -4(-2x + 1) + 2 = 8x - 2$$

(B) If $f(x) = 3x - 1$, then

$$f(-2x + 1) = 3(-2x + 1) - 1 = -6x + 2$$

Choice (B) is correct.

18. A

$$2x - 3y + z = 11$$ First equation

$$x - 2y = 2$$ Second equation

Multiply both sides of the second equation by -2 and add to the first equation.

$$2x - 3y + z = 11$$ First equation

$$+ \underline{\left|-2x + 4y \quad\;\; = -4\right.}$$ Second equation multiplied by -2

$$y + z = 7$$

19. E

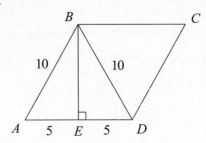

$\triangle ABD$ is an equilateral, so $\triangle ABE$ is a $30°\text{-}60°\text{-}90°$.

$$AE = \frac{1}{2}AB = 5$$

$$BE = AE \cdot \sqrt{3} = 5\sqrt{3}$$

Area of $\triangle ABD = \dfrac{1}{2}(10)(5\sqrt{3}) = 25\sqrt{3}$

Area of quadrilateral $ABCD$
$$= 2 \cdot \text{Area of } \triangle ABD = 50\sqrt{3} \approx 86.6$$

20. E

$$y = \sqrt{3}x - 2$$

If $x = 0$, $y = \sqrt{3}(0) - 2 = -2$

If $x = 6$, $y = \sqrt{3}(6) - 2 = 6\sqrt{3} - 2$

The length of the line segment with endpoints $(0, -2)$ and $(6, 6\sqrt{3} - 2)$ is

$$d = \sqrt{(6 - 0)^2 + [(6\sqrt{3} - 2) + 2]^2}$$
$$= \sqrt{36 + 108}$$
$$= \sqrt{144}$$
$$= 12$$

21. D

$$\frac{2x^2 + 5x - 3}{(x + 3)} \times \left(\frac{2x - 1}{x}\right)^{-1}$$

$$= \frac{(2x - 1)(x + 3)}{(x + 3)} \times \left(\frac{x}{2x - 1}\right)$$

$$= x$$

22. B

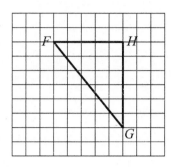

In the figure, $FH = 5$ and $GH = 6$.

$FG^2 = GH^2 + FH^2$

$\quad\quad = 6^2 + 5^2 = 61$

$FG = \sqrt{61} \approx 7.81$

$\sin \angle FGH = \dfrac{FH}{FG} = \dfrac{5}{\sqrt{61}} \approx 0.64$

23. C

The first step in writing an indirect proof is to assume that the desired conclusion is not true.

"If laser printers are on sale, then inkjet printers are not on sale."

An indirect proof of the statement could begin with "Assume inkjet printers are on sale …"

Choice (C) is correct.

24. A

$\dfrac{1}{2}$ and -4 are both zeros of the polynomial $p(x)$.

Then $p(x) = (x - \dfrac{1}{2})(x + 4)$

$\quad\quad\quad = (x^2 + \dfrac{7}{2}x - 2)$

is one possible equation of the polynomial. Multiplying the equation by 2, we get

$p(x) = 2x^2 + 7x - 4$.

The polynomial still has the same zeros.

Choice (A) is correct.

25. C

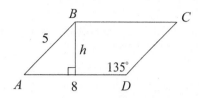

$m\angle A = 45°$　　Consecutive interior angles of $\square$ are supplementary.

$5 = h \cdot \sqrt{2}$　　$45°$-$45°$-$90°$ triangle ratio

$h = \dfrac{5}{\sqrt{2}}$

Area of parallelogram $ABCD$

$= b \cdot h = 8 \cdot \dfrac{5}{\sqrt{2}} \approx 28.3$

26. D

$1 - (\sin x - \cos x)^2$

$= 1 - (\sin^2 x - 2\sin x \cos x + \cos^2 x)$

$= 1 - (1 - 2\sin x \cos x) \quad\quad \sin^2 x + \cos^2 x = 1$

$= 2\sin x \cos x$

27. D

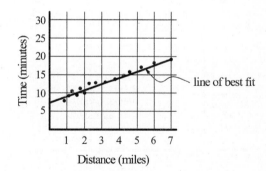

Choose 2 points from the scatter plot such as $(2,10)$ and $(7,19)$. The approximate slope of the line passing through these points is

$m = \dfrac{19 - 10}{7 - 2} = 1.8$

The y-intercept is about 7 or 8.

Among the answer choices, $t = 2d + 5$ best represents the relation between the time and the distance.

Choice (D) is correct.

28. C

A relation is a function if and only if no vertical line intersects its graph more than once.

(A)

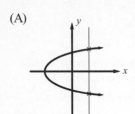

A vertical line has two points of intersection. Not a function

(B)

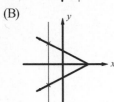

A vertical line has two points of intersection. Not a function

(C)

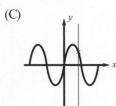

Each vertical line has only one point of intersection. It is a function.

(D)

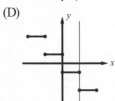

A vertical line has two points of intersection. Not a function

(E)

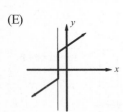

A vertical line has more than two points of intersection. Not a function

29. B

$$f(x) = x$$

$$g(x) = \frac{x^2 + 2x}{x+2} = \frac{x(x+2)}{x+2} = x$$

$g(x)$ is undefined at $x = -2$, since $x = -2$ makes the denominator zero. In other words, the graph of $g(x)$ is not continuous at $x = -2$. At all values other than $x = -2$, the graph of g coincides with the graph of $f(x) = x$.

30. D

$$f(x) = -2x - 7$$
$$f(g(-1)) = 5$$

If $x = g(-1)$, $-2x - 7 = 5 \Rightarrow x = -6$.
Therefore $g(-1) = -6$.

Test each answer choice.

(A) If $g(x) = -3x - 1$, $g(-1) = -3(-1) - 1 = 2$
  $g(-1) \neq -6$

(B) If $g(x) = 3x - 1$, $g(-1) = 3(-1) - 1 = -4$
  $g(-1) \neq -6$

(C) If $g(x) = -4x + 2$, $g(-1) = -4(-1) + 2 = 6$
  $g(-1) \neq -6$

(D) If $g(x) = 4x - 2$, $g(-1) = 4(-1) - 2 = -6$
  $g(-1) = -6$

Choice (D) is correct.

31. D

Let $y =$ the electrical resistance in ohms of a wire, and $x =$ the length of the wire.

$y = kx$	Direct variation
$8 = k \cdot 120$	$y = 8$ and $x = 120$
$k = \dfrac{8}{120} = \dfrac{1}{15}$	
$y = \dfrac{1}{15} x$	An equation of direct variation
$y = \dfrac{1}{15}(270)$	$x = 270$
$= 18$	

32. B

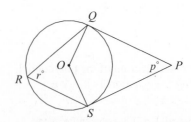

If a line is tangent to a circle, then it is $\perp$ to the radius drawn to the point of tangency. Therefore
$$m\angle OQP = m\angle OSP = 90°$$

In quadrilateral $OQPS$,
$$m\angle O + m\angle OQP + m\angle OSP + m\angle P = 360$$

$$m\angle O + 90 + 90 + p = 360 \qquad \text{Substitution}$$
$$m\angle O + p = 180$$

In a circle the measure of an inscribed angle is equal to one-half the measure of its intercepted arc.
$$r = \frac{1}{2}m\angle O \implies m\angle O = 2r$$
Therefore $2r + p = 180$.

33. B

$$(3+i)(1-i)$$
$$= 3 - 3i + i - i^2$$
$$= 3 - 2i + 1$$
$$= 4 - 2i$$

34. A

$f(x) = \dfrac{2x-5}{3}$ To find an inverse function,

1. Replace $f(x)$ with y: $\quad y = \dfrac{2x-5}{3}$

2. Interchange x and y: $\quad x = \dfrac{2y-5}{3}$

3. Solve for y:

$$x = \frac{2y-5}{3} \implies 3x = 2y - 5$$

$$\implies 2y = 3x + 5 \implies y = \frac{3x+5}{2}$$

35. C

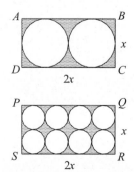

The radius of the two congruent circles inscribed in rectangle $ABCD$ is $\dfrac{1}{2}x$.

The radius of the eight congruent circles inscribed in rectangle $PQRS$ is $\dfrac{1}{4}x$.

The area of the shaded region in rectangle $ABCD$
$$= (2x)(x) - 2[\pi(\tfrac{1}{2}x)^2] = 2x^2 - \frac{\pi x^2}{2}$$

The area of the shaded region in rectangle $PQRS$
$$= (2x)(x) - 8[\pi(\tfrac{1}{4}x)^2] = 2x^2 - \frac{\pi x^2}{2}$$

Therefore the ratio of the areas of the two shaded regions equals 1.

36. A

Solve the equations for x and make substitutions to find the y-coordinates of the points of intersection.

$$x + y^2 = 3 \implies x = 3 - y^2$$
$$x + 2y = 0 \implies x = -2y$$

Make substitutions and solve for y.
$$3 - y^2 = -2y$$
$$\implies y^2 - 2y - 3 = 0$$
$$\implies (y-3)(y+1) = 0$$
$$\implies y = 3 \text{ or } y = -1$$

37. C

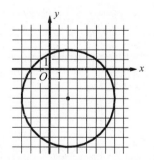

The center of the circle is $(2, -3)$ and the radius is 5.
The standard form of the equation is
$$(x-2)^2 + (y+3)^2 = 5^2$$
$$x^2 - 4x + 4 + y^2 + 6y + 9 = 25$$
$$x^2 + y^2 - 4x + 6y - 12 = 0$$

38. B

$$8^a = 5^b$$
$$\log 8^a = \log 5^b \qquad \text{Take log on both sides.}$$
$$a \log 8 = b \log 5 \qquad \log M^p = p \log M$$
$$\frac{a}{b} = \frac{\log 5}{\log 8} \qquad \text{Cross product.}$$
$$\approx 0.774$$

39. E

$$a_1 = -11$$
$$a_n = a_1 + (n-1)d$$
$$a_7 = a_1 + (7-1)d$$
$$7 = -11 + (7-1)d \qquad a_7 = 7$$
$$d = 3$$
$$a_{99} = -11 + (99-1)3$$
$$= 283$$

40. B

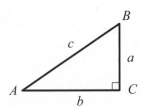

$$(\tan A + \tan B)\sin A$$
$$= (\frac{a}{b} + \frac{b}{a})\frac{a}{c}$$
$$= (\frac{a^2 + b^2}{ab})\frac{a}{c}$$
$$= (\frac{c^2}{ab})\frac{a}{c} \qquad a^2 + b^2 = c^2$$
$$= \frac{c}{b}$$

41. C

The graph of $|x| \le 3$ is the region that falls between $x = -3$ and $x = 3$.

The graph of $|y| \ge 1$ is the region that lies below

$y = -1$ and above $y = 1$.

Choice (C) is correct.

42. D

Since the dimensions of the rectangular prism are integers, find the integer factors of 12 and 21.

$$\begin{aligned} 12 &= 1 \cdot 12 & 21 &= 1 \cdot 21 \\ &= 2 \cdot 6 & &= 3 \cdot 7 \\ &= 3 \cdot 4 \end{aligned}$$

The possible dimensions of the rectangular prism are 3, 4, and 7.

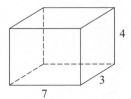

Volume of the rectangular prism
$$= 3 \cdot 4 \cdot 7 = 84$$

43. C

$$\log_3 9a$$
$$= \log_3 9 + \log_3 a \qquad \log M \cdot N = \log M + \log N$$
$$= \log_3 3^2 + k \qquad \text{Substitute: } \log_3 a = k$$
$$= 2\log_3 3 + k \qquad \log M^p = p \log M$$
$$= 2 + k \qquad \log_3 3 = 1$$

44. C

If a ball is picked at random from the bag, the probability that the ball is red is $\frac{3}{8}$.

$$\frac{\text{number of red balls}}{\text{total number of balls}} = \frac{3}{8}$$

$$\Rightarrow \frac{r}{r+b+g} = \frac{3}{8} \Rightarrow 8r = 3(r+b+g)$$

$$\Rightarrow 5r = 3(b+g) \quad \Rightarrow \frac{b+g}{r} = \frac{5}{3}$$

45. B

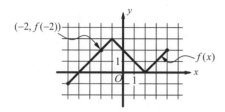

The graph above shows $f(-2) = 2$.

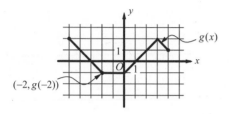

The graph above shows $g(-2) = -1$.

$\dfrac{g(f(-2))}{f(g(-2))}$

$= \dfrac{g(2)}{f(-1)}$ Substitute: $f(-2) = 2$ and

$= \dfrac{1}{3}$ $g(-2) = -1$

                         $g(2) = 1$ and $f(-1) = 3$

46. B

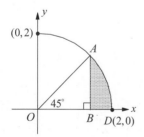

Area of sector $OAD = \pi(2)^2 \cdot \dfrac{45}{360} = \dfrac{\pi}{2}$

ΔOAB is a $45°$-$45°$-$90°$ triangle with hypotenuse of length 2. Therefore $OB = AB = \sqrt{2}$.

Area of $\Delta OAB = \dfrac{1}{2}(\sqrt{2})(\sqrt{2}) = 1$

Area of the shaded region
$=$ Area of sector $OAD -$ Area of ΔOAB
$= \dfrac{\pi}{2} - 1 = \dfrac{\pi - 2}{2}$

47. C

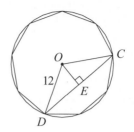

$m\angle DOC = \dfrac{3}{9} \cdot 360° = 120°$

$m\angle DOE = \dfrac{1}{2} m\angle DOC = 60°$

ΔDOE is a $30°$-$60°$-$90°$ triangle with hypotenuse of length is 12. Therefore $OE = \dfrac{1}{2} OD = 6$, and

$DE = \sqrt{3} \cdot OE = 6\sqrt{3}$.

$CD = 2 \cdot DE = 12\sqrt{3} \approx 20.8$

48. D

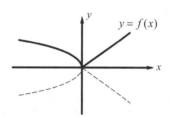

The graph of $y = -f(x)$ is the reflection of $y = f(x)$ about the x-axis.

Choice (D) is correct.

49. A

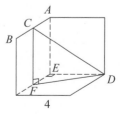

In ΔDEF, $DF^2 = DE^2 + EF^2$
$\Rightarrow DF^2 = 4^2 + 2^2 = 20$

In $\triangle CDF$, $CD^2 = CF^2 + DF^2$

$\Rightarrow\ CD^2 = 4^2 + 20 = 36$

$\Rightarrow\ CD = \sqrt{36} = 6$

50. E

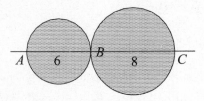

Two semicircles with diameters 6 and 8 are rotated about side $\overline{AC}$ to generate spheres.

If two solids are similar with corresponding sides in the ratio of $a : b$, their volumes have a ratio of $a^3 : b^3$. Since the ratio of the two diameters is $\dfrac{3}{4}$, the ratio of their volumes is $\dfrac{3^3}{4^3}$, or $\dfrac{27}{64}$.

Test Form C
Mathematics Level 1

Answer Sheet

1 Ⓐ Ⓑ Ⓒ Ⓓ Ⓔ	21 Ⓐ Ⓑ Ⓒ Ⓓ Ⓔ	41 Ⓐ Ⓑ Ⓒ Ⓓ Ⓔ
2 Ⓐ Ⓑ Ⓒ Ⓓ Ⓔ	22 Ⓐ Ⓑ Ⓒ Ⓓ Ⓔ	42 Ⓐ Ⓑ Ⓒ Ⓓ Ⓔ
3 Ⓐ Ⓑ Ⓒ Ⓓ Ⓔ	23 Ⓐ Ⓑ Ⓒ Ⓓ Ⓔ	43 Ⓐ Ⓑ Ⓒ Ⓓ Ⓔ
4 Ⓐ Ⓑ Ⓒ Ⓓ Ⓔ	24 Ⓐ Ⓑ Ⓒ Ⓓ Ⓔ	44 Ⓐ Ⓑ Ⓒ Ⓓ Ⓔ
5 Ⓐ Ⓑ Ⓒ Ⓓ Ⓔ	25 Ⓐ Ⓑ Ⓒ Ⓓ Ⓔ	45 Ⓐ Ⓑ Ⓒ Ⓓ Ⓔ
6 Ⓐ Ⓑ Ⓒ Ⓓ Ⓔ	26 Ⓐ Ⓑ Ⓒ Ⓓ Ⓔ	46 Ⓐ Ⓑ Ⓒ Ⓓ Ⓔ
7 Ⓐ Ⓑ Ⓒ Ⓓ Ⓔ	27 Ⓐ Ⓑ Ⓒ Ⓓ Ⓔ	47 Ⓐ Ⓑ Ⓒ Ⓓ Ⓔ
8 Ⓐ Ⓑ Ⓒ Ⓓ Ⓔ	28 Ⓐ Ⓑ Ⓒ Ⓓ Ⓔ	48 Ⓐ Ⓑ Ⓒ Ⓓ Ⓔ
9 Ⓐ Ⓑ Ⓒ Ⓓ Ⓔ	29 Ⓐ Ⓑ Ⓒ Ⓓ Ⓔ	49 Ⓐ Ⓑ Ⓒ Ⓓ Ⓔ
10 Ⓐ Ⓑ Ⓒ Ⓓ Ⓔ	30 Ⓐ Ⓑ Ⓒ Ⓓ Ⓔ	50 Ⓐ Ⓑ Ⓒ Ⓓ Ⓔ
11 Ⓐ Ⓑ Ⓒ Ⓓ Ⓔ	31 Ⓐ Ⓑ Ⓒ Ⓓ Ⓔ	
12 Ⓐ Ⓑ Ⓒ Ⓓ Ⓔ	32 Ⓐ Ⓑ Ⓒ Ⓓ Ⓔ	
13 Ⓐ Ⓑ Ⓒ Ⓓ Ⓔ	33 Ⓐ Ⓑ Ⓒ Ⓓ Ⓔ	
14 Ⓐ Ⓑ Ⓒ Ⓓ Ⓔ	34 Ⓐ Ⓑ Ⓒ Ⓓ Ⓔ	
15 Ⓐ Ⓑ Ⓒ Ⓓ Ⓔ	35 Ⓐ Ⓑ Ⓒ Ⓓ Ⓔ	
16 Ⓐ Ⓑ Ⓒ Ⓓ Ⓔ	36 Ⓐ Ⓑ Ⓒ Ⓓ Ⓔ	
17 Ⓐ Ⓑ Ⓒ Ⓓ Ⓔ	37 Ⓐ Ⓑ Ⓒ Ⓓ Ⓔ	
18 Ⓐ Ⓑ Ⓒ Ⓓ Ⓔ	38 Ⓐ Ⓑ Ⓒ Ⓓ Ⓔ	
19 Ⓐ Ⓑ Ⓒ Ⓓ Ⓔ	39 Ⓐ Ⓑ Ⓒ Ⓓ Ⓔ	
20 Ⓐ Ⓑ Ⓒ Ⓓ Ⓔ	40 Ⓐ Ⓑ Ⓒ Ⓓ Ⓔ	

Reference Information

The following information is for your reference in answering some of the questions on this test.

Volume of a right circular cone with radius r and height h: $V = \frac{1}{3}\pi r^2 h$

Lateral area of a right circular cone with base circumference C and slant height ℓ: $S = \frac{1}{2}C\ell$

Volume of a sphere with radius r: $V = \frac{4}{3}\pi r^3$

Surface area of a sphere with radius r: $S = 4\pi r^2$

Volume of a pyramid with base area B and height h: $V = \frac{1}{3}Bh$

Test Form C
SAT Subject Test in Mathematics Level 1

50 Questions   1 hour

For each of the following problems, decide which is the BEST of the choices given. If the exact numerical value is not one of the choices, select the choice that best approximates this value. Then fill in the corresponding circle on the answer sheet.

Notes: (1) A calculator will be necessary for answering some of the questions on this test. For each question you will have to decide whether or not you should use a calculator. Programmable calculators and calculators that can display graphs are permitted.

(2) The only angle measure used on the Math Level 1 Test is degree measure. Make sure your calculator is in the degree mode.

(3) Figures that accompany problems on this test are intended to provide information useful in solving the problems. They are drawn as accurately as possible EXCEPT when it is stated in a specific problem that the figure is not drawn to scale. All figures lie in a plane unless otherwise indicated.

(4) Unless otherwise specified, the domain of any function f is assumed to be the set of all real numbers x for which $f(x)$ is a real number.

(5) Reference information that may be useful in answering the questions on this test can be found on the page preceding Question 1.

1. If $a = 6b$, $c = 4a$, and $bc \neq 0$, what is the value of $\dfrac{bc}{a^2}$?

    (A) $\dfrac{1}{24}$ (B) $\dfrac{2}{3}$ (C) $\dfrac{3}{2}$ (D) 12   (E) 24

2. For all real numbers a and b, let the operation $*$ be defined as $a*b = |a-b|$. What is the value of $[7*(-5)]-[(-5)*7]$?

    (A) −14
    (B) −10
    (C) 0
    (D) 10
    (E) 24

3. There are 3-point and 4-point questions on a final exam containing 32 questions. If the total points for the exam is 100, how many 3-point questions are on the exam?

    (A) 26   (B) 28   (C) 30   (D) 32   (E) 34

4. If $4^x + 4^x + 4^x + 4^x = \dfrac{1}{256}$, what is the value of x?

    (A) −1   (B) −2   (C) −3   (D) −4   (E) −5

5. Figure 1 shows a quadrilateral with side lengths of 7, 8, 17, and x. Which of the following is not a possible value of x?

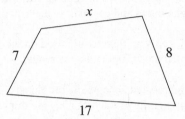

Figure 1

    (A) 2

    (B) 7

    (C) 8

    (D) 17

    (E) 31

6. $\sqrt[3]{-16x^3 y^7} =$

    (A) $4xy^2 \sqrt[3]{2y}$

    (B) $-4xy^2 \sqrt[3]{2y}$

    (C) $2xy^2 \sqrt[3]{2y}$

    (D) $-2xy^2 \sqrt[3]{2y}$

    (E) $-2xy \sqrt[3]{2y^2}$

7. $(x - y + 2)(x + y - 2) =$

    (A) $(x^2 - y^2) - 4$

    (B) $x^2 - 2x - 2y + y^2 - 4$

    (C) $x^2 - 4y + y^2 - 4$

    (D) $(x^2 - y^2) + 4y - 4$

    (E) $(x^2 - y^2) - 4x - 4$

8. $\dfrac{\sqrt{3}-3}{\sqrt{3}+1} =$

    (A) $-2\sqrt{3}$

    (B) $3+\sqrt{3}$

    (C) $3-\sqrt{3}$

    (D) $3+2\sqrt{3}$

    (E) $3-2\sqrt{3}$

9. In Figure 2, $ABCDE$ is a regular pentagon. What is the measure of $\angle BEA$?

    (A) $30°$

    (B) $32°$

    (C) $36°$

    (D) $38°$

    (E) $40°$

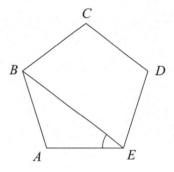

Figure 2

10. What are all values of x for which $|3x-2| \geq 5$?

    (A) $x \leq -1$ or $x \geq \dfrac{7}{3}$

    (B) $x \leq -\dfrac{7}{3}$ or $x \geq 1$

    (C) $x \geq -\dfrac{7}{3}$

    (D) $-1 \leq x \leq \dfrac{7}{3}$

    (E) $-\dfrac{7}{3} \leq x \leq 1$

11. A digital camera with a list price of c dollars was first discounted by 20%, and then an additional discount of 10% was given to card club members. What is the final price of the digital camera in terms of c, after the two discounts?

(A) $0.68c$

(B) $0.7c$

(C) $0.72c$

(D) $0.75c$

(E) $0.78c$

12. For which of the points shown in Figure 3 is $|x - 2y| > 9$?

(A) P

(B) Q

(C) R

(D) S

(E) T

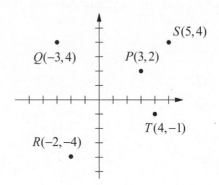

Figure 3

13. If $f(x)$ is a linear function such that $f(-1) = 6$ and $f(2) = 3$, then $f(5) =$

(A) –3   (B) –1   (C) 0   (D) 2   (E) 8

14. At an electronics store the number of a certain item sold is inversely proportional to the price of item. If 350 items are sold at a price of $48, what price should be charged to raise the number of items sold to 450?

(A) $35.95

(B) $37.33

(C) $39.67

(D) $40.98

(E) $41.56

15. For $x \neq 3$, $\dfrac{1}{x-3} + \dfrac{1}{3-x} =$

(A) 0

(B) $\dfrac{2}{x-3}$

(C) $\dfrac{2}{3-x}$

(D) $\dfrac{1}{(x-3)^2}$

(E) $\dfrac{1}{(x+3)(x-3)}$

16. In Figure 4, $\triangle ABC$ is a right triangle and $\overline{AC} \perp \overline{BD}$.
    If $AD = 10$ and $CD = 5$, what is the length of $\overline{BD}$?

(A) 6.2

(B) 6.8

(C) 7.1

(D) 7.9

(E) 8.6

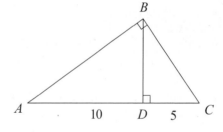

Figure 4

17. If the point $(-2, 7)$ is the midpoint of $(x, 3)$ and $(5, y)$,
    what is the value of $x + y$?

(A) −3   (B) 0   (C) 2   (D) 3   (E) 5

18. If $x^3 + 64 = -64$, then $x =$

(A) −8.00

(B) −5.04

(C) 0

(D) 5.04

(E) 8.00

19. If $t = \sqrt{\dfrac{2s}{g^2}}$ and g, s, and t are positive, which of the following

is equal to g?

(A) $\dfrac{2s}{t}$ (B) $\dfrac{t}{2s}$ (C) $\dfrac{t}{\sqrt{2s}}$ (D) $\dfrac{\sqrt{2s}}{t}$ (E) $\sqrt{\dfrac{2s}{t}}$

20. In Figure 5, the box-and-whisker plot shows the weights, in kilograms, of 15 students in a classroom. Which of the following is NOT true about the plot?

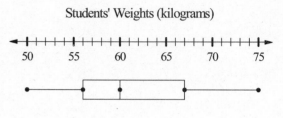

Students' Weights (kilograms)

Figure 5

(A) The median weight is 60 kilograms.

(B) The range of the data is 25.

(C) The lower quartile is 56 kilograms.

(D) 50% of the students weigh more than 60 kilograms.

(E) About 40% of the students weigh less than 60 kilograms.

21. If $i^2 = -1$, then all of the following expressions are equivalent to each other EXCEPT

(A) $i + i^5$

(B) $-i^3 + i^5$

(C) $i - i^7$

(D) $-i + i^{11}$

(E) $2i$

22. If the equation $ax^2 - 3x + 3 = 0$ has two real roots, which of the following is true about the value(s) of a?

(A) $a > \dfrac{3}{4}$

(B) $a < 0$

(C) $-\dfrac{3}{4} < a < \dfrac{3}{4}$

(D) $a > 0$

(E) $a < \dfrac{3}{4}$

23. If $x - \dfrac{1}{2}$ is a factor of $2x^3 - 3x^2 + kx - 1$, then $k =$

    (A) −3   (B) −1   (C) 3   (D) 4   (E) 6

24. Figure 6 shows the graph of $y = h(x)$. If the function f is

    defined as $f(x) = h(\dfrac{1}{2}x) + 3$, what is the value of $f(-4)$?

    (A) 0   (B) $\dfrac{1}{2}$ (C) 2   (D) $\dfrac{7}{2}$ (E) 5

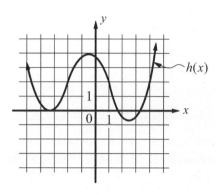

Figure 6

25. If $f(x) = \sqrt{x} + 4$ and $g(x) = f(f(x))$, then $g(\dfrac{1}{4}) =$

    (A) 2.7   (B) 3.3   (C) 4.5   (D) 5.6   (E) 6.1

26. Which of the following graphs represents the inequality

    $(x+3)(x^2 - 7x + 10) \geq 0$?

(A)

        2   5

(B)
    −3   2   5

(C)
    −3   2   5

(D)
    −3   2

(E)
    −3   5

27. If $0° < x < 90°$, then $\dfrac{\sin x}{\tan x} =$

(A) $\cos x$

(B) $\sec x$

(C) 0

(D) $\sin x \cos x$

(E) $\dfrac{\cos x}{\sin x}$

28. Figure 7 shows a dart board that is 20 inches long and 15 inches wide, on which twelve identical blue circles are painted. If 100 darts hit the board and of these 20 hit the blue circles, what is the approximate area of each circle in square inches?

(A) 3

(B) 5

(C) 8

(D) 10

(E) 12

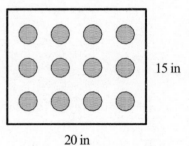

15 in

20 in

Figure 7

29. Which of the following could be the center of a circle tangent to the line $x = -4$ and the line $y = 3$?

(A) $(-3, 1)$

(B) $(-2, 0)$

(C) $(-2, -1)$

(D) $(-1, 1)$

(E) $(0, -1)$

30. If the 12th term of an arithmetic sequence is 50 and the 50th term is -26, what is the 1st term of the sequence?

(A) 54   (B) 60   (C) 66   (D) 72   (E) 78

31. If $f(x) = -(x-1)^2 + 3$ for $-1 \le x \le 2$, then which of
the following is the range of f?

(A) $\{y : -4 \le y \le 2\}$

(B) $\{y : -1 \le y \le 2\}$

(C) $\{y : -1 \le y \le 3\}$

(D) $\{y : 1 \le y \le 3\}$

(E) $\{y : 2 \le y \le 7\}$

32. If $f(x) = \sqrt{2-x}$ and $g(x) = x^2 - 1$, which of the
following could be the graph of $y = g(f(x))$?

(A)

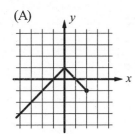

(B)

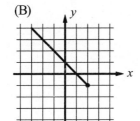

(C)

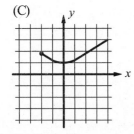

(D)

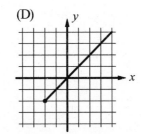

(E)

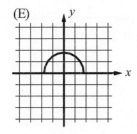

33. $\dfrac{3}{\csc^2 x} + \dfrac{3}{\sec^2 x} =$

    (A) $\dfrac{1}{3}$

    (B) 3

    (C) $3\tan^2 x$

    (D) $3\sin^2 x$

    (E) $3\cos^2 x$

34. If rectangle $ABCD$, shown in Figure 8, is rotated about side $\overline{BC}$, what is the volume of the space figure generated by the rotation?

    (A) 24π

    (B) 36π

    (C) 64π

    (D) 96π

    (E) 144π

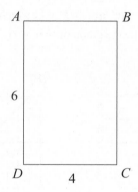

Figure 8

35. Figure 9 shows the graph of $f(x) = 2x + 1$. If θ is the angle formed by f and the x-axis, what is the angle measure of θ?

    (A) 63

    (B) 66

    (C) 69

    (D) 72

    (E) 75

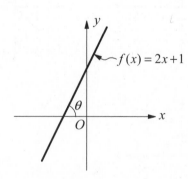

Figure 9

36. A class of 16 students was surveyed about the number of letters in their last names, with the following results:

- The average (arithmetic mean) number of letters in the last name was 5.75.

- The median number of letters in the last name was 5.5.

- The mode of the number of letters in the last name was 5.

Which of the following graphs could be a display of the survey results?

(A)

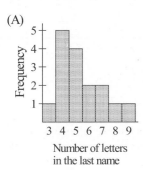

Number of letters
in the last name

(B)

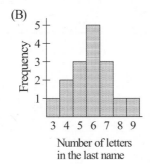

Number of letters
in the last name

(C)

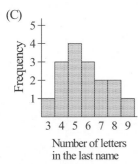

Number of letters
in the last name

(D)

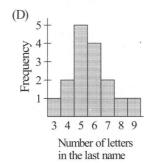

Number of letters
in the last name

(E)

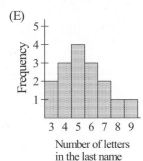

Number of letters
in the last name

37. A certain city has a population of 25,000 people at the end of 2002. If the population is increasing at a rate of 3 percent per year, what will the population of the town be at the end of 2012?

(A) 26,105

(B) 29,782

(C) 33,598

(D) 35,675

(E) 42,046

38. Figure 10 shows a right triangle ABC. If $CD = 5$, what is the area of the shaded region?

(A) 28

(B) 32

(C) 40

(D) 48

(E) 52

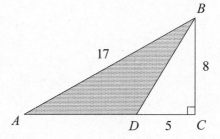

Figure 10

39. If the volume of a sphere is $\frac{9}{2}\pi$ in^3, what is the surface area of the sphere in square inches?

(A) 3π (B) $\frac{9}{2}\pi$ (C) 6π (D) 9π (E) $\frac{27}{2}\pi$

40. If $\log z = \frac{1}{2}\log w + \log x - 2\log y$, then $z =$

(A) $\frac{1}{2}(w + x) - 2y$

(B) $\sqrt{w} \cdot x - y^2$

(C) $\frac{w \cdot x}{4y}$

(D) $\frac{w \cdot x}{2y^2}$

(E) $\frac{\sqrt{w} \cdot x}{y^2}$

41. The radius of each wheel of a car is 1 foot. If the wheels are turning at the rate of 792 revolutions per minute, how many miles will the car travel in 3 hours? (1 mile = 5280 ft)

   (A) 42π miles

   (B) 46π miles

   (C) 50π miles

   (D) 54π miles

   (E) 58π miles

42. In a stack of 6 cards, each card is labeled with a different integer from 1 through 6. If two cards are selected at random without replacement, what is the probability that their sum will be more than 8?

   (A) $\dfrac{4}{15}$ (B) $\dfrac{1}{3}$ (C) $\dfrac{2}{5}$ (D) $\dfrac{7}{15}$ (E) $\dfrac{3}{5}$

43. In Figure 11, a plane parallel to the base of the cone passes through 9 cm from the base and divides the cone into two pieces. What is the volume of the smaller cone whose height is 6?

   (A) 6π

   (B) 8π

   (C) 10π

   (D) 12π

   (E) 14π

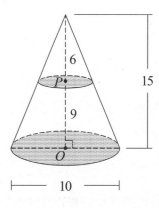

Figure 11

44. Which of the following equations could represent all points in a plane that are less than 4 units from the origin?

   (A) $x + y < 2$

   (B) $x + y < 4$

   (C) $x^2 + y^2 < 2$

   (D) $x^2 + y^2 < 4$

   (E) $x^2 + y^2 < 16$

45. The graph of the polynomial function $y = f(x)$ is shown in Figure 12. Which of the following is true about the graph of $y = f(x)$?

   I. $f(x)$ is decreasing on the interval $(-2, 1)$.

   II. $f(x)$ is positive on the interval $(0, \infty)$.

   III. $f(x)$ has three real zeros.

(A) I only

(B) I and II only

(C) II and III only

(D) I and III only

(E) I, II, and III

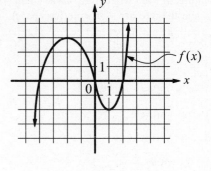

Figure 12

46. Joe walked from his home to the library at an average speed of 4 miles per hour, and returned home at an average speed of 3.2 miles per hour. If the total walking time for the round trip was 54 minutes, what is the distance from his home to the library?

(A) 1.2 miles

(B) 1.4 miles

(C) 1.6 miles

(D) 1.8 miles

(E) 2.0 miles

47. A transformation T maps every point (x, y) to the point $(2x, y-1)$. If P' and Q' are the image points of $P(-1, 3)$ and $Q(5, -2)$ under the transformation T, what is the length of $\overline{P'Q'}$?

(A) 9

(B) $6\sqrt{3}$

(C) 11

(D) $5\sqrt{5}$

(E) 13

48. In Figure 14, a square is inscribed in a quarter circle with radius 4. What is the perimeter of the shaded region?

(A) 8.0

(B) $4 + 4\sqrt{2}$

(C) 12.0

(D) $6 + 4\sqrt{2}$

(E) $8 + 4\sqrt{2}$

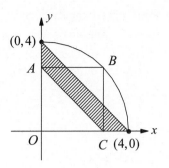

Figure 14

49. If $f(x) = \dfrac{x^2 + 3x + 2}{x + 1}$, which of the following is the graph of f?

(A)
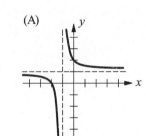

(B)
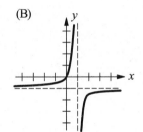

(C)
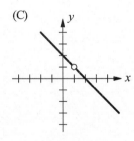

(D)
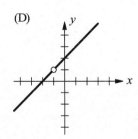

(E)
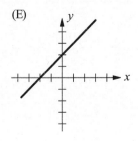

50. Figure 15 shows a right triangle where the length of side $\overline{AC}$ is x and the measure of angle A is $60°$. With A as the center and $\overline{AC}$ as a radius, an arc is drawn as shown. What is the area of the shaded region in terms of x?

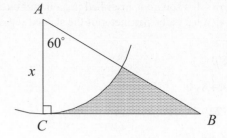

Figure 15

(A) $\dfrac{x^2(2\sqrt{2}-\pi)}{6}$

(B) $\dfrac{x^2(3\sqrt{2}-\pi)}{6}$

(C) $\dfrac{x^2(2\sqrt{3}-\pi)}{6}$

(D) $\dfrac{x^2(3\sqrt{3}-\pi)}{6}$

(E) $\dfrac{x^2(3\sqrt{3}-2\pi)}{6}$

STOP

IF YOU FINISH BEFORE TIME IS CALLED, YOU MAY CHECK YOUR WORK ON THIS TEST ONLY.
DO NOT TURN TO ANY OTHER TEST IN THIS BOOK.

Answer Key

1. B	2. C	3. B	4. E	5. A
6. D	7. D	8. E	9. C	10. A
11. C	12. B	13. C	14. B	15. A
16. C	17. C	18. B	19. D	20. E
21. D	22. E	23. C	24. E	25. E
26. B	27. A	28. B	29. E	30. D
31. C	32. B	33. B	34. D	35. A
36. C	37. C	38. C	39. D	40. E
41. D	42. A	43. B	44. E	45. D
46. C	47. E	48. C	49. D	50. D

Answers and Explanations

1. B

$$\frac{bc}{a^2} = \frac{b(4a)}{a^2} \qquad c = 4a$$
$$= \frac{4b}{a}$$
$$= \frac{4b}{6b} \qquad a = 6b$$
$$= \frac{4}{6} = \frac{2}{3}$$

2. C

$$a * b = |a - b|$$

$$[7 * (-5)] - [(-5) * 7]$$
$$= |7 - (-5)| - |(-5) - 7|$$
$$= |12| - |-12|$$
$$= 0$$

3. B

Let x = the number of 3-point questions, then
$32 - x$ = the number of 4-point questions.

$$3x + 4(32 - x) = 100$$

$$\Rightarrow \ 3x + 128 - 4x = 100$$
$$\Rightarrow \ 3x - 4x + 128 = 100$$
$$\Rightarrow \ x = 28$$

4. E

$$4^x + 4^x + 4^x + 4^x = \frac{1}{256}$$

$$\Rightarrow \ 4 \cdot 4^x = \frac{1}{256} \ \Rightarrow \ 4^{x+1} = \frac{1}{256}$$

$$\Rightarrow \ 4^{x+1} = \frac{1}{4^4} \ \Rightarrow \ 4^{x+1} = 4^{-4}$$

$$\Rightarrow \ x + 1 = -4 \ \Rightarrow \ x = -5$$

5. A

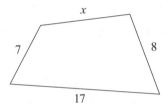

The length of a side of a quadrilateral cannot be greater than sum of the lengths of the other three sides.
Therefore $x < 7 + 17 + 8 \ \Rightarrow \ x < 32$, and
$17 < x + 7 + 8 \ \Rightarrow \ x > 2$.

The correct answer is (A).

6. D

$$\sqrt[3]{-16 x^3 y^7}$$
$$= (-2^4 x^3 y^7)^{\frac{1}{3}}$$
$$= (2 \cdot (-2)^3 x^3 y^6 \cdot y)^{\frac{1}{3}}$$
$$= (2y)^{\frac{1}{3}} \cdot (-2) x y^2$$
$$= -2 x y^2 \sqrt[3]{2y}$$

7. D

$$(x - y + 2)(x + y - 2)$$
$$= [(x - y) + 2][(x + y) - 2]$$

$$= (x-y)(x+y) - 2(x-y) + 2(x+y) - 4$$
$$= (x^2 - y^2) - 2x + 2y + 2x + 2y - 4$$
$$= (x^2 - y^2) + 4y - 4$$

8. E

$$\frac{\sqrt{3}-3}{\sqrt{3}+1}$$

$$= \frac{(\sqrt{3}-3)(\sqrt{3}-1)}{(\sqrt{3}+1)(\sqrt{3}-1)}$$

$$= \frac{3 - \sqrt{3} - 3\sqrt{3} + 3}{3-1}$$

$$= \frac{6 - 4\sqrt{3}}{2}$$

$$= 3 - 2\sqrt{3}$$

9. C

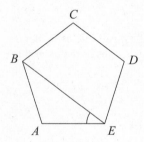

Each interior angle of a regular pentagon
$$= \frac{(n-2)180}{n} = \frac{(5-2)180}{5} = 108$$
In $\triangle ABE$, $AB = AE$, therefore
$m\angle EBA = m\angle BEA$.

$$m\angle BEA = \frac{1}{2}(180 - 108) = 36$$

10. A

$$|3x - 2| \geq 5$$
$$\Rightarrow \quad 3x - 2 \leq -5 \quad \text{or} \quad 3x - 2 \geq 5$$
$$\Rightarrow \quad 3x \leq -3 \quad \text{or} \quad 3x \geq 7$$
$$\Rightarrow \quad x \leq -1 \quad \text{or} \quad x \geq \frac{7}{3}$$

11. C

Price of the camera after the first discount
$$= c - 0.2c = 0.8c$$

Price of the camera after the second discount

$$\underset{\substack{\text{new price after} \\ \text{the first discount}}}{= \quad 0.8c} \quad \underset{\substack{\text{additional 10\%} \\ \text{discount off new price}}}{-0.1(0.8c)} = 0.72c$$

12. B

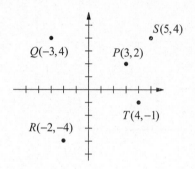

$$|x - 2y| > 9$$

Test each answer choice.

(A) $P(3,2)$ $|3 - 2(2)| > 9$ Not true

(B) $Q(-3,4)$ $|-3 - 2(4)| > 9$ True

(C) $R(-2,-4)$ $|-2 - 2(-4)| > 9$ Not true

(D) $S(5,4)$ $|5 - 2(4)| > 9$ Not true

(E) $T(4,-1)$ $|4 - 2(-1)| > 9$ Not true

13. C

If $f(x)$ is a linear function, then $f(x) = mx + b$.
$$f(-1) = 6 \Rightarrow m(-1) + b = 6 \Rightarrow -m + b = 6$$
$$f(2) = 3 \Rightarrow m(2) + b = 3 \Rightarrow 2m + b = 3$$

Solve the equations for b, and make substitutions.

$$\left.\begin{array}{l} b = m + 6 \\ b = -2m + 3 \end{array}\right\} \Rightarrow m + 6 = -2m + 3$$
$$\Rightarrow m = -1$$
$$\Rightarrow b = 5$$

Therefore $f(x) = -x + 5$.
$$f(5) = -(5) + 5 = 0$$

14. B

Let $y =$ the number of items sold, and $x =$ the price of the item.

$y = \dfrac{k}{x}$ Inverse variation

$350 = \dfrac{k}{48}$ $y = 350$ and $x = 48$

$k = 16,800$

$y = \dfrac{16,800}{x}$ An equation of inverse variation

$450 = \dfrac{16,800}{x}$ $y = 450$

$x = 37.33$

15. A

$\dfrac{1}{x-3} + \dfrac{1}{3-x}$

$= \dfrac{1}{x-3} + \dfrac{1}{-(x-3)}$

$= \dfrac{1}{x-3} - \dfrac{1}{x-3}$

$= 0$

16. C

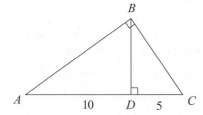

In the figure above $\triangle ABD \sim \triangle BCD$.

$\dfrac{AD}{BD} = \dfrac{BD}{CD} \Rightarrow \dfrac{10}{BD} = \dfrac{BD}{5}$

$\Rightarrow BD^2 = 50 \Rightarrow BD = \sqrt{50} \approx 7.07$

17. C

Use the midpoint formula.

$(-2, 7) = \left(\dfrac{x+5}{2}, \dfrac{3+y}{2}\right)$

$\Rightarrow -2 = \dfrac{x+5}{2}$ and $7 = \dfrac{3+y}{2}$

$\Rightarrow x = -9$ and $y = 11$

$x + y = -9 + 11 = 2$

18. B

$x^3 + 64 = -64$

$x^3 = -128$

$x = (-128)^{\frac{1}{3}} \approx -5.04$

19. D

$t = \sqrt{\dfrac{2s}{g^2}}$

$(t)^2 = \left(\sqrt{\dfrac{2s}{g^2}}\right)^2$ Square both sides.

$t^2 = \dfrac{2s}{g^2}$

$g^2 = \dfrac{2s}{t^2}$

$g = \sqrt{\dfrac{2s}{t^2}} = \dfrac{\sqrt{2s}}{t}$

20. E

Students' Weights (kilograms)

The box-and-whisker plot shows that the median number is 60. We can conclude that about 50% of the students weigh less than 60 kilograms and about 50% of the students weigh more than 60 kilograms.

The range is $75 - 50$, or 25.

All the answer choices give correct information about the box-and-whisker plot except (E).

21. D

$i^2 = -1$ and $i^4 = i^2 \cdot i^2 = (-1)(-1) = 1$

(A) $i + i^5 = i + i^4 \cdot i = 2i$

(B) $-i^3 + i^5 = -i \cdot i^2 + i \cdot i^4 = i + i = 2i$

(C) $i - i^7 = i - i^4 \cdot i^2 \cdot i = i - (1)(-1)i = 2i$

(D) $-i + i^{11} = -i + (i^4)^2 \cdot i^3 = -i + i^3 = -i - i = -2i$

(E) $2i$

22. E

If a quadratic equation $ax^2 + bx + c = 0$ has two real roots, then $b^2 - 4ac > 0$.

$ax^2 - 3x + 3 = 0$

$(-3)^2 - 4(a)(3) > 0$

$9 - 12a > 0$

$9 > 12a$

$\dfrac{9}{12} > a$, or $\dfrac{3}{4} > a$

23. C

$f(x) = 2x^3 - 3x^2 + kx - 1$

If $x - \dfrac{1}{2}$ is a factor of $f(x)$, then $f(\dfrac{1}{2}) = 0$

$f(\dfrac{1}{2}) = 2(\dfrac{1}{2})^3 - 3(\dfrac{1}{2})^2 + k(\dfrac{1}{2}) - 1 = 0$

$\Rightarrow \dfrac{1}{4} - \dfrac{3}{4} + \dfrac{1}{2}k - 1 = 0 \Rightarrow \dfrac{1}{2}k = \dfrac{3}{2}$

$\Rightarrow k = 3$

24. E

$(-2, h(-2))$

25. E

$f(x) = h(\dfrac{1}{2}x) + 3$

$f(-4) = h(\dfrac{1}{2} \cdot -4) + 3 = h(-2) + 3$

The graph shows that $h(-2) = 2$.

Therefore $f(-4) = h(-2) + 3 = 2 + 3 = 5$.

25. E

$f(x) = \sqrt{x} + 4$ and $g(x) = f(f(x))$

$g(\dfrac{1}{4}) = f(f(\dfrac{1}{4}))$ 　　　　　　$x = \dfrac{1}{4}$

$\quad = f(\sqrt{\dfrac{1}{4}} + 4)$ 　　　　　$f(\dfrac{1}{4}) = \sqrt{\dfrac{1}{4}} + 4$

$\quad = f(\dfrac{1}{2} + 4)$ 　　　　　　$\sqrt{\dfrac{1}{4}} = \dfrac{1}{2}$

$\quad = f(\dfrac{9}{2})$

$\quad = \sqrt{\dfrac{9}{2}} + 4$ 　　　　　　$f(\dfrac{9}{2}) = \sqrt{\dfrac{9}{2}} + 4$

$\quad \approx 2.1 + 4 = 6.1$

26. B

$(x + 3)(x^2 - 7x + 10) \geq 0$

$(x + 3)(x - 2)(x - 5) \geq 0$

The left side of the inequality equals zero for $x = -3$, $x = 2$, and $x = 5$. These three numbers divide the number line into four intervals.

Eliminate answer choices (A), (D), and (E).

Test values in each part of the interval.

Try $x = 0$. $(0 + 3)(0 - 2)(0 - 5) \geq 0$ 　　True.

Try $x = 3$. $(3 + 3)(3 - 2)(3 - 5) \geq 0$ 　　Not True.

Choice (B) is correct.

27. A

$\dfrac{\sin x}{\tan x} = \dfrac{\sin x}{\dfrac{\sin x}{\cos x}} = \dfrac{\sin x \cos x}{\sin x} = \cos x$

28. B

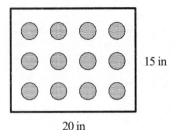

15 in

20 in

Let r = the radius of each circle.

Area of each circle = πr^2

Area of 12 circles = $12\pi r^2$

Since 20 out of 100 darts hit the blue circles,

$$\frac{\text{Area of 12 circles}}{\text{Area of rectangle}} = \frac{12\pi r^2}{20 \cdot 15} = \frac{20}{100}$$

$\Rightarrow 1200\pi r^2 = 6000$

$\Rightarrow \pi r^2 = \dfrac{6000}{1200} = 5$.

The area of each circle is about 5 in^2.

29. E

Make a drawing.

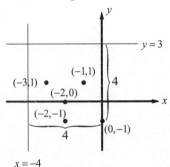

If the center of a circle is tangent to the line $x = -4$ and the line $y = 3$, the distance from the center to $x = -4$ and $y = 3$ must be equal. The distance from $(0, -1)$ to $x = -4$ is $|-4 - 0| = 4$, and the distance from $(0, -1)$ to $y = 3$ is $|3 - (-1)| = 4$.

Choice (E) is correct.

30. D

The nth term of an arithmetic sequence is

$a_n = a_1 + (n-1)d$

$a_{12} = a_1 + (12-1)d = 50$ 12th term is 50.

$a_{50} = a_1 + (50-1)d = -26$ 50th term is -26.

Simplify the two equations and subtract one equation from the other.

$a_1 + 11d = 50$

$-\underline{\begin{vmatrix} a_1 + 49d = -26 \end{vmatrix}}$

$\quad -38d = 76$

$\qquad d = -2$

$a_1 + 11(-2) = 50$ Substitute $d = -2$.

$a_1 = 72$

31. C

Use a graphing calculator to graph

$f(x) = -(x-1)^2 + 3$ for $-1 \le x \le 2$.

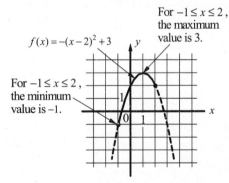

For $-1 \le x \le 2$, the range of f is $\{y : -1 \le y \le 3\}$.

32. B

$f(x) = \sqrt{2-x}$ and $g(x) = x^2 - 1$

$g(f(x)) = g(\sqrt{2-x})$

$\qquad\quad = (\sqrt{2-x})^2 - 1$

$\qquad\quad = 1 - x$

$\sqrt{2-x}$ must be defined for x to be in the domain of $g(f(x))$.

$2 - x \ge 0 \Rightarrow x \le 2$

$g(f(x))$ is defined when $x \le 2$.

(B) is the correct answer.

33. B

$$\frac{3}{\csc^2 x} + \frac{3}{\sec^2 x}$$

$$= 3\sin^2 x + 3\cos^2 x$$

$$= 3(\sin^2 x + \cos^2 x)$$

$$= 3$$

34. D

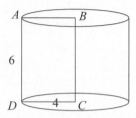

The cylinder generated by rotating the rectangle about side $\overline{BC}$ has radius 4 and height 6.

Volume of the cylinder $= \pi r^2 h = \pi(4)^2 \cdot 6 = 96\pi$

35. A

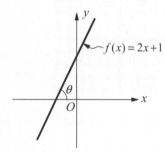

$f(x) = 2x + 1$ The slope of f is 2.

$$\tan\theta = \frac{\text{rise}}{\text{run}} = \frac{2}{1}$$

$$\theta = \tan^{-1}(2) \approx 63.43°$$

36. C

- The average (arithmetic mean) number of letters in the last name was 5.75.

- The median number of letters in the last name was 5.5.

- The mode of the number of letters in the last name was 5.

To save time, find the median and mode in each answer choice before finding the average.

(A)

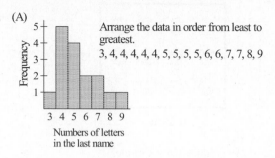

Arrange the data in order from least to greatest.

3, 4, 4, 4, 4, 4, 5, 5, 5, 5, 6, 6, 7, 7, 8, 9

Median $= 5$ and mode $= 4$.

(A) is not the correct answer.

(B)

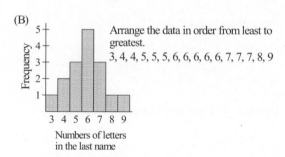

Arrange the data in order from least to greatest.

3, 4, 4, 5, 5, 5, 6, 6, 6, 6, 7, 7, 7, 8, 9

Median $= 6$ and mode $= 6$.

(B) is not the correct answer.

(C)

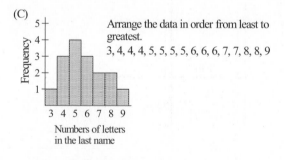

Arrange the data in order from least to greatest.

3, 4, 4, 4, 5, 5, 5, 5, 6, 6, 6, 7, 7, 8, 8, 9

Median $= \frac{5+6}{2} = 5.5$ and mode $= 5$.

$$\text{Average} = \frac{3 + 4 \cdot 3 + 5 \cdot 4 + 6 \cdot 3 + 7 \cdot 2 + 8 \cdot 2 + 9}{16}$$

$$= 5.75$$

(C) is the correct answer.

37. C

Use the compound interest formula.

$A = P(1+r)^t$, where $P = $ the initial population count, $r = $ the growth rate, and $t = $ the number of years elapsed.

$A = 25,000(1+0.03)^{10}$

$\quad = 25,000(1.03)^{10}$

$\quad = 33,598$

38. C

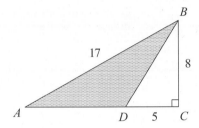

$AB^2 = AC^2 + BC^2$ Pythagorean theorem

$17^2 = AC^2 + 8^2$

$AC^2 = 17^2 - 8^2 = 225$

$AC = \sqrt{225} = 15$

$AD = AC - DC = 15 - 5 = 10$

Area of the shaded region

$= \frac{1}{2} AD \cdot BC$

$= \frac{1}{2}(10)(8)$

$= 40$

39. D

Volume of the sphere $= \frac{9}{2}\pi$

$\Rightarrow \frac{4}{3}\pi r^3 = \frac{9}{2}\pi \Rightarrow r^3 = \frac{27}{8}$

$\Rightarrow r = \frac{3}{2}$

Surface area of the sphere

$= 4\pi r^2$

$= 4\pi(\frac{3}{2})^2$

$= 9\pi$

40. E

$\log z$

$= \frac{1}{2}\log w + \log x - 2\log y$

$= \log w^{\frac{1}{2}} + \log x - \log y^2$ $\log_b M^p = p \cdot \log_b M$

$= \log \frac{w^{\frac{1}{2}} \cdot x}{y^2}$ Properties of logs

$z = \frac{\sqrt{w} \cdot x}{y^2}$ Answer

41. D

The distance traveled by a wheel

$= 2\pi r \cdot$ number of revolutions

$= 2\pi(1 \text{ ft}) \cdot (792\text{rpm}) \cdot (60\text{min}) \cdot (3 \text{ hours})$

$= 285,120\pi$ ft

$= 285,120\pi \text{ ft} \cdot \frac{1 \text{ mile}}{5280 \text{ ft}}$

$= 54\pi$ miles

42. A

Make a diagram. The diagram shows a total of 15 outcomes.

1,2 2,3 3,4 <u>4,5</u> <u>5,6</u>

1,3 2,4 3,5 <u>4,6</u>

1,4 2,5 <u>3,6</u>

1,5 2,6

1,6

Four of them have a sum of at least 9.

$P(\text{sum is more than 8}) = \frac{4}{15}$

43. B

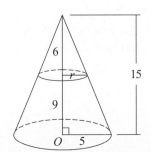

Set up a proportion to find the radius of the smaller cone.

$$\frac{6}{r} = \frac{15}{5} \Rightarrow r = 2$$

Volume of the smaller cone

$$= \frac{1}{3}\pi(2)^2(6) = 8\pi$$

44. E

The locus of points that are 4 units from the origin is the circle whose center is $(0,0)$ and radius is 4.

The equation is $x^2 + y^2 = 4^2$.

The locus of points that are less than 4 units from the origin is all the points inside the circle.

The inequality $x^2 + y^2 < 4^2$ represents the locus of points that are less than 4 units from the origin.

45. D

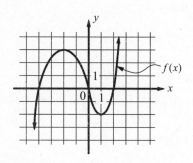

$f(x)$ is increasing on the intervals $(-\infty, -2)$, and $(1, \infty)$.

$f(x)$ is decreasing on the interval $(-2, 1)$.

$f(x)$ is negative on the intervals $(-\infty, -4)$, and $(0, 2)$.

$f(x)$ is positive on the intervals $(-4, 0)$, and $(2, \infty)$.

-4, 0, and 2 are the zeros of the function. Therefore $f(x)$ has three real zeros.

Roman numerals I and III are true.

46. C

Let $d =$ the distance from home to the library, and $t =$ the time in hours it took for Joe to walk from his home to the library.

Then $\frac{54}{60} - t$, or $\frac{9}{10} - t$, is the time in hours it took for Joe to walk from the library to his home.

Use the formula $d = r \cdot t$.

$d = 4t$	Going distance in terms of t.
$d = 3.2\left(\frac{9}{10} - t\right)$	Returning distance in terms of t.
$4t = 3.2\left(\frac{9}{10} - t\right)$	Going distance and returning distance are the same.

$$\Rightarrow 4t = 2.88 - 3.2t$$
$$\Rightarrow 7.2t = 2.88$$
$$\Rightarrow t = 0.4$$

$$d = 4t = 4(0.4) = 1.6$$

47. E

Mapping T maps each point (x, y) to the point $(2x, y-1)$. For points P and Q, multiply the x-coordinate by 2, and subtract 1 from the y-coordinate.

$$T : (x, y) \rightarrow (2x, y-1)$$
$$T : (-1, 3) \rightarrow (2 \cdot (-1), 3-1) = (-2, 2) = P'$$
$$T : (5, -2) \rightarrow (2 \cdot 5, -2-1) = (10, -3) = Q'$$

$$P'Q' = \sqrt{(10+2)^2 + (-3-2)^2}$$
$$= \sqrt{169}$$
$$= 13$$

48. C

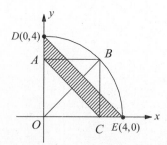

In the figure above, the radius of the quarter circle is 4, and $ABCD$ is a square, so $OB = AC = 4$.

Triangle AOC is a $45°$-$45°$-$90°$ triangle, so

$$AC = \sqrt{2} \cdot AO \implies 4 = \sqrt{2} \cdot AO$$

$$\implies AO = \frac{4}{\sqrt{2}} = \frac{4\sqrt{2}}{\sqrt{2} \cdot \sqrt{2}} = \frac{4\sqrt{2}}{2} = 2\sqrt{2} \ .$$

$$AD = DO - AO = 4 - 2\sqrt{2}$$

Triangle DOE is also a $45°$-$45°$-$90°$ triangle, so

$$DE = \sqrt{2} \cdot DO = 4\sqrt{2} \ .$$

Perimeter of the shaded region
$$= AD + DE + CE + AC$$
$$= (4 - 2\sqrt{2}) + 4\sqrt{2} + (4 - 2\sqrt{2}) + 4$$
$$= 12$$

49. D

$$f(x) = \frac{x^2 + 3x + 2}{x+1} = \frac{(x+1)(x+2)}{x+1} = x + 2$$

The graph of $f(x)$ is the same as the graph of $y = x + 2$, except that it is not continuous at $x = -1$, where $f(x)$ is undefined.

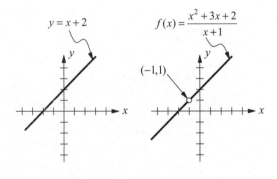

(D) is the correct answer.

50. D

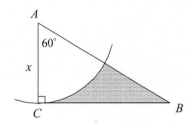

Triangle ABC is a $30°$-$60°$-$90°$ triangle, so

$$BC = \sqrt{3}x \ .$$

Area of $\triangle ABC = \frac{1}{2}(x)(\sqrt{3}x) = \frac{\sqrt{3}x^2}{2}$

Area of the sector $= \pi x^2 \cdot \frac{60}{360} = \frac{\pi x^2}{6}$

Area of the shaded region
$$= \text{Area of } \triangle ABC - \text{Area of sector}$$
$$= \frac{\sqrt{3}x^2}{2} - \frac{\pi x^2}{6}$$
$$= \frac{3\sqrt{3}x^2 - \pi x^2}{6}$$
$$= \frac{x^2(3\sqrt{3} - \pi)}{6}$$

Test Form D
Mathematics Level 1

Answer Sheet

1 Ⓐ Ⓑ Ⓒ Ⓓ Ⓔ		21 Ⓐ Ⓑ Ⓒ Ⓓ Ⓔ		41 Ⓐ Ⓑ Ⓒ Ⓓ Ⓔ			
2 Ⓐ Ⓑ Ⓒ Ⓓ Ⓔ		22 Ⓐ Ⓑ Ⓒ Ⓓ Ⓔ		42 Ⓐ Ⓑ Ⓒ Ⓓ Ⓔ			
3 Ⓐ Ⓑ Ⓒ Ⓓ Ⓔ		23 Ⓐ Ⓑ Ⓒ Ⓓ Ⓔ		43 Ⓐ Ⓑ Ⓒ Ⓓ Ⓔ			
4 Ⓐ Ⓑ Ⓒ Ⓓ Ⓔ		24 Ⓐ Ⓑ Ⓒ Ⓓ Ⓔ		44 Ⓐ Ⓑ Ⓒ Ⓓ Ⓔ			
5 Ⓐ Ⓑ Ⓒ Ⓓ Ⓔ		25 Ⓐ Ⓑ Ⓒ Ⓓ Ⓔ		45 Ⓐ Ⓑ Ⓒ Ⓓ Ⓔ			
6 Ⓐ Ⓑ Ⓒ Ⓓ Ⓔ		26 Ⓐ Ⓑ Ⓒ Ⓓ Ⓔ		46 Ⓐ Ⓑ Ⓒ Ⓓ Ⓔ			
7 Ⓐ Ⓑ Ⓒ Ⓓ Ⓔ		27 Ⓐ Ⓑ Ⓒ Ⓓ Ⓔ		47 Ⓐ Ⓑ Ⓒ Ⓓ Ⓔ			
8 Ⓐ Ⓑ Ⓒ Ⓓ Ⓔ		28 Ⓐ Ⓑ Ⓒ Ⓓ Ⓔ		48 Ⓐ Ⓑ Ⓒ Ⓓ Ⓔ			
9 Ⓐ Ⓑ Ⓒ Ⓓ Ⓔ		29 Ⓐ Ⓑ Ⓒ Ⓓ Ⓔ		49 Ⓐ Ⓑ Ⓒ Ⓓ Ⓔ			
10 Ⓐ Ⓑ Ⓒ Ⓓ Ⓔ		30 Ⓐ Ⓑ Ⓒ Ⓓ Ⓔ		50 Ⓐ Ⓑ Ⓒ Ⓓ Ⓔ			
11 Ⓐ Ⓑ Ⓒ Ⓓ Ⓔ		31 Ⓐ Ⓑ Ⓒ Ⓓ Ⓔ					
12 Ⓐ Ⓑ Ⓒ Ⓓ Ⓔ		32 Ⓐ Ⓑ Ⓒ Ⓓ Ⓔ					
13 Ⓐ Ⓑ Ⓒ Ⓓ Ⓔ		33 Ⓐ Ⓑ Ⓒ Ⓓ Ⓔ					
14 Ⓐ Ⓑ Ⓒ Ⓓ Ⓔ		34 Ⓐ Ⓑ Ⓒ Ⓓ Ⓔ					
15 Ⓐ Ⓑ Ⓒ Ⓓ Ⓔ		35 Ⓐ Ⓑ Ⓒ Ⓓ Ⓔ					
16 Ⓐ Ⓑ Ⓒ Ⓓ Ⓔ		36 Ⓐ Ⓑ Ⓒ Ⓓ Ⓔ					
17 Ⓐ Ⓑ Ⓒ Ⓓ Ⓔ		37 Ⓐ Ⓑ Ⓒ Ⓓ Ⓔ					
18 Ⓐ Ⓑ Ⓒ Ⓓ Ⓔ		38 Ⓐ Ⓑ Ⓒ Ⓓ Ⓔ					
19 Ⓐ Ⓑ Ⓒ Ⓓ Ⓔ		39 Ⓐ Ⓑ Ⓒ Ⓓ Ⓔ					
20 Ⓐ Ⓑ Ⓒ Ⓓ Ⓔ		40 Ⓐ Ⓑ Ⓒ Ⓓ Ⓔ					

Reference Information

The following information is for your reference in answering some of the questions on this test.

Volume of a right circular cone with radius r and height h: $V = \dfrac{1}{3}\pi r^2 h$

Lateral area of a right circular cone with base circumference C and slant height ℓ: $S = \dfrac{1}{2}C\ell$

Volume of a sphere with radius r: $V = \dfrac{4}{3}\pi r^3$

Surface area of a sphere with radius r: $S = 4\pi r^2$

Volume of a pyramid with base area B and height h: $V = \dfrac{1}{3}Bh$

Test Form D
SAT Subject Test in Mathematics Level 1

50 Questions   1 hour

For each of the following problems, decide which is the BEST of the choices given. If the exact numerical value is not one of the choices, select the choice that best approximates this value. Then fill in the corresponding circle on the answer sheet.

Notes: (1) A calculator will be necessary for answering some of the questions on this test. For each question you will have to decide whether or not you should use a calculator. Programmable calculators and calculators that can display graphs are permitted.

(2) The only angle measure used on the Math Level 1 Test is degree measure. Make sure your calculator is in the degree mode.

(3) Figures that accompany problems on this test are intended to provide information useful in solving the problems. They are drawn as accurately as possible EXCEPT when it is stated in a specific problem that the figure is not drawn to scale. All figures lie in a plane unless otherwise indicated.

(4) Unless otherwise specified, the domain of any function f is assumed to be the set of all real numbers x for which $f(x)$ is a real number.

(5) Reference information that may be useful in answering the questions on this test can be found on the page preceding Question 1.

1. If $-(3-2x) = x+3$, then $x =$

(A) -2 (B) -1 (C) 0 (D) 1 (E) 6

2. Which of the following is the slope of the line $2x + 3y = 5$?

(A) $-\dfrac{2}{3}$ (B) $-\dfrac{3}{2}$ (C) $\dfrac{2}{3}$ (D) $\dfrac{5}{2}$ (E) $\dfrac{5}{3}$

3. If $8x^{-3} = -1$, what is the value of $(\dfrac{x}{6})^{-2}$?

(A) 9 (B) 3 (C) $\dfrac{1}{3}$ (D) $-\dfrac{1}{3}$ (E) -3

4. Which of the following is the counterexample to the statement "For all integer values of n, $n^2 + n - 7$ is a prime number"?

(A) 3   (B) 4   (C) 5   (D) 6   (E) 9

5. In Figure 1, $AB = 3BC$ and M is the midpoint of $\overline{AB}$. If $MC = 10$, then $AC =$

(A) 12   (B) 14   (C) 16   (D) 18   (E) 20

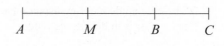

Figure 1

6. What is the number of digits in the number obtained by multiplying 12,345,678 and 8910?

(A) 10   (B) 11   (C) 12   (D) 13   (E) 14

7. Bart wanted to buy a certain CD whose original price was p. During a special sale, the price of the CD was reduced to 75%. If the sales tax was 8% and Bart paid the cashier $15 and received $1.27 in change, which of the following equations can be used to find the original price p of the CD?

(A) $(15 - p)0.75 \times 1.08 = 1.27$

(B) $15 - (0.75p) \times 1.08 = 1.27$

(C) $(15 - 0.75p) \cdot 1.08 = 1.27$

(D) $(15 - 1.08p) \times 0.75 = 1.27$

(E) $(15 - 0.75p) + 1.08 = 1.27$

8. For $a > 0$, $\dfrac{\sqrt[6]{a}}{\sqrt{a}} =$

(A) $\sqrt[3]{a}$ (B) $\sqrt{a}$ (C) $\dfrac{1}{\sqrt[3]{a}}$ (D) $\dfrac{1}{\sqrt{a}}$ (E) $\dfrac{1}{\sqrt[4]{a}}$

9. If the point $P(a,b)$ is the midpoint of the x-intercept and y-intercept of the line $y = \dfrac{1}{2}x + 3$, what is the value of $a+b$?

 (A) $-\dfrac{9}{2}$ (B) $-\dfrac{3}{2}$ (C) $-\dfrac{1}{2}$ (D) $\dfrac{3}{2}$ (E) $\dfrac{5}{2}$

10. The stem-and-leaf plot in Figure 2 shows the lifespans of 12 animals in the wild. Which of the following is true of the lifespans of the wild animals?

 I. The average (arithmetic mean) lifespan is less than 16.

 II. The median lifespan is 15.

 III. About 50% of the wild animals have lifespans of at least 20 years.

 (A) I only

 (B) II only

 (C) I and II only

 (D) I and III only

 (E) I, II, and III

0	7
1	0 0 2 2 5 5 5
2	0 5
3	2
4	2

$2 \mid 9 = 29$ years

Figure 2

11. If $\dfrac{x}{x+1} - \dfrac{3}{x-2} = \dfrac{11}{x^2 - x - 2}$, which of the following is the solution set for the equation?

 (A) $\{-2\}$

 (B) $\{-7\}$

 (C) $\{-2, -7\}$

 (D) $\{-2, 7\}$

 (E) $\{-2, 5\}$

12. If $f(x) = \dfrac{x}{x+2}$, then $f(\sqrt{2}-3) =$

(A) $1-2\sqrt{2}$

(B) $-1+2\sqrt{2}$

(C) $-1-2\sqrt{2}$

(D) $\dfrac{-2-\sqrt{2}}{2}$

(E) $\dfrac{1-\sqrt{2}}{2}$

13. In Figure 3, if $\triangle OPQ$ is equilateral, what is the slope of segment PQ?

(A) $-\sqrt{3}$

(B) $-\dfrac{\sqrt{3}}{2}$

(C) $\sqrt{3}$

(D) $-\dfrac{1}{\sqrt{3}}$

(E) $\dfrac{2}{\sqrt{3}}$

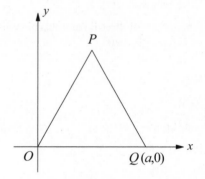

Figure 3

14. What are all values of x for which $3x - x^2 \geq -x$?

(A) $0 \leq x \leq 2$

(B) $-4 \leq x \leq 0$

(C) $0 \leq x \leq 4$

(D) $x \leq 0$ or $x \geq 4$

(E) $x \leq -4$ or $x \geq 0$

15. What is the domain of $f(x) = \sqrt[3]{9 - x^2}$?

    (A) $x \leq 3$

    (B) $x \geq 3$

    (C) $-3 \leq x \leq 3$

    (D) $x \leq -3$ or $3 \leq x$

    (E) All real numbers

16. In Figure 4, the equation of line ℓ is

    (A) $x - y = -3$

    (B) $x + y = -3$

    (C) $x = -3$

    (D) $x = 0$

    (E) $y = -3$

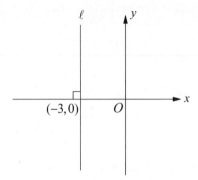

Figure 4

17. Which of the following equations have two distinct real solutions?

    I. $x^2 = 6x - 9$

    II. $x^3 - 8 = 0$

    III. $x^2 = -x$

    (A) I only

    (B) II only

    (C) III only

    (D) I and II only

    (E) II and III only

18. If $a - 2$, a, and $a + 6$ are the first three terms of a geometric sequence, what is the value of a?

    (A) 3   (B) 6   (C) 9   (D) 12   (E) 15

19. If points $(-3,0)$, $(0,5)$, $(6,2)$, and $(3,k)$ are the vertices of a parallelogram, then $k =$

   (A) -1 (B) -2 (C) -3 (D) -4 (E) -5

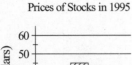

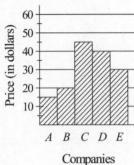
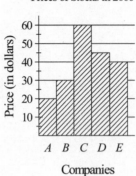

Figure 5

20. The graph in Figure 5 shows the prices of stocks of selected companies in 1995 and 2000. Which company's stocks had the greatest percent increase from 1995 to 2000?

   (A) A   (B) B   (C) C   (D) D   (E) E

21. In Figure 6, quadrilateral $PQRS$ is inscribed in a circle. Which of the following must be true?

   I. $m\angle P + m\angle R = m\angle Q + m\angle S$

   II. $\overline{PQ} \cong \overline{RS}$

   III. $m\angle S = \dfrac{1}{2}m\widehat{PQR}$

   (A) I only

   (B) II only

   (C) III only

   (D) I and III only

   (E) I, II, and III

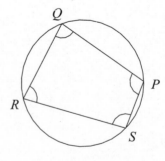

Figure 6

22. At a certain gift shop, a box of greeting cards costs between $12 and 18. Which of the following inequalities can be used to determine the price c of a box of greeting cards?

(A) $|c-6| \le 12$

(B) $|c-12| \le 6$

(C) $|c-12| \le 3$

(D) $|c-15| \le 3$

(E) $|c-15| \le 6$

23. In Figure 5, a rectangular region is divided into a square and three smaller rectangular regions. If the area of the square is x^2 and the areas of two of the rectangular regions are $7x$ and $3x$, what is the area of the shaded region?

(A) 18

(B) 21

(C) 24

(D) 27

(E) 30

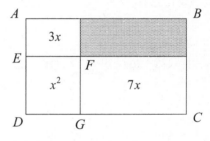

Figure 5

24. The margin of sampling error is modeled by an expression $2\sqrt{\dfrac{p(1-p)}{n}}$, where p is the percentage of people who responded to the survey in a certain way and n is the size of the sample (number of people surveyed). In a survey taken at local high school, 650 students were randomly selected and 82% of those surveyed said they preferred a certain extracurricular activity. What is the margin of error to the nearest percent?

(A) 2%

(B) 3%

(C) 4%

(D) 5%

(E) 6%

25. If $0° < \theta < 90°$, then $\dfrac{\cos(90° - \theta)}{\cos\theta} =$

(A) -1

(B) 1

(C) $-\tan\theta$

(D) $\cot\theta$

(E) $\tan\theta$

26. The table in Figure 6 shows the number of DVD players that were sold during a special holiday sale at a certain electronics store. If the prices of models A, B, and C are \$79, \$109, and \$159, respectively, which of the following matrix representations gives the total income, in dollars, received from the sales of DVD players for each day of the sale?

	Friday	Saturday	Sunday
Model A	23	45	32
Model B	18	38	26
Model C	15	34	24

Figure 6

(A) $\begin{bmatrix} 23 & 45 & 32 \\ 18 & 38 & 26 \\ 15 & 34 & 24 \end{bmatrix} \cdot \begin{bmatrix} 79 & 109 & 159 \end{bmatrix}$

(B) $\begin{bmatrix} 79 & 109 & 159 \end{bmatrix} \cdot \begin{bmatrix} 23 & 45 & 32 \\ 18 & 38 & 26 \\ 15 & 34 & 24 \end{bmatrix}$

(C) $\begin{bmatrix} 23 & 45 & 32 \\ 18 & 38 & 26 \\ 15 & 34 & 24 \end{bmatrix} \cdot \begin{bmatrix} 79 \\ 109 \\ 159 \end{bmatrix}$

(D) $\begin{bmatrix} 79 \\ 109 \\ 159 \end{bmatrix} \cdot \begin{bmatrix} 23 & 45 & 32 \\ 18 & 38 & 26 \\ 15 & 34 & 24 \end{bmatrix}$

(E) $\begin{bmatrix} 23 & 45 & 32 \\ 18 & 38 & 26 \\ 15 & 34 & 24 \end{bmatrix} \cdot \begin{bmatrix} 79 + 109 + 159 \end{bmatrix}$

27. If $(2 - i)^2 - 3 = a - bi$, where a and b are real numbers and $i^2 = -1$, what is the value of a?

(A) -4 (B) -2 (C) 0 (D) 2 (E) 5

28. In a right triangle, one of the acute angles measures $52°$. If the length of the longer leg is 10, what is the area of the triangle to the nearest integer?

   (A) 39   (B) 46   (C) 54   (D) 64   (E) 78

29. Which of the following shaded regions could be the graph of $\begin{cases} 2x - y \le 1 \\ x \le 1 \end{cases}$?

(A)
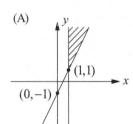

(B)
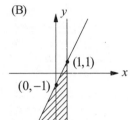

(C)
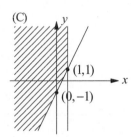

(D)
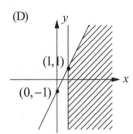

(E)
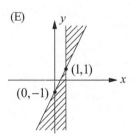

30. If a cube has a total surface area of 294 cm^2, what is the volume of the cube in square centimeters?

   (A) 27   (B) 64   (C) 125   (D) 216   (E) 343

31. The value of a certain piece of equipment is decreasing at the rate of 9% per year. If the equipment is now worth $7900, how much will it be worth 5 years from now?

    (A) $4,345

    (B) $4,670

    (C) $4,930

    (D) $5,120

    (E) $5,745

32. In Figure 7, if *ABCDEF* is a regular hexagon, what is the *y*-coordinate of *E*?

    (A) 6.0

    (B) 7.24

    (C) 7.73

    (D) 8.20

    (E) 9.0

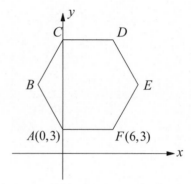

Figure 7

33. Which of the following are the *y*-intercepts of the circle $(x-2)^2 + (y+1)^2 = 10$?

    (A) $(0, 2.26)$ and $(0, -1.26)$

    (B) $(0, 1.75)$ and $(0, -2.75)$

    (C) $(0, 2)$ and $(0, -3)$

    (D) $(0, 3)$ and $(0, -2)$

    (E) $(0, 1.45)$ and $(0, -3.45)$

34. A chemist is mixing 40 liters of a solution that is 60% acid with *x* liters of a solution that is 35% acid. If the mixture is a solution that is 45% acid, what is the value of *x*?

    (A) 48   (B) 54   (C) 60   (D) 64   (E) 68

35. What is the locus of all points in a plane that are equidistant from the sides of a given angle?

    (A) a point

    (B) two points interior of the given angle

    (C) a triangle

    (D) an angle bisector of the given angle

    (E) a circle

36. In a rectangular coordinate system in Figure 8, point P is on the circle whose center is at the origin. What is the value of $\sin\theta$?

    (A) 0.5

    (B) 0.6

    (C) 0.75

    (D) 0.8

    (E) 0.86

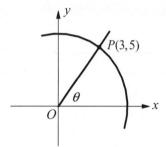

Figure 8

37. Which of the following lines is perpendicular to the line $2x - y = 7$?

    (A) $y = -2x + 7$

    (B) $y = 2x - 7$

    (C) $y = -\dfrac{1}{2}x + 7$

    (D) $y = \dfrac{1}{2}x - 7$

    (E) $y = x - 7$

38. In the xy-coordinate system, $(-1, c)$ is one of the points of intersection of the graphs $y = x^2 - 5$ and $y = 2x + b$, where b and c are constants. What is the value of b?

    (A) −5   (B) −2   (C) 0   (D) 2   (E) 5

39. If y varies directly as x, which of the following could be the graph of y as a function of x?

(A)
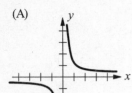

(B)
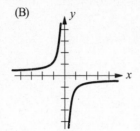

(C)
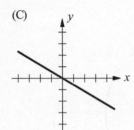

(D)
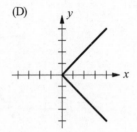

(E)
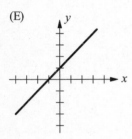

40. Figure 9 shows a rectangle where the length of side $\overline{AD}$ is 6 and the length of side $\overline{CD}$ is 8. With C as the center and $\overline{CD}$ as a radius, an arc is drawn as shown. What is the value of $\sin \theta$?

(A) 0.45

(B) 0.5

(C) 0.6

(D) 0.75

(E) 0.8

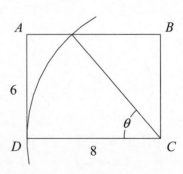

Figure 9

41. If $f(x) = x^3 - 1$ and $f(g(x)) = x$, then $g(x) =$

   (A) $1 - \sqrt[3]{x}$

   (B) $\sqrt[3]{x} - 1$

   (C) $\sqrt[3]{x} + 1$

   (D) $\sqrt[3]{x-1}$

   (E) $\sqrt[3]{x+1}$

42. Figure 10 shows a regular octagon with four of its sides
   on the sides of square $ABCD$. If the length of a side of
   the octagon is 1, what is the area of square $ABCD$?

   (A) $2 + 2\sqrt{2}$

   (B) $3 + 2\sqrt{2}$

   (C) $2 + 2\sqrt{3}$

   (D) $3 + 2\sqrt{3}$

   (E) $3 + 3\sqrt{2}$

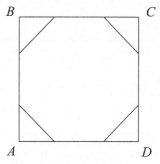

Figure 10

43. $\log_2 8 + \dfrac{1}{2}\log_2 9 - \log_2 6 =$

   (A) 2

   (B) 6

   (C) $\log_2 12$

   (D) $\log_2 18$

   (E) $\log_2 24$

44. In Figure 11, a pyramid with vertices $ABCD$ is inscribed
   in a rectangular prism. What is the ratio of the volume
   of the pyramid to the volume of the rectangular prism?

   (A) $\dfrac{1}{8}$ (B) $\dfrac{1}{6}$ (C) $\dfrac{1}{4}$ (D) $\dfrac{1}{3}$ (E) $\dfrac{1}{2}$

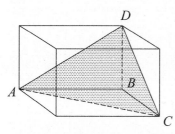

Figure 11

45. What is the minimum value of $f(x) = 2(x+1)^2 - 9$?

    (A) –9   (B) –7   (C) –1   (D) 0   (E) 9

46. Figure 12 shows the graph of $x = y^2$ and three inscribed rectangles. What is the sum of the areas of the three rectangles?

    (A) 3.6

    (B) 4.1

    (C) 5.3

    (D) 6.0

    (E) 7.2

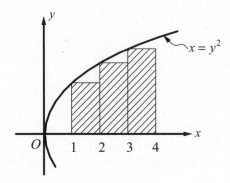

Figure 12

47. There are 500 students in Eastlake High School. If 240 students take Geometry, 140 take Biology, and 80 take both Geometry and Biology, what is the probability that a student selected at random takes either Geometry or Biology, or both?

    (A) $\dfrac{2}{5}$ (B) $\dfrac{13}{25}$ (C) $\dfrac{3}{5}$ (D) $\dfrac{17}{25}$ (E) $\dfrac{19}{25}$

48. In Figure 13, circle O with radius 10 is tangent to the square at points A and D. If the length of $\overline{AB}$ is 8, what is the length of $\overline{PQ}$?

    (A) 10

    (B) 11

    (C) 12

    (D) 13

    (E) 14

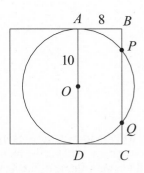

Figure 13

49. In Figure 14, point P is the y-intercept and point S is the vertex of the graph of $y = \frac{1}{2}(x - h)^2$, where h is a positive real number. If point Q lies on the graph, and $OPQR$ is a rectangle whose perimeter is 21, what is the value of h?

   (A) 4.5   (B) 4   (C) 3.5   (D) 3   (E) 2.5

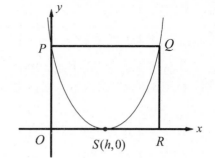

Figure 14

50. If $f(x) = \sqrt{2 - x}$ and $g(x) = x^2 - 2$, which of the following could be the graph of $y = f(g(x))$?

 (A)
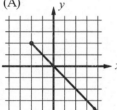

(B)
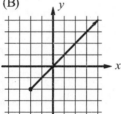

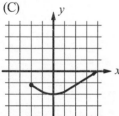 (C)

(D)
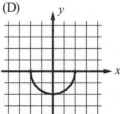

 (E)
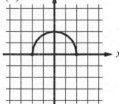

STOP

**IF YOU FINISH BEFORE TIME IS CALLED, YOU MAY CHECK YOUR WORK ON THIS TEST ONLY.
DO NOT TURN TO ANY OTHER TEST IN THIS BOOK.**

Answer Key

1. E	2. A	3. A	4. D	5. C
6. C	7. B	8. C	9. B	10. B
11. D	12. C	13. A	14. C	15. E
16. C	17. C	18. A	19. C	20. B
21. D	22. D	23. B	24. B	25. E
26. B	27. C	28. A	29. C	30. E
31. C	32. D	33. E	34. C	35. D
36. E	37. C	38. B	39. C	40. D
41. E	42. B	43. A	44. B	45. A
46. B	47. C	48. C	49. D	50. E

Answers and Explanations

1. E

$$-(3-2x) = x+3 \implies -3+2x = x+3$$
$$\implies x = 6$$

2. A

$$2x+3y = 5$$
$$\implies 3y = -2x+5 \implies y = \frac{-2}{3}x+\frac{5}{3}$$

Therefore the slope is $-\frac{2}{3}$.

3. A

$$8x^{-3} = -1$$
$$\implies 8 \cdot \frac{1}{x^3} = -1 \implies 8 = -x^3$$
$$\implies x^3 = -8 \implies x = -2$$
$$(\frac{x}{6})^{-2} = (\frac{-2}{6})^{-2} = (\frac{-1}{3})^{-2} = (\frac{3}{-1})^{2} = 9$$

4. D

"For all integer values of n, n^2+n-7 is a prime number."

To find the counterexample, test each answer choice.

  (A) If $n = 3$
$$n^2+n-7 = (3)^2+3-7 = 5 \text{, which is prime.}$$
  (B) If $n = 4$
$$n^2+n-7 = (4)^2+4-7 = 13 \text{, which is prime.}$$
  (C) If $n = 5$
$$n^2+n-7 = (5)^2+5-7 = 23 \text{, which is prime.}$$
  (D) If $n = 6$
$$n^2+n-7 = (6)^2+6-7 = 35 \text{, which is not prime.}$$

Therefore (D) is the correct answer.

5. C

Let $BC = x$, then $AB = 3BC = 3x$.
Since M is the midpoint of $\overline{AB}$,
$$MB = \frac{1}{2}AB = \frac{1}{2}(3x) = \frac{3}{2}x$$
$$MC = MB + BC = \frac{3}{2}x + x = 10$$
$$\implies \frac{5}{2}x = 10 \implies x = 4$$

$$AC = AB + BC = 3x + x = 4x = 4(4) = 16$$

6. C

Use a calculator.
$12345678 \times 8910 = 1.09999991 \in 11$,
which means $1.09999991 \times 10^{11}$. Therefore the number has 12 digits.

7. B

Original price $= p$
Sale price $= 0.75p$
Price after tax $= 0.75p(1+0.08)$

$$\underbrace{15}_{\substack{\text{amount paid} \\ \text{to cashier}}} - \underbrace{(0.75p) \times 1.08}_{\substack{\text{price of CD} \\ \text{after tax}}} = \underbrace{1.27}_{\text{change}}$$

8. C

$$\frac{\sqrt[6]{a}}{\sqrt{a}} = \frac{a^{\frac{1}{6}}}{a^{\frac{1}{2}}} = a^{\frac{1}{6}-\frac{1}{2}} = a^{-\frac{1}{3}} = \frac{1}{a^{\frac{1}{3}}} = \frac{1}{\sqrt[3]{a}}$$

9. B

$$y = \frac{1}{2}x + 3$$

To find the x-intercept of the line let $y = 0$.

$$0 = \frac{1}{2}x + 3 \implies x = -6$$

$(-6, 0)$ is the x-intercept of the line.

To find the y-intercept of the line let $x = 0$.

$$y = \frac{1}{2}(0) + 3 \implies y = 3$$

$(0, 3)$ is the y-intercept of the line.

Use the midpoint formula.

$$(a, b) = (\frac{-6+0}{2}, \frac{0+3}{2}) \implies a = -3 \text{ and } b = \frac{3}{2}$$

$$a + b = -3 + \frac{3}{2} = -\frac{3}{2}$$

10. B

0	7
1	0 0 2 2 5 5 5
2	0 5
3	2
4	2

2 | 9 = 29 years

Arrange the data in order from least to greatest.

$7, 10, 10, 12, 12, 15, 15, 15, 20, 25, 32, 42$

The average (arithmetic mean) lifespan

$$= \frac{7+10+10+12+12+15+15+15+20+25+32+42}{12}$$

$$= \frac{215}{12} \approx 17.9$$

There are two middle numbers, which are 15 and 15. Therefore, the median is $\frac{15+15}{2} = 15$.

Only 4 wild animals have lifespans of at least 20 years. $\frac{4}{20} = 0.2$, or 20%.

11. D

$$\frac{x}{x+1} - \frac{3}{x-2} = \frac{11}{x^2 - x - 2}$$

$$\implies \frac{x}{x+1} - \frac{3}{x-2} = \frac{11}{(x+1)(x-2)}$$

$$\implies \frac{x(x-2) - 3(x+1)}{(x+1)(x-2)} = \frac{11}{(x+1)(x-2)}$$

$$\implies x(x-2) - 3(x+1) = 11$$

$$\implies x^2 - 5x - 3 = 11$$

$$\implies x^2 - 5x - 14 = 0$$

$$\implies (x+2)(x-7) = 0$$

$$\implies x = -2 \text{ or } x = 7$$

12. C

$$f(x) = \frac{x}{x+2}$$

$$f(\sqrt{2}-3) = \frac{\sqrt{2}-3}{(\sqrt{2}-3)+2} = \frac{\sqrt{2}-3}{\sqrt{2}-1}$$

$$= \frac{(\sqrt{2}-3)(\sqrt{2}+1)}{(\sqrt{2}-1)(\sqrt{2}+1)} = \frac{2+\sqrt{2}-3\sqrt{2}-3}{2+\sqrt{2}-\sqrt{2}-1}$$

$$= \frac{-1-2\sqrt{2}}{1} = -1 - 2\sqrt{2}$$

13. A

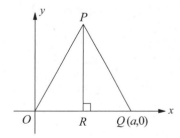

Draw $\overline{PR}$, which is perpendicular to the x-axis. $\triangle OPQ$ is equilateral, and $\triangle PQR$ is a $30°$-$60°$-$90°$ triangle.

In a $30°$-$60°$-$90°$ triangle, the ratio of the longer leg to the shorter leg is $\sqrt{3}:1$.

Slope of $\overline{PQ} = \dfrac{\text{rise}}{\text{run}} = -\dfrac{PR}{RQ} = -\dfrac{\sqrt{3}}{1} = -\sqrt{3}$

14. C

$3x - x^2 \geq -x$

$\Rightarrow x^2 - 4x \leq 0 \Rightarrow x(x-4) \leq 0$

The number line is divided into 3 intervals.

Pick a number from each interval and plug it into the inequality. The inequality is less than or equal to zero when $0 \leq x \leq 4$.

15. E

$f(x) = \sqrt[3]{9 - x^2}$

The expression under a cube root can represent any real number, since a negative number under a cube root can represent a real number.
Therefore the domain of f is all real numbers.

16. C

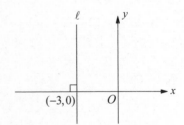

The equation of a vertical line is $x = a$, where a is the x-intercept.
The equation of line ℓ is $x = -3$.

17. C

Method 1:

I. $x^2 = 6x - 9 \Rightarrow x^2 - 6x + 9 = 0$

$\Rightarrow (x-3)^2 = 0 \Rightarrow x = 3$

There is only one solution.

II. $x^3 - 8 = 0 \Rightarrow x^3 = 8 \Rightarrow x = 2$
There is only one solution.

III. $x^2 = -x \Rightarrow x^2 + x = 0$

$\Rightarrow x(x+1) = 0 \Rightarrow x = 0$ or $x = -1$

The equation has two real solutions.

Method 2:

Use a graphing calculator.
I. $x^2 = 6x - 9 \Rightarrow x^2 - 6x + 9 = 0$
Graph $y_1 = x^2 - 6x + 9$. The graph shows only one x-intercept, which is the solution of the equation.

II. Graph $y_1 = x^3 - 8$. The graph shows only one x-intercept, so there is only one solution.

III. $x^2 = -x \Rightarrow x^2 + x = 0$
Graph $y_1 = x^2 + x$. The graph shows two x-intercepts, so there are two solutions.

18. A

$a - 2$, a, and $a + 6$ are the first three terms of a geometric sequence.

In a geometric sequence, the ratio of successive terms is always the same.
Let $r = $ the ratio of successive terms, then

$\dfrac{a}{a-2} = r$ and $\dfrac{a+6}{a} = r$.

$\Rightarrow \dfrac{a}{a-2} = \dfrac{a+6}{a} \Rightarrow a^2 = (a-2)(a+6)$

$\Rightarrow a^{\cancel{2}} = a^{\cancel{2}} + 4a - 12 \Rightarrow 4a - 12 = 0 \Rightarrow a = 3$

19. C

First make a drawing as accurately as possible, and approximate the value of k when $x = 3$.

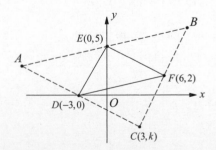

When 3 points are given there are 3 possible parallelograms we can draw, with each side of the triangle as a diagonal of the parallelogram. Since $(3, k)$ is the coordinate of the fourth point, point A or point B cannot be the fourth point of the parallelogram.

In a parallelogram, the slopes of opposite sides are the same. Use the slope formula to find the slope of $\overline{EF}$ and $\overline{CD}$.

Slope of $\overline{EF} = \dfrac{2-5}{6-0} = -\dfrac{1}{2}$

Slope of $\overline{CD} = \dfrac{0-k}{-3-3} = \dfrac{-k}{-6} = \dfrac{k}{6}$

$-\dfrac{1}{2} = \dfrac{k}{6} \ \Rightarrow \ k = -3$

(C) is the correct answer.

20. B

Percent increase $= \dfrac{\text{amount increased}}{\text{original amount}}$

% increase of company $A = \dfrac{20-15}{15} = \dfrac{1}{3} \approx 33\%$

% increase of company $B = \dfrac{30-20}{20} = \dfrac{1}{2} = 50\%$

% increase of company $C = \dfrac{60-45}{45} = \dfrac{1}{3} \approx 33\%$

% increase of company $D = \dfrac{45-40}{40} = \dfrac{1}{8} = 12.5\%$

% increase of company $E = \dfrac{40-30}{30} = \dfrac{1}{3} \approx 33\%$

21. D

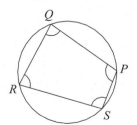

I. If a quadrilateral is inscribed in a circle, then its opposite angles are supplementary.

$m\angle P + m\angle R = 180$ and $m\angle Q + m\angle S = 180$.
Therefore $m\angle P + m\angle R = m\angle Q + m\angle S$.

II. $\overline{PQ}$ and $\overline{RS}$ are not necessarily congruent.

III. The measure of an inscribed angle is equal to half the measure of its intercepted arc.

Therefore $m\angle S = \dfrac{1}{2} m\widehat{PQR}$.

22. D

The price c of a box of greeting cards ranges from $12 to $18.
$\Rightarrow \ 12 \le c \le 18$

Solve the inequality in each answer choice.

(A) $|c-6| \le 12 \ \Rightarrow \ -12 \le c - 6 \le 12$
$\Rightarrow \ -6 \le c \le 18$

(B) $|c-12| \le 6 \ \Rightarrow \ -6 \le c - 12 \le 6$
$\Rightarrow \ 6 \le c \le 18$

(C) $|c-12| \le 3 \ \Rightarrow \ -3 \le c - 12 \le 3$
$\Rightarrow \ 9 \le c \le 15$

(D) $|c-15| \le 3 \ \Rightarrow \ -3 \le c - 15 \le 3$
$\Rightarrow \ 12 \le c \le 18$

(D) is correct answer.

23. B

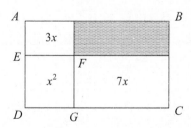

Since the area of the square is x^2, $DE = DG = x$.

Since the areas of the two rectangular regions are $7x$ and $3x$, we can conclude $CG = 7$ and $AE = 3$.

Area of the shaded region $= 7 \cdot 3 = 21$.

24. B

Margin of sampling error

$$= 2\sqrt{\frac{p(1-p)}{n}} = 2\sqrt{\frac{0.82(1-0.82)}{650}} \approx 0.03$$

25. E

$$\frac{\cos(90° - \theta)}{\cos\theta}$$

$$= \frac{\sin\theta}{\cos\theta} \qquad\qquad \cos(90° - \theta) = \sin\theta$$

$$= \tan\theta$$

26. B

(A) $M_{3\times3}$ and $M_{1\times3}$ cannot be multiplied.

(B) $\begin{bmatrix} 79 & 109 & 159 \end{bmatrix} \cdot \begin{bmatrix} 23 & 45 & 32 \\ 18 & 38 & 26 \\ 15 & 34 & 24 \end{bmatrix}$

$$= \begin{bmatrix} 79\cdot23 & 79\cdot45 & 79\cdot32 \\ +109\cdot18 & +109\cdot38 & +109\cdot26 \\ +159\cdot15 & +159\cdot34 & +159\cdot24 \end{bmatrix}$$

$$= \begin{bmatrix} 6164 & 13{,}103 & 9178 \end{bmatrix}$$
$$\quad\uparrow \qquad\quad \uparrow \qquad\quad \uparrow$$

Friday's   Saturday's   Sunday's
total   total   total

(C) $M_{3\times3} \cdot M_{3\times1} = M_{3\times1}$

$$\begin{bmatrix} 23 & 45 & 32 \\ 18 & 38 & 26 \\ 15 & 34 & 24 \end{bmatrix} \cdot \begin{bmatrix} 79 \\ 109 \\ 159 \end{bmatrix} = \begin{bmatrix} R_1 \\ R_2 \\ R_3 \end{bmatrix}$$

where $R_1 = 23\cdot79 + 45\cdot109 + 32\cdot159$

This does not give the correct representation of the sales amount because $45\cdot109$ represents the number of model A× the price of model B.

(D) $M_{3\times1} \cdot M_{3\times3}$ cannot be multiplied.

(E) $\begin{bmatrix} 23 & 45 & 32 \\ 18 & 38 & 26 \\ 15 & 34 & 24 \end{bmatrix} \cdot \begin{bmatrix} 79 + 109 + 159 \end{bmatrix}$

$$\Rightarrow \begin{bmatrix} 23 & 45 & 32 \\ 18 & 38 & 26 \\ 15 & 34 & 24 \end{bmatrix} \cdot \begin{bmatrix} 347 \end{bmatrix}$$

$M_{3\times3} \cdot M_{1\times1}$ cannot be multiplied.

27. C

$$(2-i)^2 - 3 = a - bi$$

$$4 - 2i - 2i + i^2 - 3 = a - bi$$

$$4 - 4i - 1 - 3 = a - bi \qquad i^2 = -1$$

$$0 - 4i = a - bi$$

Therefore $a = 0$ and $b = 4$.

28. A

Draw a triangle.

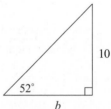

The side opposite of the $52°$ angle is the longer leg because the $52°$ angle is bigger than the other acute angle.

$$\tan52° = \frac{10}{b} \quad\Rightarrow\quad b\cdot\tan52° = 10$$

$$\Rightarrow\quad b = \frac{10}{\tan52°} \approx 7.8$$

Area of the triangle

$$= \frac{1}{2}b\cdot h = \frac{1}{2}(7.8)(10) = 39$$

29. C

$$\begin{cases} 2x - y \le 1 \\ x \le 1 \end{cases}$$

Test an ordered pair that is not on the boundary to see if it satisfies the given inequality. The origin is a convenient point to use.

$\begin{cases} 2(0)-0 \le 1 \\ 0 \le 1 \end{cases}$

$(0,0)$ does satisfy both inequalities, therefore the point $(0,0)$ should be in the shaded region.

The graph in (C) is the only one with $(0,0)$ in the shaded region.

30. E

Total surface area of a cube is $294\,\text{cm}^2$.

Area of each face of the cube $= \dfrac{294}{6} = 49\text{cm}^2$

Length of the edge of the cube $= \sqrt{49} = 7$

Volume of the cube $= 7 \cdot 7 \cdot 7 = 343$

31. C

Use the compound interest formula.

$A = P(1-r)^t$

$A = 7900(1-0.09)^5$ Value is decreasing $r\%$ per year.

$= 7900(0.91)^5$

$= 4929.85$

32. D

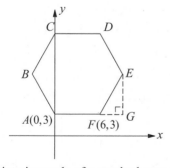

Each interior angle of a regular hexagon

$= \dfrac{(n-2)180°}{n} = \dfrac{(6-2)180°}{6} = 120°$

Therefore $\angle EFG$ measures $60°$. Since $AF = 6$, the length of each side of the regular hexagon is 6. Use the $30°$-$60°$-$90°$ triangle ratio to find the length of $\overline{EG}$.

$EF = 6 \Rightarrow FG = 3 \Rightarrow EG = 3\sqrt{3}$

Then the y-coordinate of E is $3\sqrt{3}$ more than the y-coordinate of F.
The y-coordinate of E is $3+3\sqrt{3}$, or 8.196.

33. E

$(x-2)^2 + (y+1)^2 = 10$
To find the y-intercept of the circle, let $x=0$.
$(0-2)^2 + (y+1)^2 = 10$
$(y+1)^2 = 6$
$y+1 = \pm\sqrt{6}$
$y = -1 \pm \sqrt{6}$
$y = -1+\sqrt{6}$ or $y = -1-\sqrt{6}$

$(0,1.45)$ and $(0,-3.45)$ are the y-intercepts of the circle.

34. C

Amount of acid in the mixture
$=$ Amount of acid in the 1st solution
$+$ Amount of acid in the 2nd solution

amount of acid in the mixture	amount of acid in the 1st solution	amount of acid in the 2nd solution
$0.45(40+x) =$	$0.6(40)$ $+$	$0.35x$

$18 + 0.45x = 24 + 0.35x$
$0.1x = 6$
$x = 60$

35. D

Draw an angle.

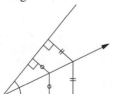

The locus of all points in a plane that are equidistant from the sides of a given angle is an angle bisector of the given angle.

36. E

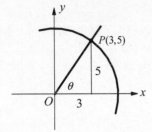

In the figure above, $OP = \sqrt{3^3 + 5^2} = \sqrt{34}$.

$\sin\theta = \dfrac{5}{\sqrt{34}} \approx 0.857$

37. C

$2x - y = 7$

$y = 2x - 7$ Solve the equation for y.

The slope of a perpendicular line is $-\dfrac{1}{2}$, which is the negative reciprocal of 2.

38. B

$y = x^2 - 5$	First equation
$c = (-1)^2 - 5$	Substitute $x = -1$ and $y = c$, since $(-1, c)$ is a point of intersection.
$c = -4$	
$y = 2x + b$	Second equation
$c = 2(-1) + b$	Substitute $x = -1$ and $y = c$.
$-4 = 2(-1) + b$	Substitute $c = -4$.
$-2 = b$	Solve for b.

39. C

A linear function defined by an equation of the form $y = kx$ is a direct variation. The graph of $y = kx$ is a line through the origin with slope k.

(C) is the correct answer.

40. D

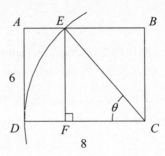

Draw a segment EF that is parallel to $\overline{BC}$ and intersects $\overline{AB}$.

Since $\overline{CD}$ and $\overline{CE}$ are radii, $CD = CE = 8$. Also, $EF = AD = 6$.

$\sin\theta = \dfrac{EF}{CE} = \dfrac{6}{8} = 0.75$

41. E

The functions f and g are inverse functions if $f(g(x)) = x$ or $g(f(x)) = x$.

$f(x) = x^3 - 1$ To find an inverse function:

1. Replace $f(x)$ with y. $y = x^3 - 1$
2. Interchange x and y. $x = y^3 - 1$
3. Solve for y. $y^3 = x + 1$

$\Rightarrow y = (x+1)^{\frac{1}{3}} \Rightarrow f^{-1}(x) = (x+1)^{\frac{1}{3}}$

$\Rightarrow g(x) = (x+1)^{\frac{1}{3}} = \sqrt[3]{x+1}$

42. B

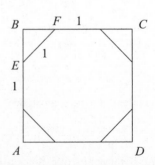

Each interior angle of a regular octagon

$= \dfrac{(n-2)180^\circ}{n} = \dfrac{(8-2)180^\circ}{8} = 135^\circ$

Therefore $\angle BEF$ and $\angle BFE$ measure $45°$, and $\triangle BEF$ is a $45°\text{-}45°\text{-}90°$ triangle.

$$BE \cdot \sqrt{2} = EF \;\Rightarrow\; BE \cdot \sqrt{2} = 1$$

$$\Rightarrow\; BE = \frac{1}{\sqrt{2}} = \frac{1 \cdot \sqrt{2}}{\sqrt{2} \cdot \sqrt{2}} = \frac{\sqrt{2}}{2}$$

The length of each side of the square

$$= \frac{\sqrt{2}}{2} + 1 + \frac{\sqrt{2}}{2} = \sqrt{2} + 1$$

Area of square $ABCD$

$$= (\sqrt{2}+1)(\sqrt{2}+1) = 2 + \sqrt{2} + \sqrt{2} + 1$$

$$= 3 + 2\sqrt{2}$$

43. A

$$\log_2 8 + \frac{1}{2}\log_2 9 - \log_2 6$$

$$= \log_2 8 + \log_2 9^{\frac{1}{2}} - \log_2 6 \quad \log_b M^p = p \cdot \log_b M$$

$$= \log_2 \frac{8 \cdot \sqrt{9}}{6} \qquad\qquad \log_b MN = \log_b M + \log_b N$$

$$\qquad\qquad\qquad\qquad \log_b \frac{M}{N} = \log_b M - \log_b N$$

$$= \log_2 \frac{24}{6} \qquad\qquad \text{Simplify the numerator.}$$

$$= \log_2 4$$

$$= \log_2 2^2$$

$$= 2\log_2 2 \qquad\qquad \log_b M^p = p \cdot \log_b M$$

$$= 2 \qquad\qquad\qquad \log_b b = 1$$

44. B

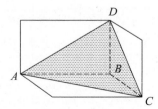

Volume of the pyramid

$$= \frac{1}{3} B \cdot h = \frac{1}{3}\left(\frac{1}{2} AB \cdot BC\right) \cdot BD$$

$$= \frac{1}{6} AB \cdot BC \cdot BD$$

Volume of the rectangular prism

$$= AB \cdot BC \cdot BD$$

$$\frac{\text{Volume of pyramid}}{\text{Volume of prism}} = \frac{\dfrac{1}{6} AB \cdot BC \cdot BD}{AB \cdot BC \cdot BD} = \frac{1}{6}$$

45. A

Use a graphing calculator to graph
$f(x) = 2(x+1)^2 - 9$.

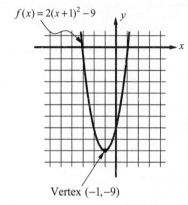

Vertex $(-1, -9)$

A quadratic function has a minimum at its vertex. The minimum value of $f(x) = 2(x+1)^2 - 9$ is -9.

46. B

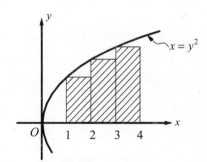

To find the heights of the rectangles, substitute the x-values into the equation of the curve $(x = y^2)$.

$$x = 1 \;\Rightarrow\; 1 = y^2 \;\Rightarrow\; y = 1$$

$$x = 2 \;\Rightarrow\; 2 = y^2 \;\Rightarrow\; y = \sqrt{2}$$

$$x = 3 \;\Rightarrow\; 3 = y^2 \;\Rightarrow\; y = \sqrt{3}$$

Sum of the areas of the three inscribed rectangles

$$= 1 \cdot 1 + 1 \cdot \sqrt{2} + 1 \cdot \sqrt{3} \approx 4.1$$

47. C

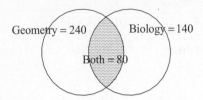

Number of students who take Geometry or Biology
$= 240 + 140 - 80 = 300$

$P(\text{Geometry, Biology, or both}) = \dfrac{300}{500} = \dfrac{3}{5}$

48. C

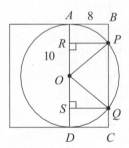

Draw $\overline{PR}$ and $\overline{QS}$ perpendicular to $\overline{AD}$.
$QS = PR = AB = 8$. $OP = OQ = 10$ since $\overline{OP}$ and $\overline{OQ}$ are radii of the same circle.

$OP^2 = OR^2 + PR^2 \Rightarrow 10^2 = OR^2 + 8^2$
$\Rightarrow OR = 6$
$OQ^2 = OS^2 + QS^2 \Rightarrow 10^2 = OS^2 + 8^2$
$\Rightarrow OS = 6$

$PQ = RS = OR + OS = 6 + 6 = 12$

49. D

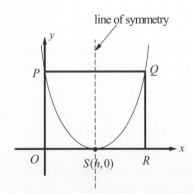

To find the y-coordinate of point P, substitute $x = 0$ into the equation of the parabola.

$y = \dfrac{1}{2}(x - h)^2$

$y = \dfrac{1}{2}(0 - h)^2 = \dfrac{1}{2}h^2$

Therefore $OP = \dfrac{1}{2}h^2$

The line of symmetry passes through the vertex, therefore $OS = SR = h$.
$OR = OS + SR = h + h = 2h$

Perimeter of rectangle $OPQR = 21$

$$\Rightarrow 2 \overbrace{(2h)}^{\text{the length}} + 2(\overbrace{\tfrac{1}{2}h^2}^{\text{the width}}) = 21$$

$\Rightarrow 4h + h^2 = 21$
$\Rightarrow h^2 + 4h - 21 = 0$
$\Rightarrow (h + 7)(h - 3) = 0$
$\Rightarrow h = -7$ or $h = 3$

Since h must be positive, $h = 3$.

50. E

$f(x) = \sqrt{x + 2}$ and $g(x) = x^2 - 2$
$y = f(g(x))$
$\quad = f(x^2 - 2)$
$\quad = \sqrt{2 - (x^2 - 2)}$
$\quad = \sqrt{4 - x^2}$

Square both sides of the equation.
$(y)^2 = (\sqrt{4 - x^2})^2 \Rightarrow y^2 = 4 - x^2$
$\Rightarrow x^2 + y^2 = 4$

This is the equation of a circle whose center is $(0, 0)$ and radius is 2.

The range of $f(g(x)) = \sqrt{4 - x^2}$ is $\{y : y \geq 0\}$, since the square root of an expression is always nonnegative.
Therefore the graph of $y = f(g(x))$ is the semicircle above the x-axis.

(E) is the correct answer.

Scaled Score Conversion Table

SAT Subject Test in Mathematics Level 1

Raw Score	Scaled Score	Raw Score	Scaled Score	Raw Score	Scaled Score	Raw Score	Scaled Score
50	800	34	640	18	500	2	380
49	790	33	630	17	500	1	370
48	780	32	620	16	490	0	360
47	770	31	610	15	480	−1	350
46	760	30	600	14	470	−2	350
45	750	29	600	13	460	−3	340
44	740	28	590	12	460	−4	330
43	730	27	580	11	450	−5	320
42	720	26	570	10	440	−6	320
41	710	25	560	9	430	−7	310
40	700	24	560	8	420	−8	300
39	690	23	550	7	420	−9	300
38	680	22	540	6	410	−10	290
37	670	21	530	5	400	−11	280
36	660	20	520	4	390	−12	270
35	650	19	510	3	390		

Calculating Your Score

Step 1: Count the number of right answers: _____

Step 2: Count the number of wrong answers: _____

Step 3: Divide the number of wrong answers by 4: _____

Step 4: Subtract the result obtained in step 3 from the total in step 1: _____

Step 5: Round the number obtained in step 4 to the nearest whole number. This is your **raw test score**: _____

Step 6: Using the table above, find the scaled score that corresponds to your raw score. Remember, this is an **approximation** of your SAT Subject Test score: _____

Math Level 2

Test Form E
Mathematics Level 2

Answer Sheet

1 Ⓐ Ⓑ Ⓒ Ⓓ Ⓔ   21 Ⓐ Ⓑ Ⓒ Ⓓ Ⓔ   41 Ⓐ Ⓑ Ⓒ Ⓓ Ⓔ
2 Ⓐ Ⓑ Ⓒ Ⓓ Ⓔ   22 Ⓐ Ⓑ Ⓒ Ⓓ Ⓔ   42 Ⓐ Ⓑ Ⓒ Ⓓ Ⓔ
3 Ⓐ Ⓑ Ⓒ Ⓓ Ⓔ   23 Ⓐ Ⓑ Ⓒ Ⓓ Ⓔ   43 Ⓐ Ⓑ Ⓒ Ⓓ Ⓔ
4 Ⓐ Ⓑ Ⓒ Ⓓ Ⓔ   24 Ⓐ Ⓑ Ⓒ Ⓓ Ⓔ   44 Ⓐ Ⓑ Ⓒ Ⓓ Ⓔ
5 Ⓐ Ⓑ Ⓒ Ⓓ Ⓔ   25 Ⓐ Ⓑ Ⓒ Ⓓ Ⓔ   45 Ⓐ Ⓑ Ⓒ Ⓓ Ⓔ
6 Ⓐ Ⓑ Ⓒ Ⓓ Ⓔ   26 Ⓐ Ⓑ Ⓒ Ⓓ Ⓔ   46 Ⓐ Ⓑ Ⓒ Ⓓ Ⓔ
7 Ⓐ Ⓑ Ⓒ Ⓓ Ⓔ   27 Ⓐ Ⓑ Ⓒ Ⓓ Ⓔ   47 Ⓐ Ⓑ Ⓒ Ⓓ Ⓔ
8 Ⓐ Ⓑ Ⓒ Ⓓ Ⓔ   28 Ⓐ Ⓑ Ⓒ Ⓓ Ⓔ   48 Ⓐ Ⓑ Ⓒ Ⓓ Ⓔ
9 Ⓐ Ⓑ Ⓒ Ⓓ Ⓔ   29 Ⓐ Ⓑ Ⓒ Ⓓ Ⓔ   49 Ⓐ Ⓑ Ⓒ Ⓓ Ⓔ
10 Ⓐ Ⓑ Ⓒ Ⓓ Ⓔ   30 Ⓐ Ⓑ Ⓒ Ⓓ Ⓔ   50 Ⓐ Ⓑ Ⓒ Ⓓ Ⓔ
11 Ⓐ Ⓑ Ⓒ Ⓓ Ⓔ   31 Ⓐ Ⓑ Ⓒ Ⓓ Ⓔ
12 Ⓐ Ⓑ Ⓒ Ⓓ Ⓔ   32 Ⓐ Ⓑ Ⓒ Ⓓ Ⓔ
13 Ⓐ Ⓑ Ⓒ Ⓓ Ⓔ   33 Ⓐ Ⓑ Ⓒ Ⓓ Ⓔ
14 Ⓐ Ⓑ Ⓒ Ⓓ Ⓔ   34 Ⓐ Ⓑ Ⓒ Ⓓ Ⓔ
15 Ⓐ Ⓑ Ⓒ Ⓓ Ⓔ   35 Ⓐ Ⓑ Ⓒ Ⓓ Ⓔ
16 Ⓐ Ⓑ Ⓒ Ⓓ Ⓔ   36 Ⓐ Ⓑ Ⓒ Ⓓ Ⓔ
17 Ⓐ Ⓑ Ⓒ Ⓓ Ⓔ   37 Ⓐ Ⓑ Ⓒ Ⓓ Ⓔ
18 Ⓐ Ⓑ Ⓒ Ⓓ Ⓔ   38 Ⓐ Ⓑ Ⓒ Ⓓ Ⓔ
19 Ⓐ Ⓑ Ⓒ Ⓓ Ⓔ   39 Ⓐ Ⓑ Ⓒ Ⓓ Ⓔ
20 Ⓐ Ⓑ Ⓒ Ⓓ Ⓔ   40 Ⓐ Ⓑ Ⓒ Ⓓ Ⓔ

Reference Information

The following information is for your reference in answering some of the questions on this test.

Volume of a right circular cone with radius r and height h: $V = \frac{1}{3}\pi r^2 h$

Lateral area of a right circular cone with base circumference C and slant height ℓ: $S = \frac{1}{2}C\ell$

Volume of a sphere with radius r: $V = \frac{4}{3}\pi r^3$

Surface area of a sphere with radius r: $S = 4\pi r^2$

Volume of a pyramid with base area B and height h: $V = \frac{1}{3}Bh$

Test Form E
SAT Subject Test in Mathematics Level 2

50 Questions   1 hour

For each of the following problems, decide which is the BEST of the answer choices given. If the exact numerical value is not one of the choices, select the choice that best approximates this value. Then fill in the corresponding circle on the answer sheet.

Notes: (1) A calculator will be necessary for answering some of the questions on this test. For each question you will have to decide whether or not you should use a calculator. Programmable calculators and calculators that can display graphs are permitted.

(2) The angle measures used on the Math Level 2 Test are in either degree measure or radian measure. Check to see which mode your calculator is in.

(3) Figures that accompany problems on this test are intended to provide information useful in solving the problems. They are drawn as accurately as possible EXCEPT when it is stated in a specific problem that its figure is not drawn to scale. All figures lie in a plane unless otherwise indicated.

(4) Unless otherwise specified, the domain of any function f is assumed to be the set of all real numbers x for which $f(x)$ is a real number.

(5) Reference information that may be useful in answering the questions on this test can be found on the page preceding Question 1.

1. If $M = z - (x + y)$ and $N = z + (x - y)$, then $M - N =$

(A) $-2x$ (B) $-2y$ (C) 0   (D) $2x$ (E) $2y$

2. For $(a^2 - 1) \neq 0$, $\dfrac{1}{a-1} - \dfrac{2}{a^2-1} =$

(A) $\dfrac{a}{a+1}$

(B) $\dfrac{a}{a-1}$

(C) $\dfrac{1}{a+1}$

(D) $\dfrac{1}{a-1}$

(E) $\dfrac{-1}{a^2-1}$

3. Which of the following is equivalent to
$\{x: x > 4 \text{ or } x < -2\}$?

(A) $\{x: x^2 - 2x > -8\}$

(B) $\{x: x^2 - 2x > 8\}$

(C) $\{x: x^2 - 2x > -6\}$

(D) $\{x: x^2 - 2x < 8\}$

(E) $\{x: x^2 - 2x < 6\}$

4. The total cost, in dollars, to send a package that weighs
n ounces by first-class mail is given by a function
$f(n) = 0.4 + 0.28[n - 0.1]$, where $[n]$ is the least integer
greater than or equal to n. If a package weighs 3.8 ounces,
what is the total cost to mail it first-class?

(A) $0.96

(B) $1.08

(C) $1.24

(D) $1.46

(E) $1.52

5. If $\sqrt[5]{4x - 9} = -3$, then $x =$

(A) −63

(B) −58.5

(C) −27.9

(D) −18

(E) −1.93

6. If $(\sqrt{a} + 2) = (\sqrt{a} - 2)^{-1}$, then $a =$

(A) 0   (B) 1   (C) 2   (D) 4   (E) 5

7. For all positive integers a, b, and c, let $\boxed{a,b,c}$ be

defined as $\boxed{a,b,c} = \dfrac{a-b^{-1}}{a+c^{-1}}$. If $\boxed{a,2,3} = 3$, then $a =$

(A) $-\dfrac{3}{4}$ (B) $-\dfrac{2}{3}$ (C) $\dfrac{1}{3}$ (D) 1   (E) 6

8. In Figure 1, if segment PQ is reflected across the line

$y = x$ (not shown), what will be the coordinates of the
reflection of point P?

(A) $(3,-4)$

(B) $(3,-2)$

(C) $(2,-4)$

(D) $(2,-3)$

(E) $(2,-4)$

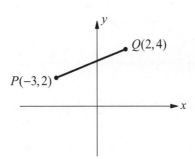

Figure 1

9. If $f(x) = 1 - x$ and $g(x) = x^2 - x$, then $g(f(x)) =$

(A) x^2

(B) $x^2 + x$

(C) $x^2 - x$

(D) $x^2 + 2x$

(E) $x^2 - 2x - 1$

10. Which of the following equations has the same solution(s)

as $|2x + 5| = x + 4$?

(A) $x + 3 = 0$

(B) $x + 1 = 0$

(C) $x - 1 = 0$

(D) $(x+1)(x-3) = 0$

(E) $(x+1)(x+3) = 0$

11. What number should be added to each of the three numbers −6, 2, and 26 so that the resulting three numbers form a geometric sequence?

(A) 8   (B) 9   (C) 10   (D) 12   (E) 16

12. A piecewise function f is defined by

$$f(x) = \begin{cases} -1 & \text{if } x \le 0 \\ x^2 - 1 & \text{if } 0 < x \le 2 \\ x + 1 & \text{if } x > 2 \end{cases}.$$

What is the value of $f(-3) + f(1) + f(3)$?

(A) 0   (B) 1   (C) 2   (D) 3   (E) 4

13. In Figure 2, $ABCDE$ is a regular pentagon with side of length 8. What is the x-coordinate of E?

(A) 2.27

(B) 2.53

(C) 2.86

(D) 3.02

(E) 3.27

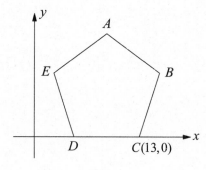

Figure 2

14. Given: 1) If the ball is yellow, then the racquet is blue.

2) The racquet is not blue.

Which of the following must be true?

(A) The ball is yellow.

(B) The racquet is yellow.

(C) The ball is not yellow.

(D) The racquet is not yellow.

(E) The ball is not blue.

15. The average (arithmetic mean) weekly earnings of 24 employees at a certain company is $585. When two new employees are added, the average of the 26 employees decreases to $579. What is the sum of the earnings of the two new employees?

(A) $1,014

(B) $1,028

(C) $1,158

(D) $1,236

(E) $1,314

16. If the equation $2x^2 - kx + 6 = 0$ has no real roots, which of the following is true about the values of k?

(A) $k < -4\sqrt{3}$

(B) $-4\sqrt{3} < k < 0$

(C) $-4\sqrt{3} < k < 4\sqrt{3}$

(D) $0 < k < 4\sqrt{3}$

(E) $k > 4\sqrt{3}$

17. In a right triangle, one of the acute angle measures $40°$. If the length of the hypotenuse is 20, what is the perimeter of the triangle?

(A) 43.7

(B) 48.2

(C) 51.3

(D) 56.8

(E) 58.9

18. After a bag of 144 golf tees was divided equally among n club members, there were 4 golf tees left. Which of the following is NOT a possible value of n?

(A) 4   (B) 10   (C) 16   (D) 28   (E) 35

19. If $f(\frac{1}{2}x+1) = \sqrt{3-2x}$ for all real numbers x, then $f(x) =$

   (A) $\sqrt{1-2x}$

   (B) $\sqrt{5-4x}$

   (C) $\sqrt{-1-2x}$

   (D) $\sqrt{7-4x}$

   (E) $\sqrt{4x+1}$

20. If $\cos x = 0.46$, what is the value of $\cos 2x$?

   (A) -0.64

   (B) -0.58

   (C) -0.46

   (D) 0.58

   (E) 0.64

21. If $x^3 + 3x^2 - 8x - 24 = (x^2 - 8)p(x)$, where $p(x)$
   is a polynomial in x, then $p(x) =$

   (A) $x^2 - 3$

   (B) $-x - 3$

   (C) $x - 3$

   (D) $-x + 3$

   (E) $x + 3$

22. If p is a positive integer and $x^{2p} - x^p - 6 = 0$ for
   $x > 0$, then $x =$

   (A) $\sqrt[p]{3}$

   (B) $\sqrt[p]{2}$

   (C) 1

   (D) 2^p

   (E) 3^p

23. If $i^2 = -1$, $(\frac{1}{\sqrt{2}} + \frac{1}{\sqrt{2}}i)^2 =$

   (A) $1+i$

   (B) $1-i$

   (C) i

   (D) $-i$

   (E) $2i$

24. What is the area of the rhombus in Figure 3?

   (A) a^2

   (B) $a^2 \sin\theta$

   (C) $a^2 \cos\theta$

   (D) $a^2 \sin\theta\cos\theta$

   (E) $a\sin\theta\cos\theta$

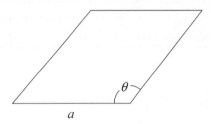

Figure 3

25. If the magnitudes of vectors **v** and **w** are 5 and 14, respectively, then the magnitude of vector $(\mathbf{w} - \mathbf{v})$ could NOT be

   (A) 8   (B) 9   (C) 12.5 (D) 14   (E) 19

26. Which of the following lines are asymptotes of the graph of $y = \dfrac{x}{x^2 + 5x}$?

   I. $x = 0$

   II. $x = -5$

   III. $y = 0$

   (A) I only

   (B) II only

   (C) I and II only

   (D) II and III only

   (E) I, II, and III

27. If $\log_2 m = n$, then what does $\log_2(\frac{m}{2})$ equal?

    (A) $n+1$

    (B) $n-1$

    (C) $\dfrac{n}{2}$

    (D) $\sqrt{n}$

    (E) $2n$

28. What is the degree measure of the largest angle in a triangle whose sides have lengths 9, 10, and 12?

    (A) $47.2°$

    (B) $54.6°$

    (C) $78.1°$

    (D) $101.9°$

    (E) $125.4°$

29. Which of the following systems of equations is represented by the graph in Figure 4?

    (A) $\begin{cases} \dfrac{x^2}{4} + \dfrac{y^2}{2} = 1 \\ x^2 + y^2 = 16 \end{cases}$

    (B) $\begin{cases} \dfrac{x^2}{4} - \dfrac{y^2}{2} = 1 \\ x^2 + y^2 = 16 \end{cases}$

    (C) $\begin{cases} \dfrac{y^2}{2} - \dfrac{x^2}{4} = 1 \\ x^2 + y^2 = 16 \end{cases}$

    (D) $\begin{cases} \dfrac{y^2}{2} + \dfrac{x^2}{4} = 1 \\ x^2 + y^2 = 16 \end{cases}$

    (E) $\begin{cases} \dfrac{x^2}{4} - \dfrac{y^2}{2} = 1 \\ x^2 - y^2 = 4 \end{cases}$

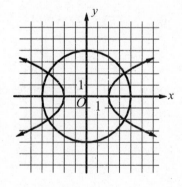

Figure 4

30. Which of the following sets of numbers has the property that the sum of any two numbers in the set is also a number in the set?

   I. The set of odd integers

   II. The set of even integers

   III. The set of negative integers

(A) I only

(B) II only

(C) III only

(D) I and II only

(E) II and III only

31. In Figure 5, $r\cos\theta + r\sin\theta =$

(A) −7

(B) −3

(C) −1

(D) 1

(E) 7

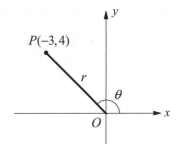

Figure 5

32. If $i^2 = -1$, which of the following equations is equivalent to $(a - \frac{1}{2}bi) = 2(a + \frac{1}{2}bi)^{-1}$, for all real numbers a and b?

(A) $\dfrac{a^2}{8} - \dfrac{b^2}{2} = 1$

(B) $\dfrac{a^2}{8} + \dfrac{b^2}{2} = 1$

(C) $\dfrac{a^2}{2} - \dfrac{b^2}{8} = 1$

(D) $\dfrac{a^2}{2} + \dfrac{b^2}{8} = 1$

(E) $4a^2 - b^2 = 0$

33. Which of the following shaded regions could be

the graph of $\begin{cases} |x|+|y| \le 3 \\ |x|+|y| \ge 1 \end{cases}$?

(A)
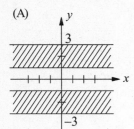

(B)
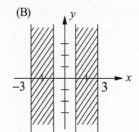

(C)
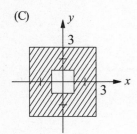

(D)
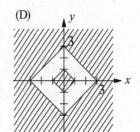

(E)
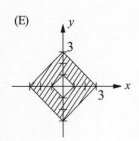

34. A sequence is recursively defined by $a_n = 1 - \dfrac{1}{a_{n-1}}$, for $n \ge 2$.

If $a_1 = k$, what is the value of a_4 in terms of k?

(A) k

(B) $\dfrac{3}{k}$

(C) $\dfrac{k-1}{k}$

(D) $\dfrac{2k-1}{k-1}$

(E) $\dfrac{k}{2k-1}$

35. A function f is an odd function if, for all values of x in the domain, $f(-x) = -f(x)$. Which of the following is an odd function?

    (A) $|x| - 3$

    (B) $x^3 + 3$

    (C) $x^3 + x$

    (D) $(x-1)^3$

    (E) $\dfrac{1}{1+x^3}$

36. Figure 6 shows the graph of $y = e^x$. What is the sum of the areas of the four inscribed rectangles?

    (A) 11.1

    (B) 17.4

    (C) 23.6

    (D) 31.2

    (E) 84.8

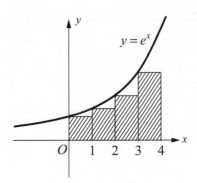

Note: Figure not drawn to scale.

Figure 6

37. Which of the following is an equation of a sine curve where $f(\frac{\pi}{3}) = 5$ is the maximum and $f(\pi) = -5$ is the minimum?

    (A) $f(x) = -5\sin x$

    (B) $f(x) = -2\sin 3x$

    (C) $f(x) = 5\sin\dfrac{3}{2}x$

    (D) $f(x) = 5\sin\dfrac{5}{2}x$

    (E) $f(x) = 5\sin 3x$

38. Figure 7 shows the graph of $f(x)$. If f^{-1} is the inverse of f, which of the following is the graph of f^{-1}?

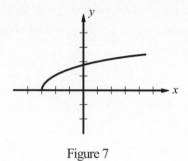

Figure 7

(A)
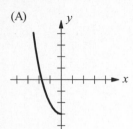

(B)
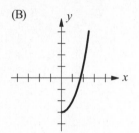

(C)
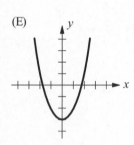

(D)
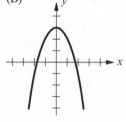

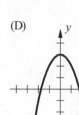

(E)
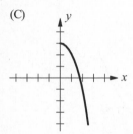

39. If $(2, 2\sqrt{3})$ is a point on a rectangular coordinate system, which of the following are the corresponding polar coordinates?

(A) $(4, \frac{\pi}{3})$

(B) $(4, \frac{\pi}{6})$

(C) $(4, \frac{2\pi}{3})$

(D) $(6, \frac{\pi}{6})$

(E) $(6, \frac{\pi}{3})$

40. If n is a positive integer, what is the remainder when
$x^{2n+1} - 2x^{2n} + 3x^{2n-1} + 4$ is divided by $x+1$?

(A) -2 (B) -1 (C) 0 (D) 1 (E) 2

41. Figure 8 shows a cube with edge of length 6. If point C is
the midpoint of $\overline{AB}$, what is the perimeter of $\triangle CDE$?

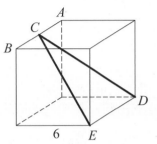

(A) $6(1+\sqrt{6})$

(B) $3(2+3\sqrt{6})$

(C) 24

(D) $6(1+2\sqrt{2})$

(E) 32

Figure 8

42. The sigma notation of the series $21+17+13+ \cdots -7$ is

(A) $\displaystyle\sum_{i=1}^{8}(21+4i)$

(B) $\displaystyle\sum_{i=1}^{8}(21-4i)$

(C) $\displaystyle\sum_{i=1}^{8}(25+4i)$

(D) $\displaystyle\sum_{i=1}^{8}(25-4i)$

(E) $\displaystyle\sum_{i=0}^{7}(25-4i)$

43. If $x = \sqrt{t} + 1$ and $y = t-1$, what is y in terms of x?

(A) $x+2$

(B) $x-2$

(C) $x^2 + x$

(D) $x^2 - 2x - 1$

(E) $x^2 - 2x$

44. At an electronics store the manager wants to display 6 different monitors in 4 different show windows. If monitors are displayed in all 4 windows, how many different arrangements are possible?

(A) 15

(B) 24

(C) 96

(D) 360

(E) 480

45. The graph of $4x^2 - 9y^2 + 32x - 36y - 80 = 0$ is a hyperbola centered at

(A) $(4, 2)$

(B) $(-4, 2)$

(C) $(-4, -2)$

(D) $(-8, -4)$

(E) $(-8, 4)$

46. A surveyor measures the angle between one side of a rectangular lot and the diagonal line from his position to the opposite corner of the lot as $35°$, as shown in Figure 9. He then measures the angle between the diagonal and the line from his position to an oak tree at the edge of the lot as $30°$. If the distance of the diagonal is 120 meters, how far is the surveyor from the oak tree?

(A) 71.3 meters

(B) 75.9 meters

(C) 82.8 meters

(D) 87.4 meters

(E) 92.5 meters

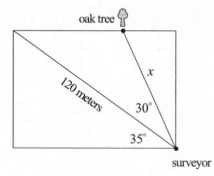

Figure 9

47. If $f(x) = \dfrac{x-16}{\sqrt{x}-4}$, what value does $f(x)$ approach as x approaches 16?

    (A) 2

    (B) 4

    (C) 8

    (D) 18

    (E) It does not approach a single number.

48. In Figure 10, a right circular cone is sliced into two pieces by a plane parallel to the base of the cone. If the height of the smaller cone (top part) is $2x$ and the height of the frustum is x, what is the ratio of the volume of the smaller cone to the volume of the frustum?

    (A) 1

    (B) $\dfrac{1}{4}$

    (C) $\dfrac{1}{3}$

    (D) $\dfrac{3}{8}$

    (E) $\dfrac{8}{19}$

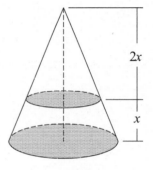

Figure 10

49. $\cos(2\sin^{-1} u) =$

    (A) $\dfrac{1+u^2}{1-u^2}$

    (B) $\dfrac{u}{1-u^2}$

    (C) $1+2u^2$

    (D) $1-2u^2$

    (E) $2u\sqrt{1-u^2}$

50. In Figure 11, a shaded region is formed by segment AB and an arc of a circle whose radius is 3. What is the volume of the space figure generated by rotating the shaded region around the x-axis?

(A) 24π

(B) 36π

(C) 45π

(D) 54π

(E) 64π

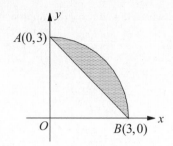

Figure 11

STOP

IF YOU FINISH BEFORE TIME IS CALLED, YOU MAY CHECK YOUR WORK ON THIS TEST ONLY.
DO NOT TURN TO ANY OTHER TEST IN THIS BOOK.

Answer Key

1. A	2. C	3. B	4. E	5. B
6. E	7. A	8. D	9. C	10. E
11. C	12. D	13. B	14. C	15. A
16. C	17. B	18. C	19. D	20. B
21. E	22. A	23. C	24. B	25. A
26. D	27. B	28. C	29. B	30. E
31. D	32. D	33. E	34. A	35. C
36. D	37. C	38. B	39. A	40. A
41. C	42. D	43. E	44. D	45. C
46. B	47. C	48. E	49. D	50. C

Answers and Explanations

1. A

$$M - N = [z - (x + y)] - [z + (x - y)]$$
$$= z - x - y - z - x + y$$
$$= -2x$$

2. C

$$\frac{1}{a-1} - \frac{2}{a^2-1} = \frac{1(a+1)}{(a-1)(a+1)} - \frac{2}{(a-1)(a+1)}$$
$$= \frac{a+1-2}{(a-1)(a+1)} = \frac{a-1}{(a-1)(a+1)}$$
$$= \frac{1}{a+1}$$

3. B

Check each answer choice.

(A) $x^2 - 2x > -8 \Rightarrow x^2 - 2x + 8 > 0$
$\Rightarrow (x+4)(x-2) > 0$

The left side of the inequality equals zero when $x = -4$ or $x = 2$. But the relevant numbers in the problem are $x = 4$ and $x = -2$.
Eliminate choice (A).

(B) $x^2 - 2x > 8 \Rightarrow x^2 - 2x - 8 > 0$
$\Rightarrow (x-4)(x+2) > 0$

The left side of the inequality equals zero when $x = 4$ or $x = -2$. Draw a number line divided into intervals by $x = -2$ and $x = 4$. Plug in one number in each interval to see if it satisfies the given inequality.

Therefore the solution set of the given inequality is $\{x : x > 4 \text{ or } x < -2\}$.

Choice (B) is correct.

4. E

$$f(n) = 0.4 + 0.28[n - 0.1]$$
$$= 0.4 + 0.28[3.8 - 0.1]$$
$$= 0.4 + 0.28[3.7]$$
$$= 0.4 + 0.28(4) \qquad \text{The least integer greater than or equal to 3.7 is 4.}$$
$$= 1.52$$

5. B

$$(\sqrt[5]{4x-9})^5 = (-3)^5 \Rightarrow 4x - 9 = -243$$
$$\Rightarrow 4x = -234 \Rightarrow x = -58.5$$

6. E

$$(\sqrt{a} + 2) = (\sqrt{a} - 2)^{-1} \Rightarrow (\sqrt{a} + 2) = \frac{1}{(\sqrt{a} - 2)}$$
$$\Rightarrow (\sqrt{a} + 2)(\sqrt{a} - 2) = 1 \Rightarrow a - 4 = 1$$
$$\Rightarrow a = 5$$

7. A

$\boxed{a,b,c}$ is defined as $\boxed{a,b,c} = \dfrac{a - b^{-1}}{a + c^{-1}}$.

$\boxed{a,2,3} = 3 \Rightarrow \boxed{a,2,3} = \dfrac{a - 2^{-1}}{a + 3^{-1}} = 3$

$\Rightarrow \dfrac{a - 1/2}{a + 1/3} = 3 \Rightarrow a - \dfrac{1}{2} = 3\left(a + \dfrac{1}{3}\right)$

$\Rightarrow a - \dfrac{1}{2} = 3a + 1 \Rightarrow -\dfrac{3}{2} = 2a \Rightarrow a = -\dfrac{3}{4}$

8. D

The graph of a function and the graph of its inverse are symmetric with respect to the line $y = x$.

Therefore the image of the reflection of $P(-3, 2)$ is $P'(2, -3)$, which is the inverse of P.

9. C

$f(x) = 1 - x$ and $g(x) = x^2 - x$

$g(f(x)) = g(1 - x)$

$\qquad = (1 - x)^2 - (1 - x)$

$\qquad = (1 - 2x + x^2) - (1 - x)$

$\qquad = x^2 - x$

10. E

If $|2x + 5| = x + 4$, then

$2x + 5 = x + 4$ or $2x + 5 = -(x + 4)$

$\qquad x = -1$ or $\qquad x = -3$

These values are the same as the solutions of the equation $(x + 1)(x + 3) = 0$.

11. C

Let x be the number which should be added to each of the three numbers, then $-6 + x$, $2 + x$, and $26 + x$ form a geometric sequence.
In a geometric sequence the ratio is the same.

Therefore $\dfrac{-6 + x}{2 + x} = \dfrac{2 + x}{26 + x}$.

$\Rightarrow (-6 + x)(26 + x) = (2 + x)(2 + x)$

$\Rightarrow x^2 + 20x - 156 = x^2 + 4x + 4$

$\Rightarrow x = 10$

12. D

A piecewise function f is defined by

$f(x) = \begin{cases} -1 & \text{if } x \le 0 \\ x^2 - 1 & \text{if } 0 < x \le 2 \\ x + 1 & \text{if } x > 2 \end{cases}$.

Since $-3 < 0$, $f(-3) = -1$.

Since $0 < 1 \le 2$, $f(1) = (1)^2 - 1 = 0$.

Since $3 > 2$, $f(3) = 3 + 1 = 4$.

$f(-3) + f(1) + f(3) = -1 + 0 + 4 = 3$

13. B

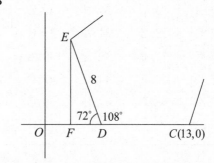

Each angle of the pentagon $= \dfrac{(5 - 2)180°}{5} = 108°$

The length of each side of the pentagon is 8.
Therefore the x-coordinate of D is $13 - 8 = 5$.

$FD = 8 \cdot \cos 72° \approx 2.47$

The x-coordinate of E is $5 - 2.47 = 2.53$.

14. C

Statement: If p, then q.
Contrapositive: If not q, then not p.

A statement and its contrapositive are logically equivalent.

Therefore if the racquet is not blue, then the ball is not yellow.

15. A

Let $x =$ the sum of the earnings of the two new employees.

$$\dfrac{\overbrace{24 \cdot 585}^{\substack{\text{sum of the earnings} \\ \text{of 24 employees}}} + \overbrace{x}^{\substack{\text{sum of the earnings} \\ \text{of 2 employees}}}}{26} = 579$$

$24 \cdot 585 + x = 26 \cdot 579$

$x = 1014$

16. C

$2x^2 - kx + 6 = 0$

In a quadratic equation, if there are no real roots, then $b^2 - 4ac < 0$.

$b^2 - 4ac = (-k)^2 - 4(2)(6) < 0$

$k^2 - 48 < 0$

$(k + \sqrt{48})(k - \sqrt{48}) < 0$

$(k + 4\sqrt{3})(k - 4\sqrt{3}) < 0$

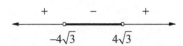

If $k < -4\sqrt{3}$ or $k > 4\sqrt{3}$, $(k + 4\sqrt{3})(k - 4\sqrt{3}) > 0$.

If $-4\sqrt{3} < k < 4\sqrt{3}$, $(k + 4\sqrt{3})(k - 4\sqrt{3}) < 0$.

Choice (C) is correct.

17. B

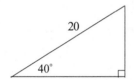

The length of the base $= 20\cos 40° \approx 15.3$

The length of the height $= 20\sin 40° \approx 12.9$

Perimeter $= 20 + 15.3 + 12.9 = 48.2$

18. C

If 4 tees were left after dividing the contents of the bag equally, that means that $144 - 4$, or 140, golf tees were divided equally without a remainder. Then n must be a number that divides 140 without a remainder. Find the prime factorization of 140.

$140 = 2 \cdot 2 \cdot 5 \cdot 7$

Then the numbers $2 \cdot 2 = 4$, $2 \cdot 5 = 10$, $2 \cdot 2 \cdot 7 = 28$, or $5 \cdot 7 = 35$ are factors of 140.

But 16 cannot divide 140 without a remainder.

19. D

Checking each answer choice is the easiest way.

(A) If $f(x) = \sqrt{1 - 2x}$, then

$f(\frac{1}{2}x + 1) = \sqrt{1 - 2(\frac{1}{2}x + 1)}$

$= \sqrt{1 - x - 2} = \sqrt{-1 - x}$

(B) If $f(x) = \sqrt{5 - 4x}$, then

$f(\frac{1}{2}x + 1) = \sqrt{5 - 4(\frac{1}{2}x + 1)}$

$= \sqrt{5 - 2x - 4} = \sqrt{1 - 2x}$

(C) If $f(x) = \sqrt{-1 - 2x}$, then

$f(\frac{1}{2}x + 1) = \sqrt{-1 - 2(\frac{1}{2}x + 1)}$

$= \sqrt{-1 - x - 2} = \sqrt{-3 - x}$

(D) If $f(x) = \sqrt{7 - 4x}$, then

$f(\frac{1}{2}x + 1) = \sqrt{7 - 4(\frac{1}{2}x + 1)}$

$= \sqrt{7 - 2x - 4} = \sqrt{3 - 2x}$

Choice (D) is correct.

20. B

$\cos 2x = 2\cos^2 x - 1$

$\quad\quad = 2(0.46)^2 - 1 \quad\quad\quad \cos x = 0.46$

$\quad\quad \approx -.58$

21. E

Divide both sides by $(x^2 - 8)$.

$$\begin{array}{r} x + 3 \\ x^2 - 8 \overline{\smash{)}x^3 + 3x^2 - 8x - 24} \\ \underline{x^3 - 8x} \downarrow \\ 3x^2 - 24 \\ \underline{3x^2 - 24} \\ 0 \end{array}$$

Therefore $p(x) = x + 3$.

22. A

Factor.

$x^{2p} - x^p - 6 = (x^p + 2)(x^p - 3) = 0$

$x^p + 2 = 0 \quad$ or $\quad x^p - 3 = 0$

$x^p = -2 \quad\quad$ or $\quad x^p = 3$

Since $x > 0$, $x^p = 3$ is the only solution.

$$(x^p)^{\frac{1}{p}} = (3)^{\frac{1}{p}}$$

$$x = (3)^{\frac{1}{p}} = \sqrt[p]{3}$$

23. C

$$(\frac{1}{\sqrt{2}} + \frac{1}{\sqrt{2}}i)^2 = (\frac{1}{\sqrt{2}} + \frac{1}{\sqrt{2}}i)(\frac{1}{\sqrt{2}} + \frac{1}{\sqrt{2}}i)$$

$$= \frac{1}{2} + \frac{1}{2}i + \frac{1}{2}i + \frac{1}{2}i^2$$

$$= \frac{1}{2} + i - \frac{1}{2} \qquad i^2 = -1$$

$$= i$$

24. B

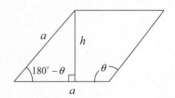

$h = a\sin(180° - \theta)$

$= a(\sin180° \cos\theta -$ Sum and difference

$\cos180° \sin\theta)$ formula

$= a(0 \cdot \cos\theta - (-1)\sin\theta)$ $\sin180° = 0$,

                      $\cos180° = -1$

$= a\sin\theta$

Area of the rhombus

$= \text{base} \cdot \text{height} = a \cdot a\sin\theta = a^2 \sin\theta$

25. A

Vector magnitude is always positive, so the magnitude of vector $\mathbf{w} - \mathbf{v}$ will be the absolute value of the sum or difference of the magnitudes of $\mathbf{v}$ and $\mathbf{w}$.

$$14 - 5 \le |\mathbf{w} - \mathbf{v}| \le 14 + 5$$

$$9 \le |\mathbf{w} - \mathbf{v}| \le 19$$

Any number between 9 and 19, inclusive, is a possible value of $|\mathbf{w} - \mathbf{v}|$.

26. D

$$y = \frac{x}{x^2 + 5x} = \frac{\cancel{x}}{\cancel{x}(x+5)} = \frac{1}{x+5}$$

A vertical asymptote occurs at a number where the denominator is zero. So the line $x = -5$ is a vertical asymptote.

A horizontal asymptote occurs where the function approaches a single number as $x \to \infty$ or $x \to -\infty$.

As x approaches infinity $\frac{1}{x+5}$ approaches 0.

So the line $y = 0$ is a horizontal asymptote.

27. B

Given: $\log_2 m = n$

$$\log_2(\frac{m}{2})$$

$$= \log_2 m - \log_2 2 \qquad \log(\frac{M}{N}) = \log M - \log N$$

$$= n - 1 \qquad\qquad \log_2 m = n \text{ and } \log_2 2 = 1$$

28. C

Sketch a triangle.

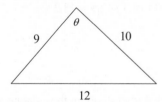

The largest angle in a triangle is the angle opposite of the longest side.

Use the Law of cosines.

$$12^2 = 9^2 + 10^2 - 2 \cdot 9 \cdot 10 \cdot \cos\theta$$

$$\cos\theta = \frac{9^2 + 10^2 - 12^2}{2 \cdot 9 \cdot 10} \approx 0.206$$

$$\theta = \cos^{-1}(0.206) = 78.1°$$

29. B

The graph shows a circle with center $(0,0)$ and radius 4. The equation of the circle is $x^2 + y^2 = 4^2$.

The graph shows a hyperbola with center $(0,0)$, a horizontal major axis, and vertices $(-2,0)$ and $(2,0)$.

The equation of the hyperbola is $\dfrac{x^2}{2^2}-\dfrac{y^2}{b^2}=1$, where a is the distance from the center to a vertex.

Choice (B) is correct.

30. E

The sum of two odd integers is an even integer, which does not belong to the set of odd integers.

The sum of even integers is an even integer.

The sum of negative integers is a negative integer.

So, Roman numerals II and III are true.

31. D

$$\cos\theta=\dfrac{-3}{r}\ \text{ and }\ \sin\theta=\dfrac{4}{r}$$

$$r\cos\theta+r\sin\theta=r(\dfrac{-3}{r})+r(\dfrac{4}{r})$$

$$=-3+4$$

$$=1$$

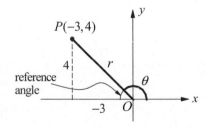

32. D

$$(a-\dfrac{1}{2}bi)=2(a+\dfrac{1}{2}bi)^{-1}$$

$$\Rightarrow (a-\dfrac{1}{2}bi)=\dfrac{2}{(a+\dfrac{1}{2}bi)}$$

$$\Rightarrow (a-\dfrac{1}{2}bi)(a+\dfrac{1}{2}bi)=2$$

$$\Rightarrow a^2+\dfrac{1}{2}abi-\dfrac{1}{2}abi-\dfrac{1}{4}b^2i^2=2$$

$$\Rightarrow a^2+\dfrac{1}{4}b^2=2$$

$$\Rightarrow \dfrac{a^2}{2}+\dfrac{b^2}{8}=1$$

33. E

The graph of $|x|+|y|=3$ consists of four line segments.

1) If $x\ge 0$ and $y\ge 0$, $x+y=3\ \Rightarrow\ y=-x+3$
2) If $x\le 0$ and $y\ge 0$, $-x+y=3\ \Rightarrow\ y=x+3$
3) If $x\le 0$ and $y\le 0$, $-x-y=3\ \Rightarrow\ y=-x-3$
4) If $x\ge 0$ and $y\le 0$, $x-y=3\ \Rightarrow\ y=x-3$

The graph of $|x|+|y|=1$ consists of four line segments.

1) If $x\ge 0$ and $y\ge 0$, $x+y=1\ \Rightarrow\ y=-x+1$
2) If $x\le 0$ and $y\ge 0$, $-x+y=1\ \Rightarrow\ y=x+1$
3) If $x\le 0$ and $y\le 0$, $-x-y=1\ \Rightarrow\ y=-x-1$
4) If $x\ge 0$ and $y\le 0$, $x-y=1\ \Rightarrow\ y=x-1$

The shaded region is inside the graph of $|x|+|y|=3$ and outside the graph of $|x|+|y|=1$.

34. A

$$a_n=1-\dfrac{1}{a_{n-1}}\ \text{ and }\ a_1=k$$

$$a_2=1-\dfrac{1}{a_1}=1-\dfrac{1}{k}=\dfrac{k-1}{k}$$

$$a_3=1-\dfrac{1}{a_2}=1-\dfrac{1}{\dfrac{k-1}{k}}=1-\dfrac{k}{k-1}=-\dfrac{1}{k-1}$$

$$a_4=1-\dfrac{1}{a_3}=1-\dfrac{1}{-\dfrac{1}{k-1}}=1+(k-1)=k$$

35. C

Check each answer choice.

(A) $f(-x)=|-x|-3=|x|-3$

$\quad\ -f(x)=-(|x|-3)=-|x|+3$

$\quad$ So, $f(-x)\ne -f(x)$.

(B) $f(-x) = (-x)^3 + 3 = -x^3 + 3$

$-f(x) = -(x^3 + 3) = -x^3 - 3$

So, $f(-x) \neq -f(x)$.

(C) $f(-x) = (-x)^3 + (-x) = -x^3 - x$

$-f(x) = -(x^3 + x) = -x^3 - x$

So, $f(-x) = -f(x)$.

Choice (C) is correct.

36. D

The sum of the areas of the four rectangles

$= 1(e^0) + 1(e^1) + 1(e^2) + 1(e^3)$

$= 1 + 2.72 + 7.39 + 20.09$

$= 31.2$

37. C

A maximum at $f(\frac{\pi}{3}) = 5$ and minimum at

$f(\pi) = -5$ means the amplitude of the sine function is 5. Test answer choices (C), (D), and (E).

(C) $f(\frac{\pi}{3}) = 5\sin\frac{3}{2}(\frac{\pi}{3}) = 5\sin(\frac{\pi}{2}) = 5$

$f(\pi) = 5\sin\frac{3}{2}(\pi) = 5\sin(\frac{3\pi}{2}) = 5(-1) = -5$

Choice (C) is correct.

38. B

Method 1:

The graphs of f and f^{-1} are symmetric with respect to the line $y = x$.

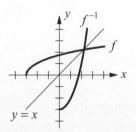

Method 2:

Choose a few points from the graph of f.

If $(-3, 0)$, $(0, 1.8)$, and $(1, 2)$ are points on the graph of f, then $(0, -3)$, $(1.8, 0)$, and $(2, 1)$ are points of f^{-1}.

Choice (B) is correct.

39. A

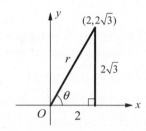

$\tan\theta = \frac{2\sqrt{3}}{2} = \sqrt{3} \Rightarrow \theta = \tan^{-1}(\sqrt{3}) = \frac{\pi}{3}$

$r^2 = 2^2 + (2\sqrt{3})^2 = 4 + 12 = 16$

$\Rightarrow r = 4$

Polar coordinates $= (r, \theta) = (4, \frac{\pi}{3})$

40. A

The remainder theorem states that if $f(x)$ is divided by $x + 1$, $f(-1)$ is the remainder.

$f(x) = x^{2n+1} - 2x^{2n} + 3x^{2n-1} + 4$

$f(-1) = (-1)^{2n+1} - 2(-1)^{2n} + 3(-1)^{2n-1} + 4$

$= -1 - 2(1) + 3(-1) + 4 = -2$

Note: $(-1)^{2n+1}$ and $(-1)^{2n-1}$ equal -1 since $2n+1$ and $2n-1$ are odd integers.

$(-1)^{2n}$ equals 1 since $2n$ is an even integer.

41. C

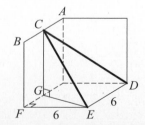

In $\triangle GEF$, $GE^2 = GF^2 + FE^2 = 3^2 + 6^2 = 45$

In $\triangle CEG$, $CE^2 = CG^2 + GE^2 = 6^2 + 45 = 81$

$CE = \sqrt{81} = 9$

Also, $CE = CD$.

Perimeter of $\triangle CED = CE + CD + DE$
$$= 9 + 9 + 6 = 24$$

42. D

To find the sigma notation of the series we need to find out a_n and the number of terms.

$a_1 = 21$ and $d = -4$
$$a_n = a_1 + (n-1)d$$
$$= 21 + (n-1)(-4)$$
$$= 25 - 4n$$

To find the number of terms, substitute -7 for a_n.
$$-7 = 25 - 4n \implies n = 8$$

Choice (D) is correct.

Choice (E) is not correct, since $i = 0$ makes the first term 25 instead of 21.

43. E

$$x = \sqrt{t} + 1$$
$$\sqrt{t} = x - 1 \qquad \text{Isolate } \sqrt{t}.$$
$$(\sqrt{t})^2 = (x-1)^2 \qquad \text{Square both sides.}$$
$$t = x^2 - 2x + 1$$
$$y = t - 1$$
$$= (x^2 - 2x + 1) - 1 \qquad \text{Substitute } x^2 - 2x + 1 \text{ for } t.$$
$$= x^2 - 2x$$

44. D

Method 1: $_6P_4 = 360$

Method 2: A diagram is also useful for solving the problem.

$\boxed{6}\ \boxed{5}\ \boxed{4}\ \boxed{3}$

There are six possible selections for the first window, five for the second window, four for the third window, and three for the last window. By the fundamental counting principle, there are $6 \cdot 5 \cdot 4 \cdot 3$, or 360, possible arrangements.

45. C

$$4x^2 - 9y^2 + 32x - 36y - 80 = 0$$
$$4(x^2 + 8x + \square) - 9(y^2 + 4y + \square) = 80$$
$$4(x^2 + 8x + 16) - 9(y^2 + 4y + 4) = 80 + 64 - 36$$
$$4(x+4)^2 - 9(y+2)^2 = 108$$

Therefore the center of the hyperbola is $(-4, -2)$.

46. B

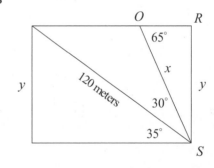

$$\sin 35° = \frac{y}{120} \implies y = 120 \cdot \sin 35° \approx 68.83$$

Since alternate interior angles are congruent, $m\angle SOR = 35 + 30 = 65$.

$$\sin 65° = \frac{y}{x} = \frac{68.83}{x} \implies x = \frac{68.83}{\sin 65°} \approx 75.94$$

47. C

$$\lim_{x \to 16} f(x) = \lim_{x \to 16} \frac{x - 16}{\sqrt{x} - 4}$$
$$= \lim_{x \to 16} \frac{(\sqrt{x} + 4)(\sqrt{x} - 4)}{\sqrt{x} - 4}$$
$$= \lim_{x \to 16} \frac{(\sqrt{x} + 4)\,(\cancel{\sqrt{x} - 4})}{\cancel{\sqrt{x} - 4}}$$

$$= \lim_{x \to 16} (\sqrt{x} + 4)$$

$$= \sqrt{16} + 4 = 8 \qquad \text{Substitute 16 for } x.$$

$$= 8$$

48. E

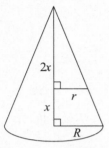

Let r = the radius of smaller cone and R = the radius of larger cone.

The two cones are similar.

$$\frac{2x}{r} = \frac{3x}{R} \implies R = \frac{3}{2}r$$

Volume of the smaller cone

$$= \frac{1}{3}\pi r^2 (2x) = \frac{2\pi r^2 x}{3}$$

Volume of the larger cone

$$= \frac{1}{3}\pi R^2 (3x) = \frac{1}{3}\pi (\frac{3}{2}r)^2 (3x) = \frac{9\pi r^2 x}{4}$$

Volume of the frustum

$$= \frac{9\pi r^2 x}{4} - \frac{2\pi r^2 x}{3} = \frac{19\pi r^2 x}{12}$$

$$\frac{\text{Volume of the smaller cone}}{\text{Volume of the frustum}}$$

$$= \frac{\dfrac{2\pi r^2 x}{3}}{\dfrac{19\pi r^2 x}{12}} = \frac{\dfrac{2}{3}}{\dfrac{19}{12}} = \frac{2 \cdot 12}{19 \cdot 3} = \frac{8}{19}$$

49. D

Let $x = \sin^{-1} u$, then

$$\sin x = \sin(\sin^{-1} u) \implies \sin x = u$$

Draw a right triangle whose acute angle is x, length of the opposite side is u, and hypotenuse has length 1.

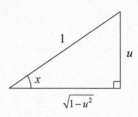

By the Pythagorean theorem the adjacent side is $\sqrt{1-u^2}$.

$$\cos(2\sin^{-1} u)$$

$$= \cos(2x) \qquad\qquad \sin^{-1} u = x$$

$$= 2\cos^2 x - 1 \qquad\quad \text{Double angle formula}$$

$$= 2(\sqrt{1-u^2})^2 - 1 \qquad \cos x = \sqrt{1-u^2}$$

$$= 2(1-u^2) - 1$$

$$= 1 - 2u^2$$

50. C

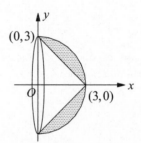

The volume of the space figure generated can be found by subtracting the volume of a cone from the volume of a hemisphere.

Volume of the hemisphere $= \dfrac{1}{2}\left[\dfrac{4}{3}\pi(3)^3 \cdot 3\right] = 54\pi$

Volume of the cone $= \dfrac{1}{3}\pi(3)^2 \cdot 3 = 9\pi$

$$54\pi - 9\pi = 45\pi$$

Test Form F
Mathematics Level 2

Answer Sheet

1 Ⓐ Ⓑ Ⓒ Ⓓ Ⓔ   21 Ⓐ Ⓑ Ⓒ Ⓓ Ⓔ   41 Ⓐ Ⓑ Ⓒ Ⓓ Ⓔ
2 Ⓐ Ⓑ Ⓒ Ⓓ Ⓔ   22 Ⓐ Ⓑ Ⓒ Ⓓ Ⓔ   42 Ⓐ Ⓑ Ⓒ Ⓓ Ⓔ
3 Ⓐ Ⓑ Ⓒ Ⓓ Ⓔ   23 Ⓐ Ⓑ Ⓒ Ⓓ Ⓔ   43 Ⓐ Ⓑ Ⓒ Ⓓ Ⓔ
4 Ⓐ Ⓑ Ⓒ Ⓓ Ⓔ   24 Ⓐ Ⓑ Ⓒ Ⓓ Ⓔ   44 Ⓐ Ⓑ Ⓒ Ⓓ Ⓔ
5 Ⓐ Ⓑ Ⓒ Ⓓ Ⓔ   25 Ⓐ Ⓑ Ⓒ Ⓓ Ⓔ   45 Ⓐ Ⓑ Ⓒ Ⓓ Ⓔ
6 Ⓐ Ⓑ Ⓒ Ⓓ Ⓔ   26 Ⓐ Ⓑ Ⓒ Ⓓ Ⓔ   46 Ⓐ Ⓑ Ⓒ Ⓓ Ⓔ
7 Ⓐ Ⓑ Ⓒ Ⓓ Ⓔ   27 Ⓐ Ⓑ Ⓒ Ⓓ Ⓔ   47 Ⓐ Ⓑ Ⓒ Ⓓ Ⓔ
8 Ⓐ Ⓑ Ⓒ Ⓓ Ⓔ   28 Ⓐ Ⓑ Ⓒ Ⓓ Ⓔ   48 Ⓐ Ⓑ Ⓒ Ⓓ Ⓔ
9 Ⓐ Ⓑ Ⓒ Ⓓ Ⓔ   29 Ⓐ Ⓑ Ⓒ Ⓓ Ⓔ   49 Ⓐ Ⓑ Ⓒ Ⓓ Ⓔ
10 Ⓐ Ⓑ Ⓒ Ⓓ Ⓔ   30 Ⓐ Ⓑ Ⓒ Ⓓ Ⓔ   50 Ⓐ Ⓑ Ⓒ Ⓓ Ⓔ
11 Ⓐ Ⓑ Ⓒ Ⓓ Ⓔ   31 Ⓐ Ⓑ Ⓒ Ⓓ Ⓔ
12 Ⓐ Ⓑ Ⓒ Ⓓ Ⓔ   32 Ⓐ Ⓑ Ⓒ Ⓓ Ⓔ
13 Ⓐ Ⓑ Ⓒ Ⓓ Ⓔ   33 Ⓐ Ⓑ Ⓒ Ⓓ Ⓔ
14 Ⓐ Ⓑ Ⓒ Ⓓ Ⓔ   34 Ⓐ Ⓑ Ⓒ Ⓓ Ⓔ
15 Ⓐ Ⓑ Ⓒ Ⓓ Ⓔ   35 Ⓐ Ⓑ Ⓒ Ⓓ Ⓔ
16 Ⓐ Ⓑ Ⓒ Ⓓ Ⓔ   36 Ⓐ Ⓑ Ⓒ Ⓓ Ⓔ
17 Ⓐ Ⓑ Ⓒ Ⓓ Ⓔ   37 Ⓐ Ⓑ Ⓒ Ⓓ Ⓔ
18 Ⓐ Ⓑ Ⓒ Ⓓ Ⓔ   38 Ⓐ Ⓑ Ⓒ Ⓓ Ⓔ
19 Ⓐ Ⓑ Ⓒ Ⓓ Ⓔ   39 Ⓐ Ⓑ Ⓒ Ⓓ Ⓔ
20 Ⓐ Ⓑ Ⓒ Ⓓ Ⓔ   40 Ⓐ Ⓑ Ⓒ Ⓓ Ⓔ

Reference Information

The following information is for your reference in answering some of the questions on this test.

Volume of a right circular cone with radius r and height h: $V = \dfrac{1}{3}\pi r^2 h$

Lateral area of a right circular cone with base circumference C and slant height ℓ: $S = \dfrac{1}{2}C\ell$

Volume of a sphere with radius r: $V = \dfrac{4}{3}\pi r^3$

Surface area of a sphere with radius r: $S = 4\pi r^2$

Volume of a pyramid with base area B and height h: $V = \dfrac{1}{3}Bh$

Test Form F
SAT Subject Test in Mathematics Level 2

50 Questions   1 hour

For each of the following problems, decide which is the BEST of the answer choices given. If the exact numerical value is not one of the choices, select the choice that best approximates this value. Then fill in the corresponding circle on the answer sheet.

Notes: (1) A calculator will be necessary for answering some of the questions on this test. For each question you will have to decide whether or not you should use a calculator. Programmable calculators and calculators that can display graphs are permitted.

      (2) The angle measures used on the Math Level 2 Test are in either degree measure or radian measure. Check to see which mode your calculator is in.

      (3) Figures that accompany problems on this test are intended to provide information useful in solving the problems. They are drawn as accurately as possible EXCEPT when it is stated in a specific problem that its figure is not drawn to scale. All figures lie in a plane unless otherwise indicated.

      (4) Unless otherwise specified, the domain of any function f is assumed to be the set of all real numbers x for which $f(x)$ is a real number.

      (5) Reference information that may be useful in answering the questions on this test can be found on the page preceding Question 1.

1. The sum of twelve and the negative of n equals p. If n equals five times p, what is the value of p?

    (A) –4   (B) –2   (C) 2   (D) 4   (E) 6

2. If $(x+3)(y-3)^{-1} = 0$, which of the following must be true?

    (A) $x = 0$ and $y = 0$

    (B) $x \neq -3$ and $y = 3$

    (C) $x = -3$ and $y \neq 3$

    (D) $x \neq -3$ and $y \neq -3$

    (E) $x = -3$ and $y = 3$

3. What is the number of digits in the number 55^9 ?

    (A) 13   (B) 14   (C) 15   (D) 16   (E) 17

4. $\dfrac{6}{\sqrt[3]{y^2}} =$

    (A) $\dfrac{6\sqrt[3]{y}}{y}$

    (B) $\dfrac{6\sqrt[3]{y^2}}{y}$

    (C) $\dfrac{6\sqrt[3]{y}}{y^2}$

    (D) $6\sqrt[3]{y}$

    (E) $6\sqrt[3]{y^2}$

5. Which of the following describes the solution set of $|x+3| \geq 8$?

    (A) All the points more than 8 units from -3

    (B) All the points at least 8 units from -3

    (C) All the points at least 8 units from 3

    (D) All the points not more than 8 unit from 3

    (E) All the points at least 5 units from -3

6. Figure 1 shows the graph of $y = g(x)$. If the function f is defined as $f(x) = g(-2x) + 1$, what is the value of $f(-\dfrac{1}{2})$?

    (A)   4

    (B) -4

    (C) $\dfrac{1}{2}$

    (D) $-\dfrac{1}{2}$

    (E)   0

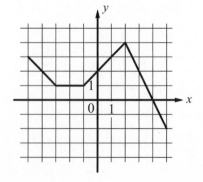

Figure 1

7. If $f(x) = x^2 - 16$ and $g(x) = x^2 - x - 20$, where $g(x) \neq 0$,

then $\dfrac{f(x)}{g(x)} =$

    (A) $\dfrac{x-4}{x+4}$

    (B) $\dfrac{x+4}{x-5}$

    (C) $\dfrac{x-4}{x+5}$

    (D) $\dfrac{x+4}{x+5}$

    (E) $\dfrac{x-4}{x-5}$

8. In right $\triangle ABC$ in Figure 2, $\sin 2x =$

    (A) 0.16

    (B) 0.40

    (C) 0.68

    (D) 0.73

    (E) 0.84

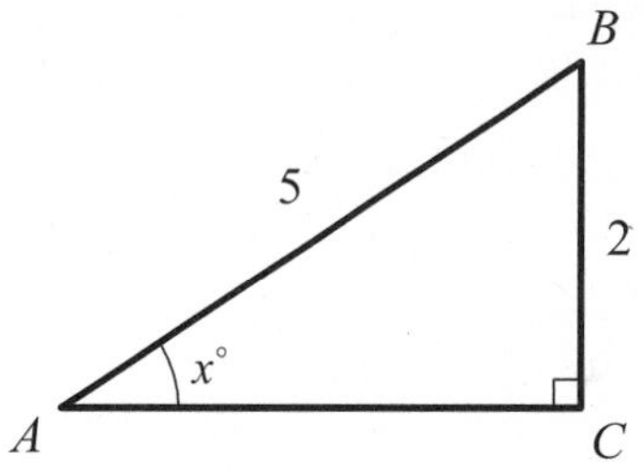

Figure 2

9. If $a^2 b^{-5} c^{11} = \dfrac{3ac^5}{b^{-5}}$, then $a =$

    (A) $\dfrac{3}{c^6}$

    (B) $\dfrac{3c^6}{b^{10}}$

    (C) $3b^{10}c^6$

    (D) $\dfrac{3b^{10}}{c^6}$

    (E) $\dfrac{c^6}{3}$

10. $\dfrac{(n+2)!}{(n+1)!} - 2 =$

(A) n

(B) $n-1$

(C) $n+1$

(D) $\dfrac{1}{n+1}$

(E) $\dfrac{-n}{n+1}$

11. If $f(g(x)) = x+2$ and $g(x) = -2x+1$, which of the following could be $f(x)$?

(A) $\dfrac{1}{2}x - \dfrac{5}{2}$

(B) $-\dfrac{1}{2}x - \dfrac{5}{2}$

(C) $-\dfrac{1}{2}x + \dfrac{5}{2}$

(D) $2x-1$

(E) $-2x+1$

12. For all real numbers x, let $x*$ be defined as

$$x* = \begin{cases} x-4 & \text{if } x \text{ is positive} \\ -\dfrac{x}{2} & \text{if } x \text{ is negative} \end{cases}.$$

Then $(2*)* =$

(A) -2

(B) -1

(C) 0

(D) 1

(E) 2

13. In a data set of n numbers, the same number k is added to each of the n numbers. Which of the following statements must be true of the new data set?

    I.   The value of the new mean is increased by k.

    II.   The new range is increased by k.

    III. The new standard deviation is increased by k.

  (A) None

  (B) I only

  (C) II only

  (D) III only

  (E) I and III only

14. A bag of fruit contains only oranges and apples. If $\frac{3}{5}$ of the oranges is equal to $\frac{1}{3}$ of the apples, what fraction of the fruits are oranges?

  (A) $\frac{1}{5}$ (B) $\frac{5}{14}$ (C) $\frac{2}{5}$ (D) $\frac{3}{7}$ (E) $\frac{4}{7}$

15. In Figure 3, circle O with radius 8 is tangent to a rectangle at points P and Q, and intersects the rectangle at points S and T. If $\theta = 55°$, what is the perimeter of trapezoid $OPRS$ to the nearest integer?

  (A) 19

  (B) 21

  (C) 23

  (D) 26

  (E) 28

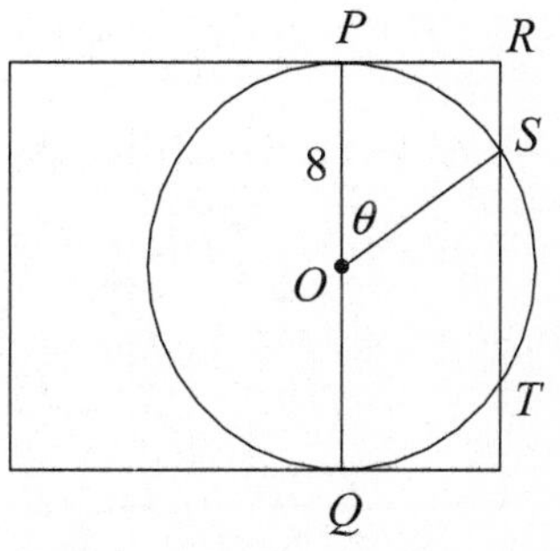

Note: Figure not drawn to scale.

Figure 3

16. If $f(x)$ is a linear function whose slope is -2, what is the slope of $f^{-1}(x)$?

  (A) -2 (B) $-\frac{1}{2}$ (C) 1   (D) $\frac{1}{2}$ (E) 2

17. An indirect proof of the statement "If $n = 19$, then n is a prime number" could begin with the assumption that

    (A) n is prime.

    (B) n is an even number.

    (C) n is not prime.

    (D) $n \neq 19$.

    (E) $n = 19$.

18. Which of the following inequalities is represented by the graph in Figure 4?

    (A) $(x - 2y)(2x - y) \leq 0$

    (B) $(x + 2y)(2x + y) \geq 0$

    (C) $(x - 2y)(2x - y) \geq 0$

    (D) $(x + 2y)(2x - y) \geq 0$

    (E) $(x + 2y)(2x - y) \leq 0$

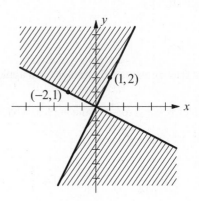

Figure 4

19. What is the range of the function defined by

$$f(x) = \begin{cases} \sqrt{x} & \text{if } x > 1 \\ \dfrac{1}{2}x + 1 & \text{if } x \leq 1 \end{cases} \quad ?$$

    (A) $y \leq \dfrac{3}{2}$

    (B) $y < 1$ or $y \geq \dfrac{3}{2}$

    (C) $1 < y \leq \dfrac{3}{2}$

    (D) All real numbers except $y = \dfrac{3}{2}$

    (E) All real numbers

20. If $(3-2i)^2 = a+bi$, where a and b are real numbers and $i^2 = -1$, then $ab =$

    (A) 156
    (B)   60
    (C)   0
    (D) −60
    (E) −156

21. In the rectangular coordinate system in Figure 5, point P is on a circle whose center is at the origin. What is the radian measure of angle θ?

    (A) 1.58
    (B) 1.68
    (C) 1.92
    (D) 2.03
    (E) 2.11

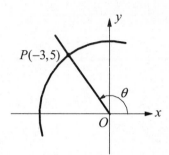

Figure 5

22. Two cars start moving from the same point and travel along two straight roads, forming an angle of $70°$. If one car travels 50 mph and the other travels 40 mph, how many miles apart are the two cars after 2 hours?

    (A) 82.3
    (B) 99.6
    (C) 104.5
    (D) 112.6
    (E) 125.8

23. When the graph of $f(x) = 2x^2$ is translated 1 unit to the right and 3 units up, the resulting graph is represented by $g(x)$. What is the value of $g(2.5)$?

    (A) 7.5   (B) 9   (C) 11   (D) 12.5 (E) 14.5

24. What is the sum of the infinite geometric series

$$2 - \frac{4}{3} + \frac{8}{9} - \frac{16}{27} + \cdots?$$

(A) 0.8 (B) 1.2 (C) 2.4 (D) 4 (E) 6

25. Which of the following shaded regions could be

the graph of $\begin{cases} |x| \leq 2 \\ |y| \leq 2 \end{cases}$?

(A)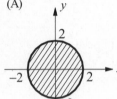

(B)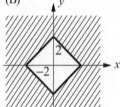

(C)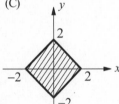

(D)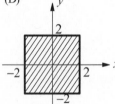

(E)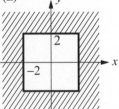

26. If $\log_b m = 3$ and $\log_b n = 4$, then $\log_b (m^2 \cdot \sqrt{n}) =$

(A) 6 (B) 8 (C) 9 (D) 12 (E) 18

27. Traffic flow is defined as the rate at which cars pass through an intersection. The value of traffic flow is modeled by the function $f(t) = 50t - 20\cos(\dfrac{t}{2})$, where t is the time measured in minutes. If the average number of cars that pass through a certain intersection over the time interval $a \le t \le b$ is defined by $\dfrac{f(b) - f(a)}{b - a}$, what is the average number of cars, to the nearest whole number, that pass through the intersection over the time interval $5 \le t \le 10$?

(A) 38

(B) 42

(C) 46

(D) 50

(E) 54

28. In Figure 6, what is the length of segment AB?

(A) 6.4

(B) 7.2

(C) 7.9

(D) 9.2

(E) 9.7

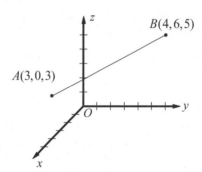

Figure 6

29. Which of the following lines are asymptotes of the graph of $y = \dfrac{4x}{x - 2}$?

   I. $x = 2$

   II. $y = 0$

   III. $y = 4$

(A) I only

(B) II only

(C) III only

(D) I and II only

(E) I and III only

30. What is the measure of one of the larger angles of a parallelogram in the xy-plane that has vertices with coordinates $(-1,3)$, $(2,5)$, $(2,0)$, and $(-1,-2)$?

(A) $116.6°$

(B) $123.7°$

(C) $128.6°$

(D) $130.9°$

(E) $135.0°$

31. If $f(x) = \dfrac{x-2}{x^2 - x - 2}$, which of the following is the graph of f?

(A)
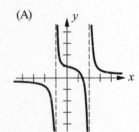

(B)
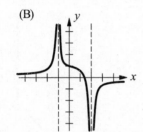

(C)
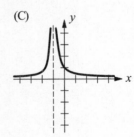

(D)
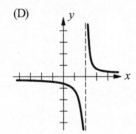

(E)
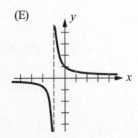

32. At how many points do the graphs of $x^2 + y^2 = 16$ and $x = 4y^2$ intersect?

    (A) None

    (B) One

    (C) Two

    (D) Three

    (E) Four

33. In Figure 7, a plane intersects a sphere in a circle. If the radius of the sphere is 8 and the length of $\overline{OP}$ is 6, what is the area of circle P?

    (A) 20π

    (B) 24π

    (C) 28π

    (D) 32π

    (E) 36π

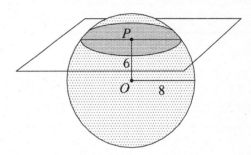

Figure 7

34. If $f(x)$ is a polynomial function and $f(i) = f(1)$, where $i = \sqrt{-1}$, which of the following could be $f(x)$?

    (A) $x^3 + x^2 - x - 1$

    (B) $x^3 - x^2 + x - 1$

    (C) $x^3 + x - 2$

    (D) $x^3 - x - 2$

    (E) $-x^3 + x + 2$

35. A sequence is recursively defined by $a_n = 1 + \dfrac{1}{a_{n-1}}$, for $n \geq 2$. If $a_1 = k$ and $a_2 \cdot a_3 = \dfrac{3}{2}$, what is the value of k?

    (A) -2 (B) -1 (C) 0 (D) 1 (E) 2

36. If $f(x) = e^x$ and the inverse function of f is denoted by f^{-1}, then what is $f^{-1}(\frac{a}{b})$ where $a > 0$ and $b > 0$?

(A) $\dfrac{e^a}{e^b}$

(B) $(\dfrac{a}{b})^e$

(C) $\ln(a-b)$

(D) $\ln a - \ln b$

(E) $\dfrac{\ln a}{\ln b}$

37. Figure 8 shows the graph of $y = f(x)$. Which of the following is the graph of $y = -|f(x)|$?

(A)

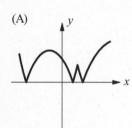

(B)

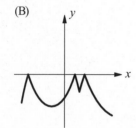

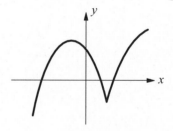

Figure 8

(C)

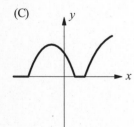

(D)

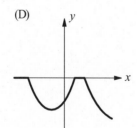

(E)

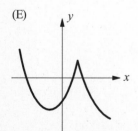

38. If **u** and **v** are two vectors such that **u** =< 7, −8 >
    and **v** =< 3, −5 >, then 2**u** − **v** =

    (A) < 11, −11 >

    (B) < 4, −3 >

    (C) < 1, 2 >

    (D) < 10, −13 >

    (E) < 17, −21 >

39. In Figure 9, what is the intersection of plane *CEF* and
    plane *ADE*?

    (A) Line *EF*

    (B) Point *E*

    (C) Line *AE*

    (D) Line *DE*

    (E) Line *EH*

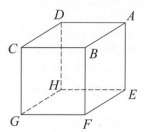

Figure 9

40. How many different 9-letter words can be formed
    from the letters in the word **committee**?

    (A) 2,835

    (B) 5,670

    (C) 11,340

    (D) 22,680

    (E) 45,360

41. If $0 < x < \dfrac{\pi}{2}$ and $\cos 2x = -\cos x$, what is the radian
    measure of *x*?

    (A) 0.67

    (B) 0.85

    (C) 1.05

    (D) 1.23

    (E) 1.62

42. What is the length of the major axis of the ellipse whose equation is $4x^2 + 3y^2 = 60$?

 (A) 3.87

 (B) 4.47

 (C) 7.74

 (D) 8.94

 (E) 15.49

43. Figure 10 shows a triangular region which contains all points (x, y). If a transformation G maps the points (x, y) in the triangular region to the points $(3x, y-2)$, what is the area of the triangular region that consists of all points $(3x, y-2)$?

 (A) 28

 (B) 34

 (C) 42

 (D) 52

 (E) 56

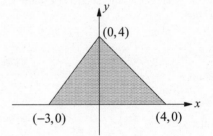

Figure 10

44. If $0 < x < \dfrac{\pi}{2}$, $\cos(\tan^{-1} x) =$

 (A) $\dfrac{1}{\sqrt{1-x^2}}$

 (B) $\dfrac{1}{\sqrt{1+x^2}}$

 (C) $\dfrac{x}{\sqrt{1+x^2}}$

 (D) $\dfrac{x}{\sqrt{1-x^2}}$

 (E) $\dfrac{1}{1+x^2}$

45. A line has parametric equations $x = 3 - \frac{1}{2}t$ and $y = 4 + 3t$, where t is the parameter. What is the slope of the line?

(A) -6 (B) $-\frac{2}{3}$ (C) $-\frac{1}{2}$ (D) $-\frac{3}{2}$ (E) $-\frac{1}{6}$

46. Which of the following is the polar equation of a curve whose rectangular-coordinate equation is $x^2 + y^2 = 9$?

(A) $(r-3)^2 = 1$

(B) $(r+3)^2 = 1$

(C) $r^2 = 3$

(D) $r = 9$

(E) $r = 3$

47. $\displaystyle\lim_{x \to -2} \frac{x^3 + 8}{x + 2} =$

(A) 4

(B) 6

(C) 8

(D) 12

(E) The limit does not exist.

48. If a cube with edge of length 4 is inscribed in a sphere, what is the volume of the sphere?

(A) $24\sqrt{3}\pi$

(B) 48π

(C) $32\sqrt{3}\pi$

(D) 64π

(E) $48\sqrt{3}\pi$

49. At a music shop two musicians have to choose 2 of 7 guitars and 3 of 6 optional accessories. How many different combinations of guitars and accessories are available to the musicians?

(A) 42

(B) 108

(C) 210

(D) 360

(E) 420

50. A trigonometric function has the following properties:

- The amplitude of the function is 3.

- The period of the function is π.

- The minimum value of the function is -2.

Which of the following could be the equation of the trigonometric function described above?

(A) $f(x) = \dfrac{1}{3}\cos 3x - \dfrac{2}{3}$

(B) $f(x) = \cos 3x - 2$

(C) $f(x) = 3\cos 2x - 1$

(D) $f(x) = 3\sin 2x + 1$

(E) $f(x) = 3\sin 2x - 2$

STOP

IF YOU FINISH BEFORE TIME IS CALLED, YOU MAY CHECK YOUR WORK ON THIS TEST ONLY.
DO NOT TURN TO ANY OTHER TEST IN THIS BOOK.

Answer Key

1. C	2. C	3. D	4. A	5. B
6. A	7. E	8. D	9. D	10. A
11. C	12. D	13. B	14. B	15. D
16. B	17. C	18. E	19. E	20. D
21. E	22. C	23. A	24. B	25. D
26. B	27. C	28. A	29. E	30. B
31. E	32. C	33. C	34. B	35. A
36. D	37. B	38. A	39. D	40. E
41. C	42. D	43. C	44. B	45. A
46. E	47. D	48. C	49. E	50. D

Answers and Explanations

1. C

$$-n+12 = p \text{ and } n = 5p$$
$$-(5p)+12 = p \qquad \text{Substitution}$$
$$12 = 6p$$
$$2 = p$$

2. C

$$(x+3)(y-3)^{-1} = 0$$
$$\Rightarrow \frac{(x+3)}{(y-3)} = 0$$

The value of a fraction is zero if the numerator is zero. Therefore $x = -3$.

A number divided by zero is undefined. Therefore $y \neq 3$.

3. D

Use your calculator. Your calculator will show a number $4.605366584 \times 10^{15}$, which means the number has 16 digits.

4. A

$$\frac{6}{\sqrt[3]{y^2}} = \frac{6}{(y^2)^{\frac{1}{3}}} = \frac{6}{y^{\frac{2}{3}}} = \frac{6y^{\frac{1}{3}}}{y^{\frac{2}{3}} \cdot y^{\frac{1}{3}}} = \frac{6y^{\frac{1}{3}}}{y} = \frac{6\sqrt[3]{y}}{y}$$

5. B

$$|x+3| \geq 8$$
$$\Rightarrow x+3 \geq 8 \quad \text{or} \quad x+3 \leq -8$$
$$\Rightarrow x \geq 5 \quad \text{or} \quad x \leq -11$$

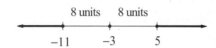

The number line shows that the solutions of the inequality are all points at least 8 units from -3.

6. A

The function f is defined as $f(x) = g(-2x)+1$.

$$f(-\frac{1}{2}) = g[-2(-\frac{1}{2})]+1 = g(1)+1$$

The graph of $y = g(x)$ shows $g(1) = 3$, therefore

$$f(-\frac{1}{2}) = g(1)+1 = 3+1 = 4.$$

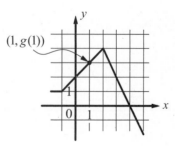

7. E

$$\frac{f(x)}{g(x)} = \frac{x^2-16}{x^2-x-20} = \frac{(x+4)(x-4)}{(x+4)(x-5)}$$
$$= \frac{x-4}{x-5}$$

8. D

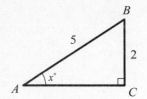

In right $\triangle ABC$ $5^2 = 2^2 + AC^2$.

$AC = \sqrt{25 - 4} = \sqrt{21}$

$\sin 2x = 2\sin x \cos x = 2 \cdot \dfrac{2}{5} \cdot \dfrac{\sqrt{21}}{5} \approx 0.73$

9. D

$a^2 b^{-5} c^{11} = \dfrac{3ac^5}{b^{-5}}$

$b^{-5} \cdot a^2 b^{-5} c^{11} = b^{-5} \cdot \dfrac{3ac^5}{b^{-5}}$ Multiply b^{-5}.

$a^2 b^{-10} c^{11} = 3ac^5$ $b^{-5} \cdot b^{-5} = b^{-10}$

$\dfrac{a^2 b^{-10} c^{11}}{a} = \dfrac{3ac^5}{a}$ Divide by a.

$ab^{-10} c^{11} = 3c^5$ Simplify.

$a = \dfrac{3c^5}{b^{-10} c^{11}}$ Divide by $b^{-10} c^{11}$.

$a = \dfrac{3b^{10}}{c^6}$ $\dfrac{1}{b^{-10}} = b^{10}$, $\dfrac{c^5}{c^{11}} = \dfrac{1}{c^6}$

10. A

$\dfrac{(n+2)!}{(n+1)!} - 2 = \dfrac{(n+2)(n+1)!}{(n+1)!} - 2$

$= (n+2) - 2$

$= n$

11. C

Check each answer choice.

(A) If $f(x) = \dfrac{1}{2}x - \dfrac{5}{2}$

$f(g(x)) = f(-2x+1) = \dfrac{1}{2}(-2x+1) - \dfrac{5}{2}$

$= -x - 2$

(B) If $f(x) = -\dfrac{1}{2}x - \dfrac{5}{2}$

$f(g(x)) = f(-2x+1) = -\dfrac{1}{2}(-2x+1) - \dfrac{5}{2}$

$= x - 3$

(C) If $f(x) = -\dfrac{1}{2}x + \dfrac{5}{2}$

$f(g(x)) = f(-2x+1) = -\dfrac{1}{2}(-2x+1) + \dfrac{5}{2}$

$= x + 2$

Choice (C) is correct.

12. D

$x* = \begin{cases} x - 4 & \text{if } x \text{ is positive} \\ -\dfrac{x}{2} & \text{if } x \text{ is negative} \end{cases}$

$(2*)* = (2-4)*$ $(2*) = 2 - 4$ since x is positive.

$= (-2)*$

$= -\dfrac{(-2)}{2}$ $(-2)* = -\dfrac{-2}{2}$ since x is negative.

$= 1$

13. B

In a data set, if the same number k is added to each number, the mean is increased by k, while the range and standard deviation are unchanged.

14. B

Let x = the number of oranges and
y = the number of apples.

Then $x + y$ = the total number of fruits in the bag.

$\dfrac{3}{5}$ of the oranges is equal to $\dfrac{1}{3}$ of the apples.

$\dfrac{3}{5}x = \dfrac{1}{3}y \implies y = \dfrac{9}{5}x$

$\dfrac{\text{the number of oranges}}{\text{total number of fruits}} = \dfrac{x}{x+y}$

$= \dfrac{x}{x + \dfrac{9}{5}x} = \dfrac{x}{\dfrac{14}{5}x} = \dfrac{5}{14}$

15. D

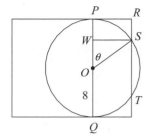

$OP = OS = 8$

$PR = WS = 8\sin 55° \approx 6.55$

$WO = 8\cos 55° \approx 4.59$

$RS = PW = 8 - 4.59 = 3.41$

Perimeter of trapezoid $OPRS$
$= OP + PR + RS + OS = 8 + 6.55 + 3.41 + 8$
$= 25.96$

16. B

$f(x)$ is a linear function whose slope is -2.

$\Rightarrow f(x) = -2x + b$

Find an inverse of f :

$y = -2x + b$ Replace $f(x)$ with y.

$x = -2y + b$ Interchange x and y.

$y = -\dfrac{1}{2}x + \dfrac{1}{2}b$ Solve for y.

The slope of $f^{-1}(x)$ is $-\dfrac{1}{2}$.

17. C

The first step in writing an indirect proof is to assume that the desired conclusion is *not* true.

An indirect proof of the given statement could begin with "Assume that n is not prime."

18. E

The equations of the lines shown are $y = -\dfrac{1}{2}x$

and $y = 2x$, or in standard form, $x + 2y = 0$ and $2x - y = 0$.

Only answer choices (D) and (E) include these equations, so discard the other choices.

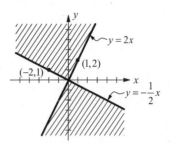

Test the remaining inequalities with the point $(0,1)$, which is in the shaded region. Substitute $x = 0$ and $y = 1$ into the inequalities.

(D) $(x + 2y)(2x - y) \geq 0$

    $(0 + 2\cdot)(2 \cdot 0 - 1) \geq 0$ Not true

(E) $(x + 2y)(2x - y) \leq 0$

    $(0 + 2 \cdot 1)(2 \cdot 0 - 1) \leq 0$ True

19. E

Graph $f(x) = \begin{cases} \sqrt{x} & \text{if } x > 1 \\ \dfrac{1}{2}x + 1 & \text{if } x \leq 1 \end{cases}$.

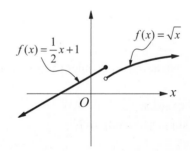

The graph shows that the range of the function is all real numbers.

20. D

$(3 - 2i)^2 = a + bi$

$9 - 6i - 6i + 4i^2 = a + bi$

$9 - 12i - 4 = a + bi$

$5 - 12i = a + bi$

$\Rightarrow a = 5$ and $b = -12$

$ab = 5(-12) = -60$

21. E

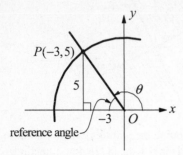

$P(-3,5)$

reference angle

Let x = the measure of the reference angle.

$\tan x = \dfrac{5}{3} \Rightarrow x = \tan^{-1}(\dfrac{5}{3}) = 1.03$

$\theta = \pi - x = \pi - 1.03 = 2.11$

22. C

Draw a diagram.

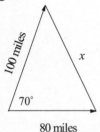

100 miles

x

70°

80 miles

The two cars had traveled 100 miles and 80 miles after 2 hours.

Use the Law of cosines.

$x^2 = 100^2 + 80^2 - 2(100)(80)\cos 70°$

$\quad = 10927.68$

$x = 104.5$

23. A

$f(x) = 2x^2$

$g(x)$ represents the graph of f translated 1 unit to the right and 3 units up:

$g(x) = f(x-1) + 3$

$\quad = 2(x-1)^2 + 3$

$g(2.5) = 2(2.5-1)^2 + 3$

$\quad = 7.5$

24. B

$2 - \dfrac{4}{3} + \dfrac{8}{9} - \dfrac{16}{27} + \cdots$

In the infinite geometric series above,

$a_1 = 2$ and $r = -\dfrac{2}{3}$.

Sum of the infinite geometric series

$= \dfrac{a_1}{1-r} = \dfrac{2}{1-(-\dfrac{2}{3})} = \dfrac{6}{5}$

25. D

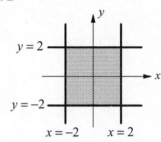

$y = 2$

$y = -2$

$x = -2$ $x = 2$

The graph of $|x| \le 2$ is the region between $x = -2$ and $x = 2$. The graph of $|y| \le 2$ is the region between $y = -2$ and $y = 2$. The shaded area in the figure above shows the overlap of these two regions.

Choice (D) is correct.

26. B

Given: $\log_b m = 3$ and $\log_b n = 4$

$\log_b (m^2 \cdot \sqrt{n}) = \log_b m^2 + \log_b \sqrt{n}$

$\quad = 2\log_b m + \log_b n^{\frac{1}{2}}$

$\quad = 2\log_b m + \dfrac{1}{2}\log_b n$

$\quad = 2\cdot 3 + \dfrac{1}{2}(4)$

$\quad = 8$

27. C

$f(t) = 50t - 20\cos(\dfrac{t}{2})$

If the unit of the variable is defined as anything other than degree measure, always use the radian mode.

Average number of cars $= \dfrac{f(10)-f(5)}{10-5}$

$= \dfrac{\left[50(10)-20\cos(\dfrac{10}{2})\right]-\left[50(5)-20\cos(\dfrac{5}{2})\right]}{10-5}$

≈ 46

28. A

$AB = \sqrt{(4-3)^2+(6-0)^2+(5-3)^2}$

$= \sqrt{41}$

$= 6.4$

29. E

$y = \dfrac{4x}{x-2}$

$\begin{array}{r} 4 \\ x-2\,\overline{)4x} \\ -\underline{|4x-8} \\ 8 \end{array}$ To simplify, divide $4x$ by $x-2$.

$y = \dfrac{4x}{x-2} = 4 + \dfrac{8}{x-2}$

A vertical asymptote occurs at a number where the denominator is zero. So the line $x=2$ is a vertical asymptote.

As x approaches infinity $\dfrac{8}{x-2}$ approaches 0.

So the line $y=4$ is a horizontal asymptote.

Choice (E) is correct.

30. B

Draw the parallelogram.

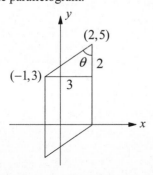

$\tan\theta = \dfrac{3}{2} \implies \theta = \tan^{-1}(\dfrac{3}{2}) = 56.3°$

In a parallelogram consecutive interior angles are supplementary.
The measure of one of the larger angles
$= 180 - 56.3 = 123.7$.

31. E

$f(x) = \dfrac{x-2}{x^2-x-2} = \dfrac{x-2}{(x-2)(x+1)} = \dfrac{1}{x+1}$

A vertical asymptote occurs at a number where the denominator is zero. So the line $x=-1$ is a vertical asymptote.

As x approaches infinity $\dfrac{1}{x+1}$ approaches 0.

So the line $y=0$ is a horizontal asymptote.
Discard choices (A), (B), and (D).
Check the value of $f(x)$ when $x=-3$.

$f(-3) = \dfrac{1}{-3+1} = -\dfrac{1}{2}$.

Choice (E) is correct.

32. C

$x^2+y^2 = 16 \implies y = \pm\sqrt{16-x^2}$

On your calculator graph $y_1 = \sqrt{16-x^2}$ and
$y_2 = -\sqrt{16-x^2}$.

$x = 4y^2 \implies y^2 = \dfrac{x}{4} \implies y = \pm\dfrac{\sqrt{x}}{2}$

Graph $y_3 = \dfrac{\sqrt{x}}{2}$ and $y_4 = -\dfrac{\sqrt{x}}{2}$.

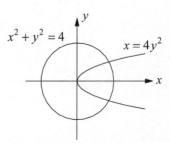

The graphs intersect at two points.

33. C

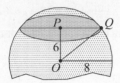

In the figure above $OQ = 8$, since all radii in a sphere are congruent.

$$OQ^2 = OP^2 + PQ^2$$
$$8^2 = 6^2 + PQ^2$$
$$PQ^2 = 28$$

The area of circle $P = \pi r^2 = \pi \cdot PQ^2 = 28\pi$

34. B

Check each answer choice.

(A) If $f(x) = x^3 + x^2 - x - 1$:

$$f(i) = (i)^3 + (i)^2 - i - 1$$
$$= -i - 1 - i - 1$$
$$= -2i - 2$$
$$f(1) = 1 + 1 - 1 - 1$$
$$= 0$$

So, $f(i) \neq f(1)$.

(B) If $f(x) = x^3 - x^2 + x - 1$:

$$f(i) = (i)^3 - (i)^2 + i - 1$$
$$= -i + 1 + i - 1$$
$$= 0$$
$$f(1) = 1 - 1 + 1 - 1$$
$$= 0$$

So, $f(i) = f(1)$.

Choice (B) is correct.

35. A

Given: $a_n = 1 + \dfrac{1}{a_{n-1}}$ and $a_1 = k$

$$a_2 = 1 + \frac{1}{a_1} = 1 + \frac{1}{k} = \frac{k+1}{k}$$

$$a_3 = 1 + \frac{1}{a_2} = 1 + \frac{1}{\frac{k+1}{k}} = 1 + \frac{k}{k+1} = \frac{2k+1}{k+1}$$

$$a_2 \cdot a_3 = \frac{3}{2} \;\Rightarrow\; \frac{k+1}{k} \cdot \frac{2k+1}{k+1} = \frac{3}{2}$$

$$\Rightarrow \frac{2k+1}{k} = \frac{3}{2}$$

$$\Rightarrow 2(2k+1) = 3k$$

$$\Rightarrow k = -2$$

36. D

$$f(x) = e^x$$

Find the inverse function:

1. Replace $f(x)$ with y. $\quad y = e^x$

2. Interchange x and y. $\quad x = e^y$

3. Solve for y. $\quad \ln x = \ln e^y$

$\Rightarrow \ln x = y \ln e$ $\qquad \ln M^P = p \ln M$

$\Rightarrow y = \ln x$ $\qquad\qquad \ln e = 1$

$\Rightarrow f^{-1}(x) = \ln x$

$$f^{-1}\left(\frac{a}{b}\right) = \ln\left(\frac{a}{b}\right) = \ln a - \ln b$$

37. B

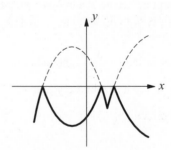

Reflect the portion of the graph of $y = f(x)$ which is above the x-axis across the x-axis. That is the graph of $y = -|f(x)|$.

Choice (B) is correct.

38. A

$$\mathbf{u} = <7, -8> \text{ and } \mathbf{v} = <3, -5>.$$
$$2\mathbf{u} = 2 <7, -8> = <14, -16>$$
$$2\mathbf{u} - \mathbf{v} = <14, -16> - <3, -5> = <11, -11>$$

39. D

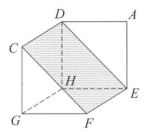

Plane *CEF* is the same as plane *CDEF*.
Plane *ADE* is the same as plane *ADHE*.

The intersection of plane *CEF* and plane *ADE* is the line *DE*.

40. E

There are 9 letters, 2 of which are m's, 2 are t's, and 2 are e's.

$$\frac{9!}{2!2!2!} = 45360$$

41. C

$$\cos 2x = -\cos x$$

$2\cos^2 x - 1 = -\cos x$ Double angle formula

$$2\cos^2 x + \cos x - 1 = 0$$

$(2\cos x - 1)(\cos x + 1) = 0$ Factor.

$$2\cos x - 1 = 0 \text{ or } \cos x + 1 = 0$$

$$\cos x = \frac{1}{2} \text{ or } \cos x = -1$$

Since $0 < x < \dfrac{\pi}{2}$, $x = \dfrac{\pi}{3} \approx 1.05$ is the only solution.

42. D

$$4x^2 + 3y^2 = 60$$

$$\frac{x^2}{15} + \frac{y^2}{20} = 1$$ Standard equation of an ellipse

So, we have $a = \sqrt{20}$ and $b = \sqrt{15}$.

The length of the major axis is

$$2a = 2 \cdot \sqrt{20} \approx 8.94$$

43. C

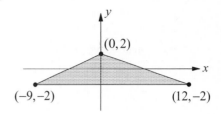

$$G : (x, y) \rightarrow (3x, y - 2)$$
$$G : (-3, 0) \rightarrow (3 \cdot -3, 0 - 2) \rightarrow (-9, -2)$$
$$G : (0, 4) \rightarrow (3 \cdot 0, 4 - 2) \rightarrow (0, 2)$$
$$G : (4, 0) \rightarrow (3 \cdot 4, 0 - 2) \rightarrow (12, -2)$$

The area of the new triangular region

$$= \frac{1}{2}(21)(4) = 42$$

44. B

Let $\theta = \tan^{-1} x$, then $\tan \theta = \tan(\tan^{-1} \theta) = x$.

Draw a right triangle whose acute angle is θ, opposite side has length x, and adjacent side has length 1.

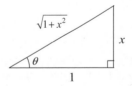

By the Pythagorean theorem the hypotenuse is $\sqrt{1 + x^2}$.

$$\cos(\tan^{-1} x)$$
$$= \cos \theta$$
$$= \frac{1}{\sqrt{1 + x^2}}$$

45. A

$$x = 3 - \frac{1}{2}t \implies \frac{1}{2}t = 3 - x \implies t = 6 - 2x$$
$$y = 4 + 3t$$
$$= 4 + 3(6 - 2x)$$
$$= -6x + 22$$

The slope of the line is -6.

46. E

Given: $x^2 + y^2 = 9$

Use the coordinate-system conversion formula.

$r^2 = x^2 + y^2 \Rightarrow r^2 = 9 \Rightarrow r = 3$

47. D

$\lim\limits_{x \to -2} \dfrac{x^3 + 8}{x + 2}$

$= \lim\limits_{x \to -2} \dfrac{(x+2)(x^2 - 2x + 4)}{x + 2}$ Sum of two cubes

$= \lim\limits_{x \to -2} (x^2 - 2x + 4)$

$= (-2)^2 - 2(-2) + 4$ Make direct substitution.

$= 12$

48. C

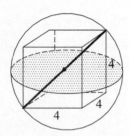

If a cube is inscribed in a sphere, the diagonal of the cube is equal to the diameter of the sphere.

Diameter of the sphere

$= \sqrt{4^2 + 4^2 + 4^2}$

$= 4\sqrt{3}$

Radius of the sphere

$= 2\sqrt{3}$

Volume of the sphere

$= \dfrac{4}{3}\pi(2\sqrt{3})^3$

$= 32\sqrt{3}\pi$

49. E

There are $_7C_2$ ways to choose 2 of 7 guitars.

There are $_6C_3$ ways to choose 3 of 6 optional accessories.

By the counting principle there are

$_7C_2 \cdot {_6C_3} = 420$ different combinations.

50. D

For the functions $f(x) = a \sin bx$ and

$f(x) = a \cos bx$, the amplitude is $|a|$ and the

period is $\dfrac{2\pi}{|b|}$.

(A) $f(x) = \dfrac{1}{3}\cos 3x - \dfrac{2}{3}$

   Amp $= \dfrac{1}{3}$, Period $= \dfrac{2\pi}{3}$

(B) $f(x) = \cos 3x - 2$

   Amp $= 1$, Period $= \dfrac{2\pi}{3}$

(C) $f(x) = 3\cos 2x - 1$

   Amp $= 3$, Period $= \dfrac{2\pi}{2} = \pi$

   Since $-1 \le \cos x \le 1$,

   Maximum $= 3(1) - 1 = 2$,

   Minimum $= 3(-1) - 1 = -4$

(D) $f(x) = 3\sin 2x + 1$

   Amp $= 3$, Period $= \dfrac{2\pi}{2} = \pi$

   Maximum $= 3 + 1 = 4$,

   Minimum $= -3 + 1 = -2$

(E) $f(x) = 3\sin 2x - 2$

   Amp $= 3$, Period $= \dfrac{2\pi}{2} = \pi$

   Maximum $= 3 - 2 = 1$,

   Minimum $= -3 - 2 = -5$

Choice (D) is correct.

Test Form G
Mathematics Level 2

Answer Sheet

1 Ⓐ Ⓑ Ⓒ Ⓓ Ⓔ   21 Ⓐ Ⓑ Ⓒ Ⓓ Ⓔ   41 Ⓐ Ⓑ Ⓒ Ⓓ Ⓔ
2 Ⓐ Ⓑ Ⓒ Ⓓ Ⓔ   22 Ⓐ Ⓑ Ⓒ Ⓓ Ⓔ   42 Ⓐ Ⓑ Ⓒ Ⓓ Ⓔ
3 Ⓐ Ⓑ Ⓒ Ⓓ Ⓔ   23 Ⓐ Ⓑ Ⓒ Ⓓ Ⓔ   43 Ⓐ Ⓑ Ⓒ Ⓓ Ⓔ
4 Ⓐ Ⓑ Ⓒ Ⓓ Ⓔ   24 Ⓐ Ⓑ Ⓒ Ⓓ Ⓔ   44 Ⓐ Ⓑ Ⓒ Ⓓ Ⓔ
5 Ⓐ Ⓑ Ⓒ Ⓓ Ⓔ   25 Ⓐ Ⓑ Ⓒ Ⓓ Ⓔ   45 Ⓐ Ⓑ Ⓒ Ⓓ Ⓔ
6 Ⓐ Ⓑ Ⓒ Ⓓ Ⓔ   26 Ⓐ Ⓑ Ⓒ Ⓓ Ⓔ   46 Ⓐ Ⓑ Ⓒ Ⓓ Ⓔ
7 Ⓐ Ⓑ Ⓒ Ⓓ Ⓔ   27 Ⓐ Ⓑ Ⓒ Ⓓ Ⓔ   47 Ⓐ Ⓑ Ⓒ Ⓓ Ⓔ
8 Ⓐ Ⓑ Ⓒ Ⓓ Ⓔ   28 Ⓐ Ⓑ Ⓒ Ⓓ Ⓔ   48 Ⓐ Ⓑ Ⓒ Ⓓ Ⓔ
9 Ⓐ Ⓑ Ⓒ Ⓓ Ⓔ   29 Ⓐ Ⓑ Ⓒ Ⓓ Ⓔ   49 Ⓐ Ⓑ Ⓒ Ⓓ Ⓔ
10 Ⓐ Ⓑ Ⓒ Ⓓ Ⓔ   30 Ⓐ Ⓑ Ⓒ Ⓓ Ⓔ   50 Ⓐ Ⓑ Ⓒ Ⓓ Ⓔ
11 Ⓐ Ⓑ Ⓒ Ⓓ Ⓔ   31 Ⓐ Ⓑ Ⓒ Ⓓ Ⓔ
12 Ⓐ Ⓑ Ⓒ Ⓓ Ⓔ   32 Ⓐ Ⓑ Ⓒ Ⓓ Ⓔ
13 Ⓐ Ⓑ Ⓒ Ⓓ Ⓔ   33 Ⓐ Ⓑ Ⓒ Ⓓ Ⓔ
14 Ⓐ Ⓑ Ⓒ Ⓓ Ⓔ   34 Ⓐ Ⓑ Ⓒ Ⓓ Ⓔ
15 Ⓐ Ⓑ Ⓒ Ⓓ Ⓔ   35 Ⓐ Ⓑ Ⓒ Ⓓ Ⓔ
16 Ⓐ Ⓑ Ⓒ Ⓓ Ⓔ   36 Ⓐ Ⓑ Ⓒ Ⓓ Ⓔ
17 Ⓐ Ⓑ Ⓒ Ⓓ Ⓔ   37 Ⓐ Ⓑ Ⓒ Ⓓ Ⓔ
18 Ⓐ Ⓑ Ⓒ Ⓓ Ⓔ   38 Ⓐ Ⓑ Ⓒ Ⓓ Ⓔ
19 Ⓐ Ⓑ Ⓒ Ⓓ Ⓔ   39 Ⓐ Ⓑ Ⓒ Ⓓ Ⓔ
20 Ⓐ Ⓑ Ⓒ Ⓓ Ⓔ   40 Ⓐ Ⓑ Ⓒ Ⓓ Ⓔ

Reference Information

The following information is for your reference in answering some of the questions on this test.

Volume of a right circular cone with radius r and height h: $V = \dfrac{1}{3}\pi r^2 h$

Lateral area of a right circular cone with base circumference C and slant height ℓ: $S = \dfrac{1}{2}C\ell$

Volume of a sphere with radius r: $V = \dfrac{4}{3}\pi r^3$

Surface area of a sphere with radius r: $S = 4\pi r^2$

Volume of a pyramid with base area B and height h: $V = \dfrac{1}{3}Bh$

Test Form G
SAT Subject Test in Mathematics Level 2

50 Questions   1 hour

For each of the following problems, decide which is the BEST of the answer choices given. If the exact numerical value is not one of the choices, select the choice that best approximates this value. Then fill in the corresponding circle on the answer sheet.

Notes: (1) A calculator will be necessary for answering some of the questions on this test. For each question you will have to decide whether or not you should use a calculator. Programmable calculators and calculators that can display graphs are permitted.

(2) The angle measures used on the Math Level 2 Test are in either degree measure or radian measure. Check to see which mode your calculator is in.

(3) Figures that accompany problems on this test are intended to provide information useful in solving the problems. They are drawn as accurately as possible EXCEPT when it is stated in a specific problem that its figure is not drawn to scale. All figures lie in a plane unless otherwise indicated.

(4) Unless otherwise specified, the domain of any function f is assumed to be the set of all real numbers x for which $f(x)$ is a real number.

(5) Reference information that may be useful in answering the questions on this test can be found on the page preceding Question 1.

1. $-0.3[x-(4x-5)]+0.7(x+1) =$

   (A) $-0.2x-0.8$

   (B) $-0.2x+2.2$

   (C) $0.8(2x-1)$

   (D) $0.8(2x+1)$

   (E) $0.8(x-1)$

2. Let the operation $*$ be defined as $a*b = a^2 - ab$, for all real numbers a and b. If $a*4 = 4*5$, then $a =$

   (A) 2

   (B) 3

   (C) 4

   (D) 5

   (E) 6

3. The formula for the surface area of a cone is given by
$S = \pi r \sqrt{r^2 + h^2}$. What is the value of h to the nearest integer, if $S = 204$ and $r = 5$?

(A) 9

(B) 10

(C) 11

(D) 12

(E) 13

4. A bag of n candies is divided into two bags such that the number of candies in the smaller bag is 9 more than one-half the number of candies in the bigger bag. Which of the following is the number of candies in the bigger bag in terms of n?

(A) $\dfrac{3}{2}n - 9$

(B) $\dfrac{2}{3}n - 6$

(C) $\dfrac{2}{3}n + 6$

(D) $\dfrac{3}{2}n + 9$

(E) $\dfrac{3n + 9}{2}$

5. For $ab \neq 0$, $\dfrac{a - b}{a^{-1} - b^{-1}} =$

(A) $\dfrac{1}{ab}$

(B) $\dfrac{-1}{ab}$

(C) ab

(D) $-ab$

(E) $\dfrac{1}{a + b}$

6. The average (arithmetic mean) age of all the members in a gym is 43. If the average age of the m males in the gym is 47 and that of the f females is 41, what is the value of $\dfrac{m}{f}$?

(A) $\dfrac{1}{2}$ (B) $\dfrac{4}{7}$ (C) $\dfrac{3}{5}$ (D) $\dfrac{5}{4}$ (E) 2

$$\begin{bmatrix} 3x = 2y - 1 \\ mx - y = 6 \end{bmatrix}$$

7. If the system of the equations shown above has no solution, what is the value of m?

(A) $-\dfrac{3}{2}$ (B) $-\dfrac{1}{2}$ (C) 0 (D) $\dfrac{1}{2}$ (E) $\dfrac{3}{2}$

8. In Figure 1, point Q (not shown) is the image of point P rotated 90 degrees counterclockwise with respect to the origin. If point Q is reflected over the x-axis to create an image point R (not shown), what are the coordinates of R?

(A) $(2,3)$

(B) $(-3,2)$

(C) $(-3,-2)$

(D) $(-2,-3)$

(E) $(2,-3)$

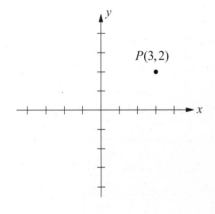

Figure 1

9. In the xy-coordinate system, $(c,-5)$ is one of the points of intersection of the graphs $y = -x^2 + 4$ and $y = \dfrac{1}{3}x^2 - k$, where k is a constant. What is the value of k?

(A) -3 (B) -1 (C) 3 (D) 5 (E) 8

10. $(x-4)^3 - 9(x-4) =$

(A) $(x-4)^2(x-9)$

(B) $(x+2)(x-2)(x-9)$

(C) $(x-1)(x-4)(x-7)$

(D) $(x+3)(x-3)(x-4)$

(E) $(x-4)(x-7)(x-9)$

11. In Figure 2, if the points B and C are points of intersection of the graphs of $y = x^2$ and $y = -x+6$, what is the area of trapezoid $ABCD$?

(A) 28

(B) 32.5

(C) 37

(D) 41.5

(E) 46

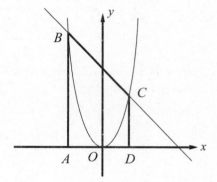

Figure 2

12. Which of the following quadratic equations has two roots whose sum is $\dfrac{1}{3}$ and product is $-\dfrac{1}{6}$?

(A) $3x^2 + x - 1 = 0$

(B) $3x^2 - x + 1 = 0$

(C) $6x^2 + 2x + 1 = 0$

(D) $6x^2 - 2x - 1 = 0$

(E) $6x^2 - 2x + 1 = 0$

13. Which of the following is a factor of the polynomial function $2x^3 + 5x^2 - 4x - 3$?

(A) $x+1$

(B) $2x-1$

(C) $2x+1$

(D) $x-3$

(E) $x-2$

14. If $f(x) = \dfrac{x^2+1}{x^2-1}$, then $f(\sqrt{2}+1) =$

(A) $1-\sqrt{2}$

(B) $1+\sqrt{2}$

(C) $\sqrt{2}$

(D) $-\sqrt{2}$

(E) $\dfrac{1-\sqrt{2}}{2}$

15. Two sides of a triangle have lengths 9 and 13, and the angle between them is $25°$. If the angle between them is increasing $3°/\min$, what is the length of the third side after 20 minutes?

(A) 15.2

(B) 16.8

(C) 18.2

(D) 19.4

(E) 21.7

16. Which of the following lines are asymptotes of the graph of $y = \dfrac{9}{x^2-4}$?

  I. $x = -2$

  II. $y = 0$

  III. $y = -\dfrac{9}{4}$

(A) I only

(B) II only

(C) III only

(D) I and II only

(E) I and III only

17. If $f(x) = x - \dfrac{1}{x}$ and $i^2 = -1$, then $f(1-i) =$

(A) $\dfrac{3-i}{2}$

(B) $\dfrac{3-2i}{2}$

(C) $\dfrac{1-3i}{2}$

(D) $\dfrac{1+3i}{2}$

(E) $\dfrac{-1+3i}{2}$

18. If $\sin\theta = 0.81$, then $\sin(\pi - \theta) =$

(A) 0

(B) 0.19

(C) −0.19

(D) 0.81

(E) −0.81

19. If $f(x) = \sqrt[3]{x-11}$, what is $f^{-1}(-2)$?

(A) −4   (B) −1   (C) 3   (D) 5   (E) 8

20. The function f is defined as $f(x) = x - [x]$, where $[x]$ is the greatest integer less than or equal to x.
If $-2 \le x < -1$, then $f(x) =$

(A) $-x-2$

(B) $-x-1$

(C) x

(D) $x+2$

(E) $x+1$

21. When a certain radioactive substance decays the amount that exists at any time t can be found by a function $f(t) = ae^{-0.00124t}$, where a is the initial amount and t is the elapsed time in years. How many years would it take for an initial amount of 15 grams to decay to 1 gram?

   (A) 1651

   (B) 1704

   (C) 1975

   (D) 2184

   (E) 2774

22. Which of the following inequalities is represented by the graph in Figure 4?

   (A) $\begin{cases} y \geq x^2 - 4 \\ x - y \geq 1 \end{cases}$

   (B) $\begin{cases} y \geq x^2 - 4 \\ x + y \geq 1 \end{cases}$

   (C) $\begin{cases} y \leq x^2 - 4 \\ x - 2y \geq 1 \end{cases}$

   (D) $\begin{cases} y \leq x^2 - 4 \\ x + y \geq 1 \end{cases}$

   (E) $\begin{cases} y \geq x^2 - 4 \\ x - 2y \geq 2 \end{cases}$

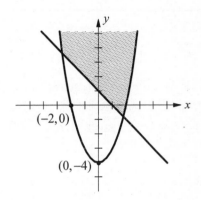

Figure 4

23. What is the value of $|2i(3 - 4i)|$?

   (A) 3

   (B) 5.385

   (C) 7.071

   (D) 7.746

   (E) 10

24. A manufacturer of navigation systems includes a tolerance limit in the specifications given for each part it makes. Suppose a part is to be 1.5 inches long with a tolerance limit of 0.005 inches. This means that it must be at least 1.495 inches long or at most 1.505 inches long. If the thickness t of a part with a certain tolerance limit is at least 0.117 inches or at most 0.123 inches, which of the following inequalities can be used to determine the specified thickness of the part?

(A) $|t - 0.006| \leq 0.123$

(B) $|t - 0.117| \geq 0.003$

(C) $|t - 0.12| \leq 0.003$

(D) $|t - 0.123| \leq 0.003$

(E) $|t - 0.12| \geq 0.003$

25. A function f is increasing if f has the property that whenever $x_1 \leq x_2$, then $f(x_1) \leq f(x_2)$. Which of the following could be the graph of f ?

(A)

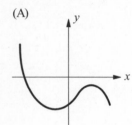

(B)

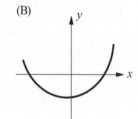

(C)

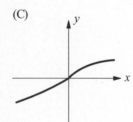

(D)

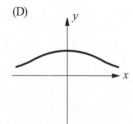

(E)

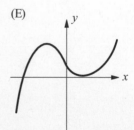

26. At how many points do the graphs of $\dfrac{y^2}{4} - \dfrac{x^2}{1} = 1$

and $\dfrac{(x-2)^2}{4} - \dfrac{y^2}{16} = 1$ intersect?

    (A) None

    (B) One

    (C) Two

    (D) Three

    (E) Four

27. In Figure 5, a rectangle is inscribed in an ellipse whose
equation is $\dfrac{x^2}{25} + \dfrac{y^2}{9} = 1$. If $AB = 8$, and $\overline{AB}$ is parallel
to the *x*-axis, what is the area of the rectangle *ABCD*?

    (A) 20.8

    (B) 22.4

    (C) 24.6

    (D) 28.8

    (E) 30.0

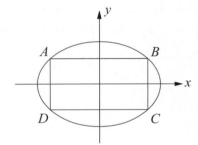

Figure 5

28. If $f(x) = \ln(2x)$, then $f^{-1}(2) =$

    (A) e (B) e^2 (C) $\dfrac{e^2}{2}$ (D) $2e$ (E) 2^e

29. If $0° < \theta < 90°$ and $4\tan^2 \theta + 3\tan\theta - 1 = 0$, what is
the angle measure of θ?

    (A) $14°$

    (B) $26.6°$

    (C) $31°$

    (D) $53.1°$

    (E) $63.4°$

30. What are the coordinates of the center of a hyperbola whose equation is $x^2 - 8y^2 - 12x + 8y - 15 = 0$?

   (A) $(-6, -\frac{1}{2})$

   (B) $(-6, -1)$

   (C) $(6, -1)$

   (D) $(6, 1)$

   (E) $(6, \frac{1}{2})$

31. Figure 6 shows the graph of $y = 2\sqrt{x}$ and three inscribed rectangles. What is the sum of the areas of the three rectangles?

   (A) 6.3

   (B) 7.6

   (C) 8.3

   (D) 9.1

   (E) 10.3

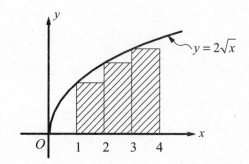

Note: Figure not drawn to scale.

Figure 6

32. Given: 1) If $a > b$, then $a > c$.

   2) $a > c$

   Which of the following is true?

   (A) $a > b$

   (B) $a < b$

   (C) $b > c$

   (D) $b < c$

   (E) No conclusion can be determined from the given information.

33. For the geometric sequence $\dfrac{3}{4}, \dfrac{1}{2}, \dfrac{1}{3}, \dfrac{2}{9}, \cdots$, which of the following is the ninth term?

  (A) $-\dfrac{5}{4}$

  (B) $\dfrac{11}{4}$

  (C) $\dfrac{16}{243}$

  (D) $\dfrac{32}{729}$

  (E) $\dfrac{64}{2187}$

34. Figure 7 shows a regular pentagon whose radius is 10. What is the area of the pentagon to the nearest whole number?

  (A) 238

  (B) 262

  (C) 294

  (D) 323

  (E) 385

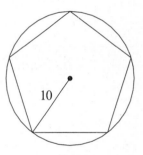

10

Figure 7

35. Which of the following is the radian measure of x that will yield the maximum of $f(x) = -\cos(x + \dfrac{\pi}{3}) + 1$?

  (A) $\dfrac{2\pi}{3}$

  (B) $\dfrac{\pi}{3}$

  (C) $\dfrac{\pi}{4}$

  (D) $\dfrac{\pi}{6}$

  (E) $-\dfrac{\pi}{3}$

36. Which of the following is equal to the positive value of csc(arcsin 0.6525) ?

    (A) 0.78

    (B) 0.92

    (C) 1.32

    (D) 1.53

    (E) 2.16

37. Figure 8 shows a rectangular solid. If $AB = 10$, $BC = 4$, and $CD = 6$, what is the distance from the center of the rectangular solid to one of the corners?

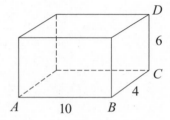

    (A) 5.8

    (B) 6.2

    (C) 6.8

    (D) 7.3

    (E) 7.9

Figure 8

38. If $\displaystyle\sum_{i=1}^{20} i = 210$, then $\displaystyle\sum_{i=1}^{20}(2i - 1) =$

    (A) 360

    (B) 400

    (C) 460

    (D) 500

    (E) 540

39. What is the sum of the infinite geometric series $20 + 18 + 16.2 + 14.58 + \cdots$?

    (A) 128

    (B) 140

    (C) 180

    (D) 200

    (E) The series has no sum.

40. In a sack there are only red and green marbles. If two red marbles are removed from the sack, the probability of randomly selecting a red marble from the sack is $\frac{1}{4}$.

If instead two green marbles are removed from the sack, the probability of randomly selecting a red marble from the sack is $\frac{3}{10}$. How many marbles in the sack are red?

(A) 6

(B) 10

(C) 12

(D) 14

(E) 15

41. Which of the following could be an equation of the graph shown in Figure 9?

(A) $y = \cos x + 2$

(B) $y = \cos \dfrac{x}{2} + 2$

(C) $y = 3\cos \dfrac{x}{2}$

(D) $y = 3\cos 2x$

(E) $y = 3\cos(x + 2)$

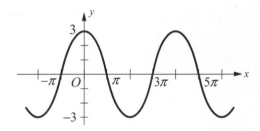

Figure 9

42. If $f(x) = \dfrac{2x^2 + 5}{3x^2 - 2x + 4}$, what value does $f(x)$ approach as x gets infinitely large?

(A) 0

(B) $\dfrac{2}{3}$

(C) $\dfrac{5}{4}$

(D) $\dfrac{7}{5}$

(E) It does not approach a single number.

43. If $r\sin\theta = -2$ is a polar equation, which of the following is the corresponding rectangular-coordinate equation?

(A) $x = -2$

(B) $xy = -2$

(C) $y = 2x$

(D) $y = -2x$

(E) $y = -2$

44. Figure 10 shows two vectors **u** and **v** whose initial point lie at the origin. If **z** is a vector such that $\mathbf{z} = \mathbf{u} + \mathbf{v}$, what is the magnitude of **z**?

(A) 7.08

(B) 7.92

(C) 8.44

(D) 9.85

(E) 11.47

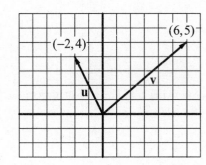

Figure 10

45. Which of the following is the y-intercept of the curve whose parametric equations are $x = \cos t$ and $y = \sin^2 t$?

(A) −1   (B) 0   (C) 1   (D) 2   (E) 4

46. What is the distance between the points $P(2,5,9)$ and $Q(10,2,3)$?

(A) 10.4

(B) 11.4

(C) 12.6

(D) 13.1

(E) 15.2

47. If $f : (x, y) \to (x, y - x)$ for every pair (x, y) in the plane, which of the following is true?

   (A) $f : (1, 1) \to (1, 2)$

   (B) $f : (1, 2) \to (1, 0)$

   (C) $f : (2, 3) \to (2, 2)$

   (D) $f : (2, 5) \to (2, 3)$

   (E) $f : (3, 4) \to (3, 2)$

48. Figure 11 shows the midpoints $C, D, F, G,$ and H of the edges of a cube. Which of the following segments are equal in length?

   (A) $\overline{AE}$ and $\overline{BF}$

   (B) $\overline{AE}$ and $\overline{DH}$

   (C) $\overline{CG}$ and $\overline{DH}$

   (D) $\overline{CG}$ and $\overline{BF}$

   (E) $\overline{BF}$ and $\overline{DH}$

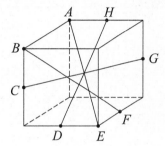

Figure 11

49. A region is formed by $x^2 + y^2 \le 25$, $x \ge 0$, and $y \ge 0$. What is the surface area of the three-dimensional figure generated by rotating that region about the x-axis?

   (A) 10π

   (B) 25π

   (C) 50π

   (D) 75π

   (E) 100π

50. Figure 12 shows a rectangle $ABCD$ with a diagonal $\overline{BD}$ of length x. With D as the center and $\overline{DB}$ as a radius, an arc is drawn as shown. What is the area of the shaded region in terms of x?

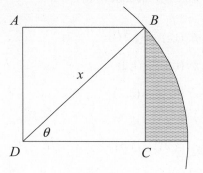

Figure 12

(A) $\dfrac{x^2}{2}(\dfrac{\pi\theta}{180} - \tan\theta)$

(B) $\dfrac{x^2}{2}(\dfrac{\pi\theta}{180} - \sin\theta\cos\theta)$

(C) $x^2(\dfrac{\pi\theta}{360} - \sin\theta\cos\theta)$

(D) $\dfrac{x^2}{4}(\dfrac{\pi\theta}{180} - 1)$

(E) $\dfrac{x^2}{4}(\dfrac{\pi\theta}{180} - \sqrt{2})$

STOP

Answer key

1. C	2. A	3. D	4. B	5. D
6. A	7. E	8. D	9. E	10. C
11. B	12. D	13. C	14. C	15. A
16. D	17. C	18. D	19. C	20. D
21. D	22. B	23. E	24. C	25. C
26. C	27. D	28. C	29. A	30. E
31. C	32. E	33. E	34. A	35. A
36. D	37. B	38. B	39. D	40. C
41. C	42. B	43. E	44. D	45. C
46. A	47. D	48. C	49. D	50. B

Answers and Explanations

1. C

$$-0.3[x-(4x-5)]+0.7(x+1)$$
$$=-0.3[-3x+5]+0.7x+0.7$$
$$=0.9x-1.5+0.7x+0.7$$
$$=1.6x-0.8$$
$$=0.8(2x-1)$$

2. A

Given: $a*b=a^2-ab$
$$a*4=a^2-a\cdot4=a^2-4a$$
$$4*5=4^2-4\cdot5=-4$$
Given: $a*4=4*5 \implies a^2-4a=-4$
$$\implies a^2-4a+4=0 \implies (a-2)^2=0$$
$$\implies a=2$$

3. D

Given: $S=\pi r\sqrt{r^2+h^2}$, $S=204$, and $r=5$
$$204=\pi\cdot5\sqrt{5^2+h^2}$$
$$\implies \sqrt{25+h^2}=\frac{204}{5\pi} \implies \sqrt{25+h^2}\approx12.99$$
$$\implies 25+h^2=168.7 \implies h=12$$

4. B

Let $x=$ the number of candies in the bigger bag,
then $\frac{1}{2}x+9=$ the number of candies in the smaller bag.

The number of candies in the smaller bag		The number of candies in the larger bag	The total number of candies
$\frac{1}{2}x+9$	$+$	x	$=$ n

$$\frac{3}{2}x+9=n \implies \frac{3}{2}x=n-9$$
$$\implies x=\frac{2}{3}(n-9) \implies x=\frac{2}{3}n-6$$

5. D

$$\frac{a-b}{a^{-1}-b^{-1}}=\frac{a-b}{\dfrac{1}{a}-\dfrac{1}{b}}=\frac{a-b}{\dfrac{b-a}{ab}}=\frac{ab(a-b)}{b-a}$$
$$=\frac{ab(a-b)}{-(a-b)}=-ab$$

6. A

Weighted average of two groups

$$=\frac{\left\{\begin{array}{c}\text{Sum of the values}\\\text{of group 1}\end{array}\right\}+\left\{\begin{array}{c}\text{Sum of the values}\\\text{of group 2}\end{array}\right\}}{\text{Total number of persons}}$$

$$43=\frac{47m+41f}{m+f}$$
$$43(m+f)=47m+41f$$
$$2f=4m$$
$$\frac{m}{f}=\frac{1}{2}$$

7. E

If a system of equations has no solution, the equations have the same slope but different y-intercepts.
Change both equations into slope-intercept form.

$$3x=2y-1 \implies 3x+1=2y \implies y=\frac{3}{2}x+\frac{1}{2}$$

$mx - y = 6 \implies y = mx - 6$

From the two equations we can conclude that

$m = \dfrac{3}{2}$.

8. D

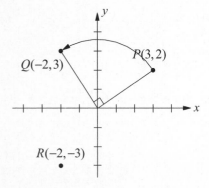

$Q(-2,3)$ $P(3,2)$ $R(-2,-3)$

If a point is rotated 90 degrees counterclockwise, $P(x, y) \to P'(-y, x)$. Therefore

$P(3,2) \to Q(-2,3)$.

If a point is reflected over the x-axis, $P(x, y) \to P'(x, -y)$. Therefore

$Q(-2,3) \to R(-2,-3)$.

9. E

$(c, -5)$ is one of the points of intersection of the graphs $y = -x^2 + 4$ and $y = \dfrac{1}{3}x^2 - k$.

$y = -x^2 + 4$	First equation
$-5 = -c^2 + 4$	Substitute: $x = c$, $y = -5$
$c^2 = 9$	Solve the equation for c^2.
$y = \dfrac{1}{3}x^2 - k$	Second equation
$-5 = \dfrac{1}{3}c^2 - k$	Substitute: $x = c$, $y = -5$
$-5 = \dfrac{1}{3}(9) - k$	Substitute: $c^2 = 9$
$-5 = 3 - k$	Simplify.
$k = 8$	Answer

10. C

$(x-4)^3 - 9(x-4)$

$= (x-4)[(x-4)^2 - 9]$

$= (x-4)[x^2 - 8x + 16 - 9]$

$= (x-4)(x^2 - 8x + 7)$

$= (x-4)(x-1)(x-7)$

11. B

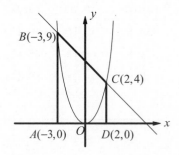

$B(-3,9)$ $C(2,4)$ $A(-3,0)$ O $D(2,0)$

$y = x^2$ and $y = -x + 6$ are the equations of the graphs. To find the points of intersection we need to eliminate one variable from the given equations. We can use a substitution method or a linear combination method to solve the equation.

$y = x^2$	First equation
$y = -x + 6$	Second equation
$x^2 = -x + 6$	Substitution: $y = x^2$
$x^2 + x - 6 = 0$	Standard form
$(x+3)(x-2) = 0$	Factor.
$x = -3$ or $x = 2$	Zero product property
$y = x^2 = (-3)^2 = 9$	Substitute: $x = -3$ $\implies B(-3,9)$
$y = x^2 = (2)^2 = 4$	Substitute: $x = 2$ $\implies C(2,4)$

Therefore the four points of the trapezoid are $A(-3,0)$, $B(-3,9)$, $C(2,4)$, and $D(2,0)$. Then $AD = 5$, $AB = 9$, and $CD = 4$.

Area of trapezoid $ABCD$

$= \dfrac{1}{2}(AB + CD) \cdot AD = \dfrac{1}{2}(9+4)5 = 32.5$

12. D

If $ax^2 + bx + c = 0$, the sum of the roots $= -\dfrac{b}{a}$

and the product of the roots $= \dfrac{c}{a}$.

Check each answer choice.

(A) $3x^2 + x - 1 = 0$

Sum of the roots $= -\dfrac{1}{3} \neq \dfrac{1}{3}$ Discard.

(B) $3x^2 - x + 1 = 0$

Sum of the roots $= -\dfrac{-1}{3} = \dfrac{1}{3}$

Product of the roots $= \dfrac{1}{3} \neq -\dfrac{1}{6}$.   Discard.

(C) $6x^2 + 2x + 1 = 0$

Sum of the roots $= -\dfrac{2}{6} \neq \dfrac{1}{3}$ Discard.

(D) $6x^2 - 2x - 1 = 0$

Sum of the roots $= -\dfrac{-2}{6} = \dfrac{1}{3}$

Product of the roots $= \dfrac{-1}{6}$.

Choice (D) is correct.

---

13. C

Use the remainder theorem.

(A) If $x + 1$ is a factor of the polynomial, then $f(-1) = 0$.

$f(-1) = 2(-1)^3 + 5(-1)^2 - 4(-1) - 3 \neq 0$

(B) If $2x - 1$ is a factor of the polynomial, then $f(\frac{1}{2}) = 0$.

$f(\frac{1}{2}) = 2(\frac{1}{2})^3 + 5(\frac{1}{2})^2 - 4(\frac{1}{2}) - 3 \neq 0$

(C) If $2x + 1$ is a factor of the polynomial, then $f(-\frac{1}{2}) = 0$.

$f(-\frac{1}{2}) = 2(-\frac{1}{2})^3 + 5(-\frac{1}{2})^2 - 4(-\frac{1}{2}) - 3 = 0$

Choice (C) is correct.

---

14. C

$f(x) = \dfrac{x^2 + 1}{x^2 - 1}$

$f(\sqrt{2} + 1)$

$= \dfrac{(\sqrt{2}+1)^2 + 1}{(\sqrt{2}+1)^2 - 1} = \dfrac{(2 + \sqrt{2} + \sqrt{2} + 1) + 1}{(2 + \sqrt{2} + \sqrt{2} + 1) - 1}$

$= \dfrac{4 + 2\sqrt{2}}{2 + 2\sqrt{2}} = \dfrac{\cancel{2}(2 + \sqrt{2})}{\cancel{2}(1 + \sqrt{2})} = \dfrac{(2 + \sqrt{2})(1 - \sqrt{2})}{(1 + \sqrt{2})(1 - \sqrt{2})}$

$= \dfrac{2 - 2\sqrt{2} + \sqrt{2} - 2}{1 - \sqrt{2} + \sqrt{2} - 2} = \dfrac{-\sqrt{2}}{-1} = \sqrt{2}$

---

15. A

After 20 minutes, the angle between the two sides of the triangle will be $25° + 20 \cdot 3°$, or $85°$.

Let $x =$ the length of the third side after 20 minutes.

Use the Law of cosines.

$x^2 = 9^2 + 13^2 - 2(9)(13)\cos 85°$

$\Rightarrow x \approx 15.15$

---

16. D

$y = \dfrac{9}{x^2 - 4} = \dfrac{9}{(x+2)(x-2)}$

A vertical asymptote occurs at a number where the denominator is zero. So the lines $x = -2$ and $x = 2$ are vertical asymptotes.

As x approaches infinity $\dfrac{9}{x^2 - 4}$ approaches 0.

So the line $y = 0$ is a horizontal asymptote.

---

17. C

$f(x) = x - \dfrac{1}{x}$

$f(1 - i) = (1 - i) - \dfrac{1}{1 - i}$

$= (1 - i) - \dfrac{1(1 + i)}{(1 - i)(1 + i)}$

$= (1 - i) - \dfrac{1 + i}{1 - i^2}$

$= (1 - i) - \dfrac{1 + i}{2}$ $i^2 = -1$

$= \dfrac{2 - 2i}{2} - \dfrac{1 + i}{2}$

$= \dfrac{1}{2}(1 - 3i)$

18. D

$\sin(\pi - \theta) = \sin\theta$, so $\sin(\pi - \theta) = 0.81$

19. C

$f(x) = \sqrt[3]{x - 11}$

To find an inverse function:

1. Replace $f(x)$ with y. $y = \sqrt[3]{x - 11}$

2. Interchange x and y. $x = \sqrt[3]{y - 11}$

3. Solve for y. $x^3 = y - 11$

$\Rightarrow\ y = x^3 + 11 \Rightarrow f^{-1}(x) = x^3 + 11$

$f^{-1}(-2) = (-2)^3 + 11 = 3$

20. D

$f(x) = x - [x]$, where $[x]$ is the greatest integer less than or equal to x. First find the values of $[x]$ for several points in the interval $-2 \le x < -1$.

$[-2] = -2$ The greatest integer less than or equal to -2 is -2.

$[-1.9] = -2$ The greatest integer less than or equal to -1.9 is -2.

$[-1.5] = -2$ The greatest integer less than or equal to -1.5 is -2.

$[-1.01] = -2$ The greatest integer less than or equal to -1.01 is -2.

Therefore when $-2 \le x < -1$, $[x] = -2$.

$f(x) = x - [x] = x - (-2) = x + 2$

21. D

$f(t) = ae^{-0.00124t}$

$1 = 15e^{-0.00124t}$ Given: $a = 15$, $f(t) = 1$

$\dfrac{1}{15} = e^{-0.00124t}$ Divide both sides by 15.

$\ln(\dfrac{1}{15}) = \ln e^{-0.00124t}$ Take ln of both sides.

$\ln(\dfrac{1}{15}) = -0.00124t \ln e$ $\ln M^p = p \ln M$

$\ln(\dfrac{1}{15}) = -0.00124t$ $\ln e = 1$

$t = \dfrac{\ln(\dfrac{1}{15})}{-0.00124} \approx 2183.9$ Divide by -0.00124.

22. B

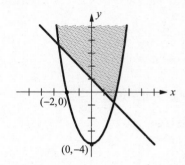

The equation of the parabola is $y = x^2 - 4$ and the equation of the line is $x + y = 1$.

Only answer choices (B) and (D) include these equations in their inequalities, so discard the other answer choices.

Test the inequalities with the point $(0, 2)$, which is in the shaded region.

(B) $\begin{cases} y \ge x^2 - 4 \\ x + y \ge 1 \end{cases}$ $\begin{cases} 2 \ge 0^2 - 4 & \text{True} \\ 0 + 2 \ge 1 & \text{True} \end{cases}$

(D) $\begin{cases} y \le x^2 - 4 \\ x + y \ge 1 \end{cases}$ $\begin{cases} 2 \le 0^2 - 4 & \text{Not true} \\ 0 + 2 \ge 1 & \text{True} \end{cases}$

Choice (B) is correct.

23. E

$\begin{aligned} |2i(3 - 4i)| &= 2|i(3 - 4i)| \\ &= 2|3i - 4i^2| \\ &= 2|4 + 3i| & i^2 = -1 \\ &= 2\sqrt{4^2 + 3^2} & |a + bi| = \sqrt{a^2 + b^2} \\ &= 10 \end{aligned}$

24. C

The thickness of the part ranges from 0.117 to 0.123 $\Rightarrow$ $0.117 \le t \le 0.123$.

Solve the inequality in each answer choice.

(A) $|t - 0.006| \le 0.123$
$\Rightarrow$ $-0.123 \le t - 0.006 \le 0.123$
$\Rightarrow$ $-0.117 \le t \le 0.129$

(B) $|t - 0.117| \ge 0.003$
$\Rightarrow$ $t - 0.117 \ge 0.003$ or $t - 0.117 \le -0.003$
$\Rightarrow$ $t \ge 0.12$ or $t \le 0.114$

(C) $|t - 0.12| \le 0.003$
$\Rightarrow$ $-0.003 \le t - 0.12 \le 0.003$
$\Rightarrow$ $0.117 \le t \le 0.123$

(C) is the correct answer.

25. C

If the graph of f rises as x increases then the function is called an increasing function.

The graph of answer choice (C) is rising over the whole domain of f.

26. C

Use your calculator to graph the equations, first solving each equation for y.

$\dfrac{y^2}{4} - \dfrac{x^2}{1} = 1$ $\Rightarrow$ $y^2 = 4x^2 + 4$
$\Rightarrow$ $y = \pm\sqrt{4x^2 + 4}$

Graph $y_1 = \sqrt{4x^2 + 4}$ and $y_2 = -\sqrt{4x^2 + 4}$.

$\dfrac{(x-2)^2}{4} - \dfrac{y^2}{16} = 1$ $\Rightarrow$ $y^2 = 4(x-2)^2 - 16$
$\Rightarrow$ $y = \pm\sqrt{4(x-2)^2 - 16}$

Graph $y_3 = \sqrt{4(x-2)^2 - 16}$ and
$y_4 = -\sqrt{4(x-2)^2 - 16}$.

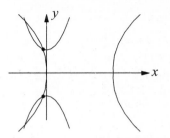

There are two points of intersection.

27. D

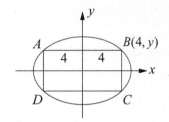

Since the ellipse is centered at $(0,0)$ and $AB = 8$, the x-coordinate of point B is 4. Substitute $x = 4$ into the equation of the parabola.

$\dfrac{4^2}{25} + \dfrac{y^2}{9} = 1$ $\Rightarrow$ $\dfrac{y^2}{9} = 1 - \dfrac{16}{25}$

$\Rightarrow$ $y^2 = \dfrac{81}{25}$ $\Rightarrow$ $y = \pm\dfrac{9}{5}$

Therefore the y-coordinate of point B is $\dfrac{9}{5}$ and

the length of $\overline{BC}$ equals $\dfrac{18}{5}$.

Area of rectangle $ABCD$
$= 8 \cdot \dfrac{18}{5} = \dfrac{144}{5} = 28.8$

28. C

$f(x) = \ln(2x)$

To find an inverse function:

1. Replace $f(x)$ with y. $\qquad y = \ln(2x)$
2. Interchange x and y. $\qquad x = \ln(2y)$
3. Solve for y. $\qquad 2y = e^x$

$\Rightarrow$ $y = \dfrac{1}{2}e^x$ $\Rightarrow$ $f^{-1}(x) = \dfrac{1}{2}e^x$

$f^{-1}(2) = \dfrac{1}{2}e^2$

29. A

$$4\tan^2\theta + 3\tan\theta - 1 = 0$$

$$(4\tan\theta - 1)(\tan\theta + 1) = 0 \qquad \text{Factor.}$$

$$4\tan\theta - 1 = 0 \quad \text{or} \quad \tan\theta + 1 = 0$$

$$\tan\theta = \frac{1}{4} \qquad \text{or} \quad \tan\theta = -1$$

$$\theta = \tan^{-1}(\frac{1}{4}) \approx 14° \text{ or } \theta = \tan^{-1}(-1) = -45°$$

Since $0° < \theta < 90°$, $\theta = 14°$.

30. E

$$x^2 - 8y^2 - 12x + 8y - 15 = 0$$

Rearrange the terms.

$$x^2 - 12x - 8(y^2 - y) = 15$$

Add $(-\frac{12}{2})^2$ to complete the square   Add $(-\frac{1}{2})^2$ to complete the square

$$(x^2 - 12x + \boxed{36}) - 8(\ y^2 - y + \boxed{\frac{1}{4}}\ ) = 15 + \boxed{36} - 8\boxed{\frac{1}{4}}$$

$$(x - 6)^2 - 8(y^2 - \frac{1}{2}) = 49$$

Center of the hyperbola $= (6, \frac{1}{2})$.

31. C

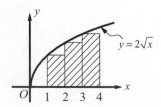

The height of the first rectangle $= f(1) = 2\sqrt{1} = 2$.

The height of the second rectangle $= f(2) = 2\sqrt{2}$.

The height of the third rectangle $= f(3) = 2\sqrt{3}$.

Sum of the areas of the three rectangles

$$= 1 \cdot 2 + 1 \cdot 2\sqrt{2} + 1 \cdot 2\sqrt{3} \approx 8.3$$

32. E

Given: 1) If $a > b$, then $a > c$.
    2) $a > c$

"If $a > c$, then $a > b$" is the converse of the given statement. The converse is not always equivalent to the given statement. Therefore, no conclusion can be drawn from the given information.

33. E

$$\frac{3}{4}, \frac{1}{2}, \frac{1}{3}, \frac{2}{9}, \dots$$

In the given geometric sequence,

$$a_1 = \frac{3}{4} \text{ and } r = \frac{2}{3}.$$

$$a_9 = a_1 \cdot r^{9-1} = \frac{3}{4}(\frac{2}{3})^8 = \frac{64}{2187}$$

34. A

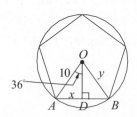

In the figure above, $m\angle AOB = 360 \div 5 = 72$ and $m\angle AOD = 72 \div 2 = 36$.

$x = 10\sin 36°$ and $y = 10\cos 36°$

Area of $\triangle AOB$

$$= \frac{1}{2}(2x)(y) = \frac{1}{2}(2 \cdot 10\sin 36°)(10\cos 36°)$$

$$\approx 47.55$$

Area of the pentagon $= 5(47.55) = 237.75$

35. A

Method 1: Since $-1 \le \cos\theta \le 1$, $f(x)$ will be at a maximum when $\cos(x + \frac{\pi}{3}) = -1$, which makes

$$f(x) = -(-1) + 1 = 2.$$

$$\cos(x + \frac{\pi}{3}) = -1 \implies x + \frac{\pi}{3} = \pi \implies x = \frac{2\pi}{3}$$

Method 2: Use a graphing calculator to find the x-coordinate when the value of f is greatest.

A maximum occurs at $x \approx 2.1$, and $\dfrac{2\pi}{3} \approx 2.1$.

36. D

Let $x = \arcsin 0.6525$, then $\sin x = 0.6525$.

$\csc(\arcsin 0.6525)$

$= \csc(x)$ $\qquad\qquad\qquad x = \arcsin 0.6525$

$= \dfrac{1}{\sin x}$ $\qquad\qquad \csc x = \dfrac{1}{\sin x}$

$= \dfrac{1}{0.6525}$ $\qquad\qquad \sin x = 0.6525$

≈ 1.533

37. B

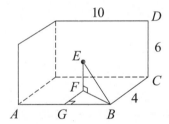

In the figure above point E is the center of the rectangular solid.

In $\triangle BFG$, $\quad BF^2 = FG^2 + BG^2$

$\qquad\qquad\qquad BF^2 = 2^2 + 5^2 = 29$

In $\triangle BEF$, $\quad BE^2 = EF^2 + BF^2$

$\qquad\qquad\qquad BE^2 = 3^2 + 29 = 38$

$\qquad\qquad\qquad BE = \sqrt{38} \approx 6.16$

38. B

Given: $\displaystyle\sum_{i=1}^{20} i = 210$

$\displaystyle\sum_{i=1}^{20} (2i-1)$

$= \displaystyle\sum_{i=1}^{20} 2i - \sum_{i=1}^{20} 1$

$= 2(210) - 20 \qquad \displaystyle\sum_{i=1}^{20} i = 210 \text{ and } \sum_{i=1}^{n} c = cn$

$= 400$

39. D

$20 + 18 + 16.2 + 14.58 + \cdots$

In the given geometric sequence,
$a_1 = 20$ and $r = 0.9$.

Sum of the infinite geometric series

$= \dfrac{a_1}{1-r} = \dfrac{20}{1-0.9} = 200$

40. C

Let $r =$ the number of red marbles
and $g =$ the number of green marbles.

The number of red marbles after
2 red marbles are removed.

$\dfrac{\overbrace{r-2}}{\underbrace{(r-2)+g}} = \dfrac{1}{4}$

Total number of marbles after
2 red marbles are removed.

$\Rightarrow 4(r-2) = r-2+g$

$\Rightarrow 3r = g+6$

$\Rightarrow g = 3r-6$

$\dfrac{r}{\underbrace{r+(g-2)}} = \dfrac{3}{10}$

Total number of marbles after
2 green marbles are removed.

$\Rightarrow 10r = 3[r+(g-2)]$

$\Rightarrow 10r = 3r+3g-6$

$\Rightarrow 7r = 3g-6$

Substitute $g = 3r-6$ into this second equation.

$7r = 3(3r-6)-6$

$7r = 9r-24$

$2r = 24$

$r = 12$

41. C

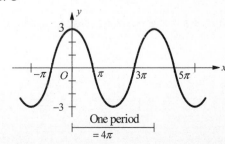

One period
$= 4\pi$

For the function $y = a\cos bx$, the amplitude is a and the period is $\dfrac{2\pi}{b}$.

The graph shows that the amplitude of the function is 3, and the period is 4π. There is no vertical shift of the graph.

Choice (C) is correct.

42. B

$$\lim_{x \to \infty} \frac{2x^2 + 5}{3x^2 - 2x + 4}$$

$$= \lim_{x \to \infty} \frac{\dfrac{2x^2}{x^2} + \dfrac{5}{x^2}}{\dfrac{3x^2}{x^2} - \dfrac{2x}{x^2} + \dfrac{4}{x^2}}$$

Divide the numerator and denominator by x^2.

$$= \lim_{x \to \infty} \frac{2 + \dfrac{5}{x^2}}{3 - \dfrac{2}{x} + \dfrac{4}{x^2}}$$

$$= \frac{2}{3}$$

As $x \to \infty$, $\dfrac{5}{x^2} \to 0$,

$\dfrac{2}{x} \to 0$, and $\dfrac{4}{x^2} \to 0$.

43. E

$r\sin\theta = -2$ Polar equation
$y = -2$ Use the coordinate-system conversion formula $y = r\sin\theta$.

Choice (E) is correct.

44. D

The graph shows that $\mathbf{u} = \,<-2, 4>$ and $\mathbf{v} = \,<6, 5>$.

$\mathbf{z} = \mathbf{v} + \mathbf{w}$

$= \,<-2, 4> + <6, 5>$

$= \,<-2 + 6, 4 + 5>$

$= \,<4, 9>$

Magnitude of $\mathbf{z} = |\mathbf{z}|$

$$= \sqrt{4^2 + 9^2}$$

$$= \sqrt{97}$$

$$\approx 9.85$$

45. C

Given: $x = \cos t$ and $y = \sin^2 t$

$y = \sin^2 t$

$= 1 - \cos^2 t$ Pythagorean identity:
$\sin^2\theta + \cos^2\theta = 1$

$= 1 - x^2$ Substitution: $x = \cos t$

The y-intercept occurs when $x = 0$.

$y = 1 - x^2$

$= 1 - 0^2$

$= 1$

46. A

$P(2, 5, 9)$ and $Q(10, 2, 3)$

$$d = \sqrt{(2 - 10)^2 + (5 - 2)^2 + (9 - 3)^2}$$

$$= \sqrt{64 + 9 + 36}$$

$$= \sqrt{109}$$

$$\approx 10.44$$

47. D

$$f : (x, y) \to (x, y - x)$$

(A) $f : (1, 1) \to (1, 1 - 1) = (1, 0)$

(B) $f : (1, 2) \to (1, 2 - 1) = (1, 1)$

(C) $f : (2, 3) \to (2, 3 - 2) = (2, 1)$

(D) $f : (2, 5) \to (2, 5 - 2) = (2, 3)$

Choice (D) is correct.

48. C

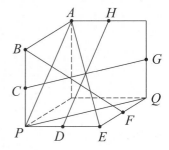

In the figure above, $CG = PQ$ and $DH = PA$,

therefore the length of $\overline{CG}$ and $\overline{DH}$ is the same as the length of the diagonal of the face.

$\overline{AE}$ is the diagonal of the cube.
$\overline{BF}$ is the segment connecting one corner to the midpoint of an edge.

Choice (C) is correct.

49. D

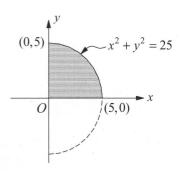

The region formed by $x^2 + y^2 \leq 25$, $x \geq 0$, and $y \geq 0$ is a quarter circle whose radius is 5.

The three dimensional figure generated is a hemisphere with radius 5.

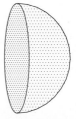

Surface area of the hemisphere

$$= \underbrace{\frac{1}{2}(4\pi r^2)}_{\substack{\text{one half the surface} \\ \text{area of sphere}}} + \overbrace{\pi r^2}^{\text{area of base}}$$

$$= \frac{1}{2}(4\pi \cdot 5^2) + \pi \cdot 5^2$$

$$= 75\pi$$

50. B

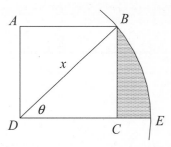

$BC = x \sin \theta$
$CD = x \cos \theta$

Area of $\triangle BCD$

$$= \frac{1}{2}(x \cos \theta)(x \sin \theta)$$

$$= \frac{1}{2}x^2 \cos \theta \sin \theta$$

Area of sector DBE

$$= \pi x^2 \cdot \frac{\theta}{360}$$

Area of the shaded region

$$= \frac{\pi x^2 \theta}{360} - \frac{1}{2}x^2 \sin \theta \cos \theta$$

$$= \frac{x^2}{2}(\frac{\pi \theta}{180} - \sin \theta \cos \theta)$$

Test Form H
Mathematics Level 2

Answer Sheet

1 Ⓐ Ⓑ Ⓒ Ⓓ Ⓔ	21 Ⓐ Ⓑ Ⓒ Ⓓ Ⓔ	41 Ⓐ Ⓑ Ⓒ Ⓓ Ⓔ
2 Ⓐ Ⓑ Ⓒ Ⓓ Ⓔ	22 Ⓐ Ⓑ Ⓒ Ⓓ Ⓔ	42 Ⓐ Ⓑ Ⓒ Ⓓ Ⓔ
3 Ⓐ Ⓑ Ⓒ Ⓓ Ⓔ	23 Ⓐ Ⓑ Ⓒ Ⓓ Ⓔ	43 Ⓐ Ⓑ Ⓒ Ⓓ Ⓔ
4 Ⓐ Ⓑ Ⓒ Ⓓ Ⓔ	24 Ⓐ Ⓑ Ⓒ Ⓓ Ⓔ	44 Ⓐ Ⓑ Ⓒ Ⓓ Ⓔ
5 Ⓐ Ⓑ Ⓒ Ⓓ Ⓔ	25 Ⓐ Ⓑ Ⓒ Ⓓ Ⓔ	45 Ⓐ Ⓑ Ⓒ Ⓓ Ⓔ
6 Ⓐ Ⓑ Ⓒ Ⓓ Ⓔ	26 Ⓐ Ⓑ Ⓒ Ⓓ Ⓔ	46 Ⓐ Ⓑ Ⓒ Ⓓ Ⓔ
7 Ⓐ Ⓑ Ⓒ Ⓓ Ⓔ	27 Ⓐ Ⓑ Ⓒ Ⓓ Ⓔ	47 Ⓐ Ⓑ Ⓒ Ⓓ Ⓔ
8 Ⓐ Ⓑ Ⓒ Ⓓ Ⓔ	28 Ⓐ Ⓑ Ⓒ Ⓓ Ⓔ	48 Ⓐ Ⓑ Ⓒ Ⓓ Ⓔ
9 Ⓐ Ⓑ Ⓒ Ⓓ Ⓔ	29 Ⓐ Ⓑ Ⓒ Ⓓ Ⓔ	49 Ⓐ Ⓑ Ⓒ Ⓓ Ⓔ
10 Ⓐ Ⓑ Ⓒ Ⓓ Ⓔ	30 Ⓐ Ⓑ Ⓒ Ⓓ Ⓔ	50 Ⓐ Ⓑ Ⓒ Ⓓ Ⓔ
11 Ⓐ Ⓑ Ⓒ Ⓓ Ⓔ	31 Ⓐ Ⓑ Ⓒ Ⓓ Ⓔ	
12 Ⓐ Ⓑ Ⓒ Ⓓ Ⓔ	32 Ⓐ Ⓑ Ⓒ Ⓓ Ⓔ	
13 Ⓐ Ⓑ Ⓒ Ⓓ Ⓔ	33 Ⓐ Ⓑ Ⓒ Ⓓ Ⓔ	
14 Ⓐ Ⓑ Ⓒ Ⓓ Ⓔ	34 Ⓐ Ⓑ Ⓒ Ⓓ Ⓔ	
15 Ⓐ Ⓑ Ⓒ Ⓓ Ⓔ	35 Ⓐ Ⓑ Ⓒ Ⓓ Ⓔ	
16 Ⓐ Ⓑ Ⓒ Ⓓ Ⓔ	36 Ⓐ Ⓑ Ⓒ Ⓓ Ⓔ	
17 Ⓐ Ⓑ Ⓒ Ⓓ Ⓔ	37 Ⓐ Ⓑ Ⓒ Ⓓ Ⓔ	
18 Ⓐ Ⓑ Ⓒ Ⓓ Ⓔ	38 Ⓐ Ⓑ Ⓒ Ⓓ Ⓔ	
19 Ⓐ Ⓑ Ⓒ Ⓓ Ⓔ	39 Ⓐ Ⓑ Ⓒ Ⓓ Ⓔ	
20 Ⓐ Ⓑ Ⓒ Ⓓ Ⓔ	40 Ⓐ Ⓑ Ⓒ Ⓓ Ⓔ	

Reference Information

The following information is for your reference in answering some of the questions on this test.

Volume of a right circular cone with radius r and height h: $V = \dfrac{1}{3}\pi r^2 h$

Lateral area of a right circular cone with base circumference C and slant height ℓ: $S = \dfrac{1}{2} C \ell$

Volume of a sphere with radius r: $V = \dfrac{4}{3}\pi r^3$

Surface area of a sphere with radius r: $S = 4\pi r^2$

Volume of a pyramid with base area B and height h: $V = \dfrac{1}{3} Bh$

Test Form H
SAT Subject Test in Mathematics Level 2

50 Questions   1 hour

For each of the following problems, decide which is the BEST of the answer choices given. If the exact numerical value is not one of the choices, select the choice that best approximates this value. Then fill in the corresponding circle on the answer sheet.

Notes: (1) A calculator will be necessary for answering some of the questions on this test. For each question you will have to decide whether or not you should use a calculator. Programmable calculators and calculators that can display graphs are permitted.

(2) The angle measures used on the Math Level 2 Test are in either degree measure or radian measure. Check to see which mode your calculator is in.

(3) Figures that accompany problems on this test are intended to provide information useful in solving the problems. They are drawn as accurately as possible EXCEPT when it is stated in a specific problem that its figure is not drawn to scale. All figures lie in a plane unless otherwise indicated.

(4) Unless otherwise specified, the domain of any function f is assumed to be the set of all real numbers x for which $f(x)$ is a real number.

(5) Reference information that may be useful in answering the questions on this test can be found on the page preceding Question 1.

1. If $x > 0$ and $3x - 1 = \dfrac{8}{3x+1}$, then which of the following could be the value of x?

   (A) -1 (B) 0 (C) 1 (D) 3 (E) 9

2. If $a - 2b - c = -3$ and $-2a + 4b + c = 2$, what is the value of c?

   (A) -4

   (B) -3

   (C) 0

   (D) 4

   (E) It cannot be determined from the information given.

3. If $3^{x^2} = 9^x \cdot 27$ and $x > 0$, then $x =$

   (A) 2 (B) 3 (C) 4 (D) 5 (E) 6

4. The hardness, h, of a mineral can be determined by hitting the mineral with a diamond and measuring the depth, d, of the indentation. The relation can be modeled by an equation $hd^2 = 1.89$. If the hardness of a certain mineral is 50, what is the depth of the indentation left by hitting the mineral with a diamond?

(A) 0.06   (B) 0.09   (C) 0.12   (D) 0.15   (E) 0.19

5. If $x + 4y = 4$ and $x + y^2 = 0$, then $y =$

(A) −2

(B) −1

(C) 0

(D) 2

(E) 4

6. Which of the following graphs is represented by the inequality $\dfrac{x^2 - 2x - 8}{x - 1} < 0$?

(A)
       −2   1   4

(B)
       −2   1   4

(C)
       −4   −2   1

(D)
       −4   −2   1

(E)
         −2   1

7. What is the remainder when $x^3 + 3x^2 - 2x - 6$ is divided by $x + 2$?

(A) −22   (B) −6   (C) 2   (D) 6   (E) 10

8. Aaron had p pounds of strawberries for sale at a price of d dollars per pound. If x is the number of pounds of strawberries he did not sell, how much did he receive from the sales of the strawberries?

(A) $pd - x$

(B) $p - dx$

(C) $d(p - x)$

(D) $p(d - x)$

(E) $x(p - d)$

9. For all positive numbers a, let the operation $\blacktriangle$ be defined as $a\blacktriangle = a^2 + 1$. If $10 = x\blacktriangle$ and $k\blacktriangle = x$, what is the value of k?

(A) $\sqrt{2}$ (B) 3   (C) 4   (D) $2\sqrt{2}$ (E) 8

10. For $mn \neq 0$, $\dfrac{mn^{-1} - 1}{m^{-1}n - 1} =$

(A) $-\dfrac{m}{n}$

(B) $\dfrac{m}{n}$

(C) $\dfrac{1}{n - m}$

(D) $\dfrac{m}{n - m}$

(E) $\dfrac{-m}{n - m}$

11. If $(n - 2)! = 12(n - 4)!$, then $n =$

(A) 5   (B) 6   (C) 7   (D) 8   (E) 9

12. Which of the following is the solution set for the equation $\sqrt{8-x}+2=x$?

(A) $\{-1, 4\}$

(B) $\{2, 4\}$

(C) $\{1, -4\}$

(D) $\{-1\}$

(E) $\{4\}$

13. Figure 1 shows a regular octagon whose radius is 6. What is the perimeter of the octagon to the nearest whole number?

(A) 33

(B) 37

(C) 40

(D) 43

(E) 49

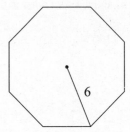

Figure 1

14. For what value of x is $f(x) = 5 - |3 - 2x|$ at its maximum?

(A) -2

(B) $-\dfrac{3}{2}$

(C) 0

(D) $\dfrac{3}{2}$

(E) 2

15. If $0 < x < \pi$ and $\cos x = \dfrac{4}{5}$, then $\tan\dfrac{x}{2} =$

    (A) $\dfrac{1}{9}$ (B) $\dfrac{1}{4}$ (C) $\dfrac{1}{3}$ (D) $\dfrac{1}{2}$ (E) $\dfrac{2}{3}$

16. Figure 2 is the graph of $f(x)$. If f^{-1} is the inverse of f, what is $f^{-1}(-1)$?

    (A) -3

    (B) -2

    (C) -1

    (D) 1

    (E) 2

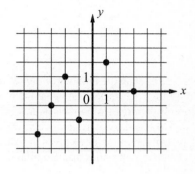

Figure 2

17. If $h(x) = \dfrac{2x-1}{x}$ and $i^2 = -1$, then $h(1 - i\sqrt{2}) =$

    (A) $\dfrac{5 - i\sqrt{2}}{3}$

    (B) $\dfrac{5 + i\sqrt{2}}{3}$

    (C) $\dfrac{5 - i\sqrt{2}}{5}$

    (D) $\dfrac{5 + i\sqrt{2}}{5}$

    (E) $5 - i\sqrt{2}$

18. The function f is defined as $f(x) = [x] - x$, where $[x]$ is the greatest integer less than or equal to x. If $1 \le x < 2$, then f is also given by $f(x) =$

    (A) $-x$

    (B) $-x - 1$

    (C) $-x + 1$

    (D) $x + 1$

    (E) $x - 1$

19. The population growth of a certain species of insect obeys the law of an exponential function $f(t) = ae^{0.384t}$, where a is the initial amount and t is the number of days elapsed. How many days would it take for the population of these insects to grow from 100 to 1000?

   (A) 5   (B) 6   (C) 7   (D) 8   (E) 9

20. Figure 3 is a table showing the number of digital cameras that were sold during two weeks in June, at the e-max electronics store. If the prices of models A, B, C, and D are $129, $189, $249, and $329, respectively, which of the following matrix representations gives the total income, in dollars, received from the sales of the digital cameras for each week?

	1st week	2nd week
Model A	25	22
Model B	34	38
Model C	18	20
Model D	14	18

Figure 3

(A) $\begin{bmatrix} 25 & 22 \\ 34 & 38 \\ 18 & 20 \\ 14 & 18 \end{bmatrix} \cdot \begin{bmatrix} 129 \\ 189 \\ 249 \\ 329 \end{bmatrix}$

(B) $\begin{bmatrix} 129 \\ 189 \\ 249 \\ 329 \end{bmatrix} \cdot \begin{bmatrix} 25 & 22 \\ 34 & 38 \\ 18 & 20 \\ 14 & 18 \end{bmatrix}$

(C) $\begin{bmatrix} 129 & 189 & 249 & 329 \end{bmatrix} \cdot \begin{bmatrix} 25 & 22 \\ 34 & 38 \\ 18 & 20 \\ 14 & 18 \end{bmatrix}$

(D) $\begin{bmatrix} 25 & 22 \\ 34 & 38 \\ 18 & 20 \\ 14 & 18 \end{bmatrix} \cdot \begin{bmatrix} 129 & 189 & 249 & 329 \end{bmatrix}$

(E) $129\begin{bmatrix} 25 & 22 \\ 34 & 38 \\ 18 & 20 \\ 14 & 18 \end{bmatrix} + 189\begin{bmatrix} 25 & 22 \\ 34 & 38 \\ 18 & 20 \\ 14 & 18 \end{bmatrix} + 249\begin{bmatrix} 25 & 22 \\ 34 & 38 \\ 18 & 20 \\ 14 & 18 \end{bmatrix} + 229\begin{bmatrix} 25 & 22 \\ 34 & 38 \\ 18 & 20 \\ 14 & 18 \end{bmatrix}$

21. If $0 < x < \dfrac{\pi}{2}$ and $5\cos^2 x - 2 = -3\cos x$, what is the radian measure of x?

(A) 0.38

(B) 0.65

(C) 0.83

(D) 1.02

(E) 1.16

22. Figure 4 shows the top view of an open rectangular box that is divided into 4 compartments, and its dimensions. When a ball is dropped into the box at random it falls into one of the compartments. If the probability that the ball will fall into the shaded compartment is $\dfrac{4}{15}$, what is the value of x?

(A) 3

(B) 4

(C) 5

(D) 6

(E) 7

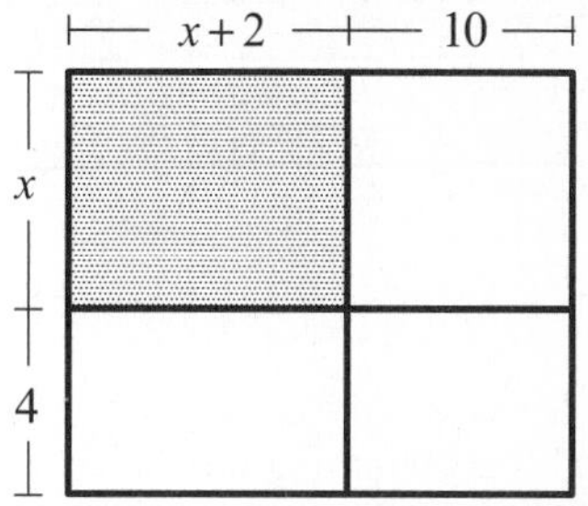

Note: Figure not drawn to scale.

Figure 4

23. What is the area of the region enclosed by $x^2 + y^2 \le 25$ and $\dfrac{x^2}{25} + \dfrac{y^2}{9} \ge 1$? (The formula for the area of an ellipse is $A = \pi ab$, where a and b are one-half the respective lengths of the major and minor axis.)

(A) 3π (B) 9π (C) 10π (D) 25π (E) 34π

24. Which of the following is equal to the positive value of $\cot(\arctan 2.98)$?

(A) 0.34   (B) 0.72   (C) 1.01   (D) 1.48   (E) 2.16

25. A sequence is recursively defined by $a_n = a_{n-1} + a_{n-2}$, for $n \geq 3$. If $a_1 = -1$ and $a_2 = 2$, then $a_5 =$

(A) 4   (B) 7   (C) 11   (D) 18   (E) 29

26. In triangle ABC in Figure 5, what is the length of $\overline{AB}$?

(A) 32.7

(B) 39.4

(C) 43.6

(D) 48.9

(E) 50.5

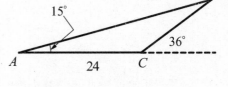

Note: Figure not drawn to scale.

Figure 5

27. A function f is a decreasing function if f has the property that whenever $x_1 \leq x_2$, then $f(x_1) \geq f(x_2)$. Which of the following is a decreasing function?

(A) $x^2 - 8$

(B) 3^x

(C) $4 - x$

(D) $|x - 3|$

(E) $\dfrac{1}{x}$

28. The probability that flight A arrives on time is $\dfrac{3}{4}$ and the probability that flight B arrives on time is $\dfrac{5}{6}$. What is the probability that flight A arrives on time but flight B does not arrive on time?

(A) $\dfrac{1}{8}$ (B) $\dfrac{1}{4}$ (C) $\dfrac{3}{8}$ (D) $\dfrac{1}{2}$ (E) $\dfrac{5}{8}$

29. In which quadrant(s) is the set of points (x, y) that satisfy $(2x+1)(y+2) < 0$ located?

    (A) Quadrant II only

    (B) Quadrant III only

    (C) Quadrants II and III only

    (D) Quadrants II, III, and IV only

    (E) Quadrants I, II, III, and IV

30. In Figure 6, the grid consists of unit squares. The initial point of the two vectors **s** and **t** lies at the origin. If **u** is a vector such that $\mathbf{u} = \mathbf{s} - \mathbf{t}$, then $\mathbf{u} =$

    (A) $<-5, 1>$

    (B) $<-5, -1>$

    (C) $<5, -1>$

    (D) $<3.5, 2.5>$

    (E) $<5.5, 2.5>$

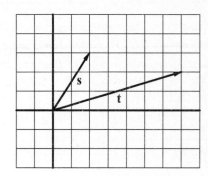

Figure 6

31. If $y = e^{2t} - 1$ and $x = e^t$, what is y in terms of x?

    (A) $2x - 1$

    (B) $2x + 1$

    (C) $x^2 - 1$

    (D) $x^2 + 1$

    (E) $x^2 - x$

32. What is the length of the major axis of the ellipse whose equation is $x^2 + 2y^2 - 2x + 8y + 7 = 0$?

    (A) 1   (B) 1.41   (C) 2   (D) 2.82   (E) 4

33. If $f(r,\theta) = r\cos\theta - r\sin\theta$, then $f(6,\frac{\pi}{6}) =$

(A) 6

(B) $6\sqrt{3}$

(C) $3(1-\sqrt{3})$

(D) $3(\sqrt{3}-1)$

(E) $3(\sqrt{3}+1)$

34. Figure 7 shows $\triangle ADE$ and square $ABCD$, which are rotated about side $\overline{CE}$ to generate a cone and a cylinder, respectively (not shown). If $m\angle AED = 30°$ and $AE = 4$, what is the ratio of the volume of the cone to the volume of the cylinder?

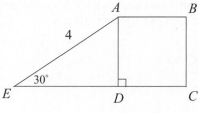

Figure 7

(A) $\dfrac{1}{3}$

(B) $\dfrac{\sqrt{3}}{3}$

(C) 1

(D) $\sqrt{3}$

(E) 3

35. If $f(x) = 2^x$ and the inverse function of f is denoted by f^{-1}, then which of the following must be true?

  I. $f^{-1}(2) = 1$

  II. $f^{-1}(6) = 1 + f^{-1}(3)$

  III. $f^{-1}(8) = 3$

(A) None

(B) I only

(C) III only

(D) I and III only

(E) I, II, and III

36. Which of the following is the fifth term in the
    expansion of $(2x - y)^7$?

    (A) $280x^3 y^4$

    (B) $-280x^2 y^5$

    (C) $280x^2 y^5$

    (D) $336x^3 y^4$

    (E) $-336x^2 y^5$

37. In Figure 8, what is the length of segment PQ?

    (A) 5.8
    (B) 6.6
    (C) 7.8
    (D) 8.5
    (E) 9.2

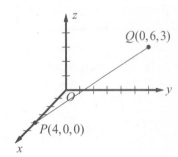

Figure 8

38. Which of the following could be the period of the
    trigonometric function $y = 2\sin\dfrac{x}{2} + 3$?

    (A) $\dfrac{\pi}{2}$ (B) π (C) 2π (D) 3π (E) 4π

39. In how many ways can 12 people be divided into
    two groups, one with 8 people and the other with
    4 people?

    (A) 384
    (B) 495
    (C) 2340
    (D) 11,880
    (E) 245,025

40. What is the surface area of a hemisphere if the volume of
the hemisphere is $\dfrac{9}{4}\pi$?

(A) 3π

(B) 4π

(C) $\dfrac{9}{2}\pi$

(D) 6π

(E) $\dfrac{27}{4}\pi$

41. The graph of $y = f(x)$ is shown in Figure 9. Which of
the following graphs could be the graph of $y = f(-x)$?

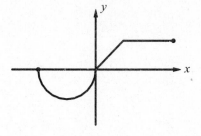

Figure 9

(A)

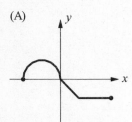

(B)

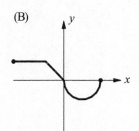

(C)

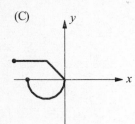

(D)

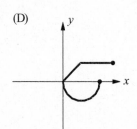

(E)

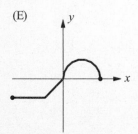

42. What is the set of all points in a plane that are 2 cm
from a line and 3 cm from a point on the line?

(A) One point

(B) Two points

(C) Four points

(D) One line

(E) Two lines

43. Which of the following inequalities is represented by
the graph in Figure 10?

(A) $(x-y)(x+y-2) \geq 0$

(B) $(x-y)(x+y-2) \leq 0$

(C) $(x+y)(x-y-2) \geq 0$

(D) $(x+y)(x-y-2) \leq 0$

(E) $(x-y)(x-y+2) \geq 0$

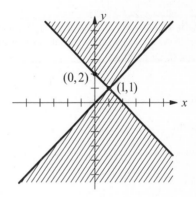

Figure 10

44. A person has two job options each with the same starting
salary of $30,000. Under the first option the salary will
increase by $1500 each year, and under the second option
the salary will increase by 4% each year. If f represents
the sum of the first ten years' income under the first option,
and s represents that of the second option, which of the
following statements is true?

(A) $f = 7317 + s$

(B) $f = 3265 + s$

(C) $s = 1560 + f$

(D) $s = 3140 + f$

(E) $s = 5085 + f$

45. Which of the following is the square root of $-5+12i$?

(A) $13i$

(B) $3-2i$

(C) $3+2i$

(D) $2+3i$

(E) $2-3i$

46. A solid with dimensions as shown in Figure 11 is to be painted on all of its faces. What is the total surface area to be painted?

(A) 768 cm^2

(B) 840 cm^2

(C) 912 cm^2

(D) 984 cm^2

(E) 1056 cm^2

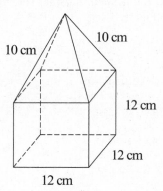

Figure 11

47. Figure 12 shows a rectangle inscribed in a semicircle. If the radius of the semicircle is r and the measure of $\angle BOC$ is θ, what is the area of the rectangle $ABCD$ in terms of r and θ ?

(A) $r^2 \sin^2 \theta$

(B) $r^2 \cos^2 \theta$

(C) $2r \tan^2 \theta$

(D) $2r \sin \theta \cos \theta$

(E) $2r^2 \sin \theta \cos \theta$

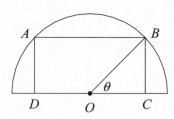

Figure 12

48. If $f(x,y) = \dfrac{x-y}{1+xy}$, then which of the following statements

must be true?

   I. $f(-x,-y) = -f(x,y)$

   II. $f(x,y) = -f(y,x)$

   III. $\dfrac{1+f(x,1)}{1-f(x,1)} = f(x,0)$

   (A) I only

   (B) I and II only

   (C) I and III only

   (D) II and III only

   (E) I, II, and III

49. Figure 13 shows the graph of $x = y^2 - 2$. Which

of the following is the graph of $x = \left| y^2 - 2 \right|$?

(A)
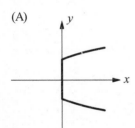

(B)
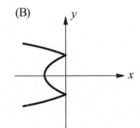

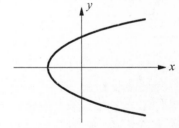

Figure 13

(C)
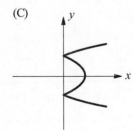

(D)
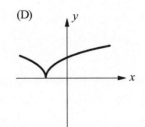

(E)
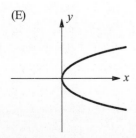

50. A polynomial function has the following properties:

- The degree of the function is 5.

- The leading coefficient is negative.

- The polynomial function has three real roots.

Which of the following could be the graph of the polynomial function?

(A)

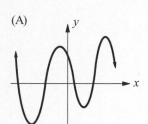

(B)

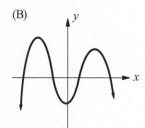

(C)

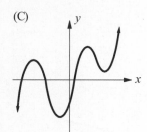

(D)

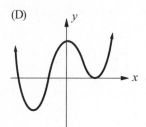

(E)

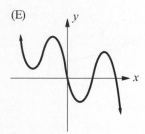

STOP

IF YOU FINISH BEFORE TIME IS CALLED, YOU MAY CHECK YOUR WORK ON THIS TEST ONLY.
DO NOT TURN TO ANY OTHER TEST IN THIS BOOK.

Answer Key

1. C	2. D	3. B	4. E	5. D
6. B	7. C	8. C	9. A	10. A
11. B	12. E	13. B	14. D	15. C
16. A	17. A	18. C	19. B	20. C
21. E	22. D	23. C	24. A	25. A
26. B	27. C	28. A	29. D	30. A
31. C	32. D	33. D	34. B	35. E
36. A	37. C	38. E	39. B	40. E
41. B	42. C	43. B	44. A	45. D
46. C	47. E	48. E	49. C	50. E

Answers and explanations

1. C

$$3x - 1 = \frac{8}{3x+1} \implies (3x-1)(3x+1) = 8$$

$$\implies 9x^2 - 1 = 8 \implies 9x^2 - 9 = 0 \implies 9(x^2 - 1) = 0$$

$$\implies x = \pm 1$$

But $x > 0$, therefore $x = 1$ is the only solution.

2. D

$$a - 2b - c = -3 \qquad \text{First equation}$$
$$-2a + 4b + c = 2 \qquad \text{Second equation}$$

To eliminate the variables a and b, multiply both sides of the first equation by 2 and add to the second equation.

$$2(a - 2b - c) = 2(-3) \implies 2a - 4b - 2c = -6$$

$$\begin{array}{r} 2a - 4b - 2c = -6 \\ + \underline{|{-2a + 4b + c = 2}} \\ -c = -4 \end{array}$$

$$\implies c = 4$$

3. B

$$3^{x^2} = 9^x \cdot 27$$

$$\implies 3^{x^2} = (3^2)^x \cdot 3^3 \implies 3^{x^2} = 3^{2x} \cdot 3^3$$

$$\implies 3^{x^2} = 3^{2x+3} \implies x^2 = 2x + 3$$

$$\implies x^2 - 2x - 3 = 0 \implies (x-3)(x+1) = 0$$

$$\implies x = 3 \text{ or } x = -1$$

Since $x > 0$, $x = 3$ is the solution.

4. E

The hardness of a certain mineral is given as 50. Substitute $h = 50$ into the equation $hd^2 = 1.89$.

$$50d^2 = 1.89 \implies d^2 = \frac{1.89}{50} = 0.0378$$

$$\implies d = \sqrt{0.0378} \approx 0.194$$

5. D

$x + 4y = 4$	First equation
$x = -4y + 4$	Solve first equation for x.
$x + y^2 = 0$	Second equation
$-4y + 4 + y^2 = 0$	Substitute first equation into the second.
$y^2 - 4y + 4 = 0$	
$(y-2)^2 = 0$	Factor.
$y = 2$	

6. B

$$\frac{x^2 - 2x - 8}{x - 1} < 0$$

Multiply both sides of the inequality by $(x-1)^2$.

Since $(x-1)^2$ is positive you don't have to change the direction of the inequality symbol.

$$\frac{x^2 - 2x - 8}{x - 1}(x-1)^2 < 0 \cdot (x-1)^2$$

$$\implies (x+2)(x-4)(x-1) < 0$$

The left side of the inequality equals zero for $x = -2$, $x = 1$, and $x = 4$. These three numbers divide the number line into four intervals.

Discard answer choices (C), (D), and (E), which don't show -2, 1, and 4 on the number line. Then test values in each interval.

If $x = 0$, $(0+2)(0-4)(0-1) < 0$ Not true
If $x = 2$, $(2+2)(2-4)(2-1) < 0$ True

Choice (B) is correct.

7. C

$f(x) = x^3 + 3x^2 - 2x - 6$

Use the remainder theorem. If $f(x)$ is divided by $x+2$, the remainder is $f(-2)$.

$$f(-2) = (-2)^3 + 3(-2)^2 - 2(-2) - 6$$
$$= -8 + 12 + 4 - 6$$
$$= 2$$

8. C

The amount he received from the sales of the strawberries
= the number of pounds sold × price per pound
$= (p - x) \cdot d$

Choice (C) is correct.

9. A

$a \blacktriangle = a^2 + 1$ Defined operation
$10 = x \blacktriangle \Rightarrow 10 = x^2 + 1$ First equation
$k \blacktriangle = x \Rightarrow k^2 + 1 = x$ Second equation

Now substitute $x = k^2 + 1$ into the first equation.

$10 = (k^2 + 1)^2 + 1$

$10 = (k^4 + 2k^2 + 1) + 1$ FOIL

$k^4 + 2k^2 - 8 = 0$ Simplify.

$(k^2 + 4)(k^2 - 2) = 0$ Factor.

$(k^2 + 4)$ cannot equal 0, since k^2 cannot be a negative number. Therefore $k^2 - 2 = 0$.

$k^2 - 2 = (k + \sqrt{2})(k - \sqrt{2}) = 0$

$k = -\sqrt{2}$ or $k = \sqrt{2}$

Since k is positive, $k = \sqrt{2}$ is the answer.

10. A

$$\frac{mn^{-1} - 1}{m^{-1}n - 1} = \frac{m\frac{1}{n} - 1}{\frac{1}{m}n - 1} = \frac{(m\frac{1}{n} - 1)mn}{(\frac{1}{m}n - 1)mn}$$
$$= \frac{m^2 - mn}{n^2 - mn} = \frac{m(m-n)}{n(n-m)}$$
$$= \frac{m(m-n)}{-n(m-n)}$$
$$= -\frac{m}{n}$$

11. B

$(n-2)! = 12(n-4)!$

$\dfrac{(n-2)!}{(n-4)!} = 12$

$\dfrac{(n-2)(n-3)(n-4)!}{(n-4)!} = 12$

$(n-2)(n-3) = 12$

$n^2 - 5n + 6 = 12$

$n^2 - 5n - 6 = 0$

$(n-6)(n+1) = 0$

$n = 6$ or $n = -1$

In factorial notation $n \geq 0$. Therefore $n = 6$.

12. E

$\sqrt{8-x} + 2 = x$

$\sqrt{8-x} = x - 2$

$(\sqrt{8-x})^2 = (x-2)^2$

$8 - x = x^2 - 4x + 4$

$x^2 - 3x - 4 = 0$

$(x-4)(x+1) = 0$

$x = 4$ or $x = -1$

Check each possible solution in the original equation.

$\sqrt{8-4} + 2 \overset{\neq}{=} 4 \Rightarrow 2 + 2 = 4$

$\sqrt{8-(-1)} + 2 \overset{\neq}{=} -1 \Rightarrow 3 + 2 \neq -1$

The solution set is $\{4\}$.

13. B

In the octagon $m\angle POQ = 360 \div 8 = 45$, and $m\angle QOR = 22.5$.

$RQ = 6\sin 22.5° \approx 2.296$

$PQ = 2(2.296) = 4.592$

Perimeter of the octagon
$= 8(4.592) = 36.736$

14. D

$f(x) = 5 - |3 - 2x|$

The expression $5 - |3 - 2x|$ is maximum when the part after the minus sign is the smallest. Since the absolute value of a number cannot be negative, the expression is maximum when $3 - 2x = 0$ or $x = \dfrac{3}{2}$.

This type of question can also be solved with a graphing calculator.

Graph $y_1 = 5 - |3 - 2x|$.

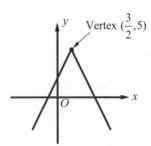

The graph shows the maximum value is 5 when $x = \dfrac{3}{2}$.

15. C

Draw a right triangle whose hypotenuse is 5 and side adjacent to angle x is 4.

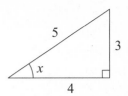

$0 < x < \pi$ and $\cos x = \dfrac{4}{5}$, and by the Pythagorean theorem the side opposite of angle x is 3.

$\tan \dfrac{x}{2} = \dfrac{\sin x}{1 + \cos x}$ Half-angle formula

$= \dfrac{3/5}{1 + 4/5}$ $\sin x = \dfrac{3}{5}$ and $\cos x = \dfrac{4}{5}$

$= \dfrac{1}{3}$

16. A

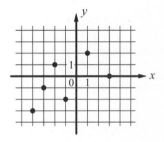

The graph of $f(x)$ shows 6 points, $(-4, -3)$, $(-3, -1)$, $(-2, 1)$, $(-1, -2)$, $(1, 2)$, and $(3, 0)$.

f^{-1} is $(-3, -4)$, $(-1, -3)$, $(1, -2)$, $(-2, -1)$, $(2, 1)$, and $(0, 3)$.

Therefore $f^{-1}(-1) = -3$.

17. A

$h(x) = \dfrac{2x - 1}{x}$

$h(1 - i\sqrt{2})$

$= \dfrac{2(1 - i\sqrt{2}) - 1}{1 - i\sqrt{2}} = \dfrac{1 - 2i\sqrt{2}}{1 - i\sqrt{2}} = \dfrac{(1 - 2i\sqrt{2})(1 + i\sqrt{2})}{(1 - i\sqrt{2})(1 + i\sqrt{2})}$

$= \dfrac{1 + i\sqrt{2} - 2i\sqrt{2} - 4i^2}{1 - 2i^2} = \dfrac{1 - i\sqrt{2} - 4(-1)}{1 - 2(-1)}$

$= \dfrac{5 - i\sqrt{2}}{3}$

18. C

$f(x) = [x] - x$ and $1 \le x < 2$

If $1 \le x < 2$, then $[x] = 1$, so

$f(x) = [x] - x = 1 - x$.

19. B

$f(t) = ae^{0.384t}$

$f(t) = 1000 =$ the final amount

$a = 100 =$ the initial amount

$1000 = 100e^{0.384t}$

$10 = e^{0.384t}$ Divide both sides by 100.

$\ln 10 = \ln e^{0.384t}$ Take natural log on both sides of the equation.

$\ln 10 = 0.384t \cdot \ln e$

$\ln 10 = 0.384t \cdot 1$

$t = \dfrac{\ln 10}{0.384} \approx 5.996$

20. C

(A) $M_{4 \times 2} \cdot M_{4 \times 1}$ cannot be multiplied.

(B) $M_{4 \times 1} \cdot M_{4 \times 2}$ cannot be multiplied.

(C) $\begin{bmatrix} 129 & 189 & 249 & 329 \end{bmatrix} \cdot \begin{bmatrix} 25 & 22 \\ 34 & 38 \\ 18 & 20 \\ 14 & 18 \end{bmatrix}$

$= \begin{bmatrix} 129 \cdot 25 & 129 \cdot 22 \\ +189 \cdot 34 & +189 \cdot 38 \\ +249 \cdot 18 & +249 \cdot 20 \\ +329 \cdot 14 & +329 \cdot 18 \end{bmatrix}$

$= [\ \underline{18739} \quad \underline{20922}\ ]$

       ↑   ↑
    first   second
week's total   week's total

(D) $M_{4 \times 2} \cdot M_{1 \times 4}$ cannot be multiplied.

(E) $129 \begin{bmatrix} 25 & 22 \\ 34 & 38 \\ 18 & 20 \\ 14 & 18 \end{bmatrix} + 189 \begin{bmatrix} 25 & 22 \\ 34 & 38 \\ 18 & 20 \\ 14 & 18 \end{bmatrix}$

$+249 \begin{bmatrix} 25 & 22 \\ 34 & 38 \\ 18 & 20 \\ 14 & 18 \end{bmatrix} + 229 \begin{bmatrix} 25 & 22 \\ 34 & 38 \\ 18 & 20 \\ 14 & 18 \end{bmatrix}$

$= (129 + 189 + 249 + 329) \begin{bmatrix} 25 & 22 \\ 34 & 38 \\ 18 & 20 \\ 14 & 18 \end{bmatrix}$

$= (896) \begin{bmatrix} 25 & 22 \\ 34 & 38 \\ 18 & 20 \\ 14 & 18 \end{bmatrix}$

This matrix does not represents the two weeks' gross income.

Choice (C) is correct.

21. E

$5\cos^2 x - 2 = -3\cos x$

$5\cos^2 x + 3\cos x - 2 = 0$

$(5\cos x - 2)(\cos x + 1) = 0$

$5\cos x - 2 = 0$ or $\cos x + 1 = 0$

$\cos x = \dfrac{2}{5} \Rightarrow x = \cos^{-1}(\dfrac{2}{5}) \approx 1.16$

$\cos x = -1 \Rightarrow x = \cos^{-1}(-1) = \pi$

Since $0 < x < \dfrac{\pi}{2}$ is given, $x = 1.16$ is the answer.

22. D

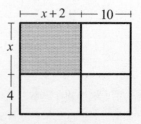

Total area $= [(x+2)+10][x+4]$

$\qquad = (x+12)(x+4)$

$\qquad = x^2 + 16x + 48$

Area of the shaded region

$\qquad = x(x+2) = x^2 + 2x$

The probability that the ball will fall into the shaded compartment is $\dfrac{4}{15}$.

$$\frac{\text{Area of shaded region}}{\text{Total area}} = \frac{x^2 + 2x}{x^2 + 16x + 48} = \frac{4}{15}$$

$15(x^2 + 2x) = 4(x^2 + 16x + 48)$ $\quad$ Cross product

$15x^2 + 30x = 4x^2 + 64x + 192$

$11x^2 - 34x - 192 = 0$

$x = \dfrac{34 \pm \sqrt{(-34)^2 - 4(11)(-192)}}{2(11)}$ $\quad$ Quadratic formula

$\quad = \dfrac{34 \pm \sqrt{9604}}{22} = \dfrac{34 \pm 98}{22}$

$x = 6$ (Discard the negative number.)

23. C

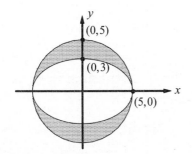

$\dfrac{x^2}{25} + \dfrac{y^2}{9} = 1 \implies a = 5$ and $b = 3$.

The area of the region enclosed by
a circle and an ellipse
= area of the circle − area of the ellipse

$= \pi(5)^2 - \pi(5)(3)$ $\quad$ Area of an ellipse $= \pi ab$

$= 10\pi$

24. A

cot(arctan 2.98)

$= \dfrac{1}{\tan(\arctan 2.98)} = \dfrac{1}{2.98} \approx 0.336$

25. A

Given: $a_n = a_{n-1} + a_{n-2}$

$\qquad a_1 = -1$ and $a_2 = 2$

$a_3 = a_2 + a_1 = 2 + (-1) = 1$

$a_4 = a_3 + a_2 = 1 + 2 = 3$

$a_5 = a_4 + a_3 = 3 + 1 = 4$

26. B

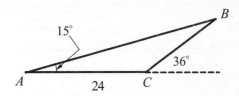

In the figure above
$m\angle ACB = 180 - 36 = 144$
$m\angle B = 180 - (144 + 15) = 21$

Use the Law of sines.

$$\frac{\sin 21^\circ}{24} = \frac{\sin 144^\circ}{AB}$$

$\implies AB = \dfrac{24 \cdot \sin 144^\circ}{\sin 21^\circ} \approx 39.36$

27. C

You can graph each equation on your calculator to see if it is increasing or decreasing.

$x^2 - 8$ $\qquad$ Decreasing on the interval $(-\infty, 0)$, and increasing on the interval $(0, \infty)$.

3^x $\qquad$ Increasing on the interval $(-\infty, \infty)$.

$4 - x$ $\qquad$ Decreasing on the interval $(-\infty, \infty)$.

$|x - 3|$ $\qquad$ Decreasing on the interval $(-\infty, 3)$, and increasing on the interval $(3, \infty)$.

$\dfrac{1}{x}$ $\qquad$ Decreasing on the interval $(-\infty, 0)$, and increasing on the interval $(0, \infty)$.

Choice (C) is correct.

28. A

$$P(\text{flight } A \text{ arrives on time}) = \frac{3}{4}$$

$$P(\text{flight } B \text{ arrives on time}) = \frac{5}{6}$$

$$\Rightarrow \quad P(\text{flight } B \text{ does not arrive on time}) = \frac{1}{6}$$

The probability that flight A arrives on time but flight B does not arrive on time

$$= \frac{3}{4} \cdot \frac{1}{6} = \frac{1}{8}$$

29. D

If $(2x+1)(y+2) < 0$

$2x+1 < 0$ and $y+2 > 0$ or
$2x+1 > 0$ and $y+2 < 0$ $\left.\right\} \Rightarrow$

$x < -\dfrac{1}{2}$ and $y > -2$ or

$x > -\dfrac{1}{2}$ and $y < -2$

Draw the graphs of $x = -\dfrac{1}{2}$ and $y = -2$.

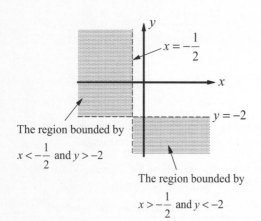

The region bounded by

$x < -\dfrac{1}{2}$ and $y > -2$

The region bounded by

$x > -\dfrac{1}{2}$ and $y < -2$

The graph above shows that the set of points (x, y) which satisfy $(2x+1)(y+2) < 0$ lies in quadrants II, III, and IV.

30. A

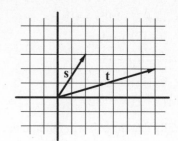

The graph shows that $\mathbf{s} = \langle 2, 3 \rangle$ and $\mathbf{t} = \langle 7, 2 \rangle$.

$\mathbf{u} = \mathbf{s} - \mathbf{t}$

$\quad = \langle 2, 3 \rangle - \langle 7, 2 \rangle$

$\quad = \langle -5, 1 \rangle$

31. C

$x = e^t$

$y = e^{2t} - 1 = (e^t)^2 - 1$

$\quad = x^2 - 1 \qquad \text{Substitution: } x = e^t$

32. D

$x^2 + 2y^2 - 2x + 8y + 7 = 0$

Complete the square.

$(x^2 - 2x + \square) + 2(y^2 + 4y + \square) = -7 + \square + 2\square$

$(x^2 - 2x + \boxed{1}) + 2(y^2 + 4y + \boxed{4}) = -7 + 1 + 8$

$(x-1)^2 + 2(y+2)^2 = 2$

$\dfrac{(x-1)^2}{2} + \dfrac{(y+2)^2}{1} = 1$

$\Rightarrow \quad a = \sqrt{2}$ and $b = 1$

Length of the major axis of the ellipse

$= 2a = 2\sqrt{2} \approx 2.82$

33. D

$f(r, \theta) = r\cos\theta - r\sin\theta$

$f(6, \dfrac{\pi}{6}) = 6\cos\dfrac{\pi}{6} - 6\sin\dfrac{\pi}{6}$

$\quad = 6(\dfrac{\sqrt{3}}{2}) - 6(\dfrac{1}{2})$

$\quad = 3\sqrt{3} - 3$

$\quad = 3(\sqrt{3} - 1)$

34. B

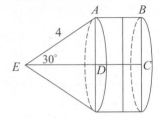

A cone and a cylinder are generated by rotating $\triangle ADE$ and square $ABCD$ about side $\overline{CE}$.

Use the $30°$-$60°$-$90°$ triangle ratio to find the radius of the cone and cylinder.

$AD = \dfrac{1}{2} AE = 2$, $ED = AD \cdot \sqrt{3} = 2\sqrt{3}$

Volume of cone $= \dfrac{1}{3}\pi r^2 h = \dfrac{1}{3}\pi(2)^2 \cdot 2\sqrt{3} = \dfrac{8\sqrt{3}}{3}\pi$

Volume of cylinder $= \pi r^2 h = \pi(2)^2 \cdot 2 = 8\pi$

$\dfrac{\text{Volume of cone}}{\text{Volume of cylinder}} = \dfrac{\dfrac{8\sqrt{3}}{3}\pi}{8\pi} = \dfrac{8\sqrt{3}}{3} \cdot \dfrac{1}{8} = \dfrac{\sqrt{3}}{3}$

35. E

$f(x) = 2^x$. To find an inverse function:

1. Replace $f(x)$ with y. $y = 2^x$

2. Interchange x and y. $x = 2^y$

3. Solve for y. $\log x = \log 2^y$

$\Rightarrow \log x = y \log 2 \Rightarrow y = \dfrac{\log x}{\log 2}$

$\Rightarrow f^{-1}(x) = \dfrac{\log x}{\log 2}$

Method I: Use the properties of logarithms.

I. $f^{-1}(2) = \dfrac{\log 2}{\log 2} = 1$

II. $f^{-1}(6) = \dfrac{\log 6}{\log 2} = \dfrac{\log(2 \cdot 3)}{\log 2}$

$= \dfrac{\log 2 + \log 3}{\log 2}$ $\log a \cdot b = \log a + \log b$

$= 1 + \dfrac{\log 3}{\log 2}$

$= 1 + f^{-1}(3)$ $f^{-1}(3) = \dfrac{\log 3}{\log 2}$

III. $f^{-1}(8) = \dfrac{\log 8}{\log 2} = \dfrac{\log 2^3}{\log 2} = \dfrac{3 \cdot \log 2}{\log 2} = 3$

Method II: Use your calculator.

I. $f^{-1}(2) = \dfrac{\log 2}{\log 2} = 1$

II. $f^{-1}(6) = \dfrac{\log 6}{\log 2} = 2.5849625$

$f^{-1}(3) = \dfrac{\log 3}{\log 2} = 1.5849625$

Therefore $f^{-1}(6) = 1 + f^{-1}(3)$.

III. $f^{-1}(8) = \dfrac{\log 8}{\log 2} = 3$

36. A

The k th term of $(a+b)^n$ is $_nC_{(k-1)}(a)^{n-(k-1)}(b)^{(k-1)}$.

The fifth term of $(2x - y)^7$ is

$_7C_4(2x)^3(-y)^4 = 35(8x^3)(y^4) = 280x^3 y^4$

37. C

$PQ = \sqrt{(0-4)^2 + (6-0)^2 + (3-0)^2}$

$= \sqrt{61}$

≈ 7.8

38. E

The period of the sine function is $\dfrac{2\pi}{b}$.

$y = 2\sin\dfrac{x}{2} + 3$

$\text{Period} = \dfrac{2\pi}{b} = \dfrac{2\pi}{1/2} = 4\pi$

39. B

When you choose 8 people to be in the first group then the other 4 people will naturally be left in the second group.

$_{12}C_8 \cdot {}_4C_4 = 495 \cdot 1 = 495$

40. E

Volume of a hemisphere

$$= \frac{1}{2}(\frac{4}{3}\pi r^3) = \frac{2}{3}\pi r^3$$

$$\frac{2}{3}\pi r^3 = \frac{9}{4}\pi \qquad \text{Volume of hemisphere is } \frac{9}{4}\pi.$$

$$r^3 = \frac{9}{4}\cdot\frac{3}{2} = \frac{27}{8}$$

$$r = \frac{3}{2} \qquad \text{Solve for } r.$$

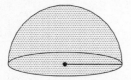

Surface area of the hemisphere

$$= \text{area of bottom circle} + \frac{1}{2} \text{ the area of a sphere}$$

$$= \pi(\frac{3}{2})^2 + \frac{1}{2}[4\pi(\frac{3}{2})^2] = \frac{9}{4}\pi + \frac{9}{2}\pi$$

$$= \frac{27}{4}\pi$$

41. B

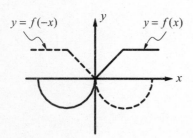

The graph of $y = f(-x)$ is the reflection of $y = f(x)$ about the y-axis.

Choice (B) is correct.

42. C

The locus of points is the intersection of two parallel lines 2 cm from the given line and a circle with radius 3 cm whose center is on the given line.

There are four points of intersection.

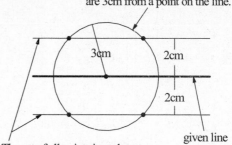

The set of all points in a plane that are 3cm from a point on the line.

3cm   2cm

2cm

given line

The set of all points in a plane that are 2cm from a line.

43. B

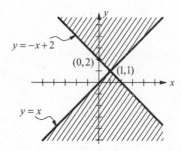

$y = -x + 2$

$(0,2)$

$(1,1)$

$y = x$

The standard form equations of the two lines are $x + y - 2 = 0$ and $x - y = 0$.

Only answer choices (A) and (B) include these equations in their inequalities.
Discard the other answer choices.

Test the point $(0,3)$, which is in the shaded region, in each inequality.

(A) $(x - y)(x + y - 2) \geq 0$
     $(0 - 3)(0 + 3 - 2) \geq 0$ Not true
(B) $(x - y)(x + y - 2) \leq 0$
     $(0 - 3)(0 + 3 - 2) \leq 0$ True

44. A

Under the first option the salary will increase by $1500 each year. The sum of the first ten years' income is an arithmetic series.

$$a_1 = 30,000$$

$$a_{10} = 30,000 + (10 - 1)\cdot 1500 = 43,500$$

$$f = S_{10} = \frac{n(a_1 + a_n)}{2} = \frac{10(30,000 + 43,500)}{2}$$

$$= 367,500$$

Under the second option the salary will increase by 4% each year. The sum of the first ten years' income is a geometric series.

$$s = 30,000 + 30,000(1.04) + 30,000(1.04)^2 + \ldots$$
$$+ 30,000(1.04)^9$$

$$= \frac{30,000(1 - 1.04^{10})}{1 - 1.04} \qquad s_n = \frac{a_1(1 - r^n)}{1 - r}$$

$$= 360,183.21$$

$$f - s = 367,500 - 360,183$$
$$= 7317$$
$$\Rightarrow f = s + 7317$$

45. **D**

If $\sqrt{-5 + 12i} = a + bi$, then $-5 + 12i = (a + bi)^2$. Square each answer choice and find out which is equivalent to $-5 + 12i$.

(A) $(13i)^2 = 169i^2 = -169$

(B) $(3 - 2i)^2 = 9 - 6i - 6i + 4i^2 = 5 - 12i$

(C) $(3 + 2i)^2 = 9 + 6i + 6i + 4i^2 = 5 + 12i$

(D) $(2 + 3i)^2 = 4 + 6i + 6i + 9i^2 = -5 + 12i$

Choice (D) is correct.

46. **C**

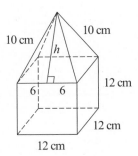

h is the lateral height of the pyramid.
$$10^2 = 6^2 + h^2 \implies h = 8$$

Total surface area
$$= 4 \cdot \text{area of triangle} + 5 \cdot \text{area of rectangle}$$
$$= 4[\frac{1}{2}(12)(8)] + 5[12 \cdot 12]$$
$$= 912$$

47. **E**

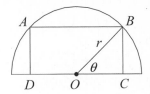

$$BC = r \sin \theta$$
$$OC = r \cos \theta$$
$$DC = 2OC = 2r \cos \theta$$

Area of rectangle $ABCD$
$$= BC \cdot DC$$
$$= r \sin \theta \cdot 2r \cos \theta$$
$$= 2r^2 \sin \theta \cos \theta$$

48. **E**

$$f(x, y) = \frac{x - y}{1 + xy}$$

I. $f(-x, -y) = \dfrac{-x - (-y)}{1 + (-x)(-y)}$

$$= \frac{-x + y}{1 + xy} = \frac{-(x - y)}{1 + xy} = -f(x, y)$$

Roman numeral I is true.

II. $-f(y, x) = -(\dfrac{y - x}{1 + yx}) = \dfrac{x - y}{1 + xy} = f(x, y)$

Roman numeral II is true.

III. $\dfrac{1 + f(x, 1)}{1 - f(x, 1)} = \dfrac{1 + \dfrac{x - 1}{1 + x \cdot 1}}{1 - \dfrac{x - 1}{1 + x \cdot 1}} = \dfrac{1 + \dfrac{x - 1}{1 + x}}{1 - \dfrac{x - 1}{1 + x}}$

$$= \frac{\left(1 + \dfrac{x - 1}{1 + x}\right)(1 + x)}{\left(1 - \dfrac{x - 1}{1 + x}\right)(1 + x)} = \frac{(1 + x) + (x - 1)}{(1 + x) - (x - 1)}$$

$$= \frac{2x}{2} = x$$

$$f(x, 0) = \frac{x - 0}{1 + x \cdot 0} = \frac{x}{1} = x$$

Therefore $\dfrac{1 - f(x, 1)}{1 + f(x, 1)} = f(x, 0)$.

Roman numeral III is true.

49. C

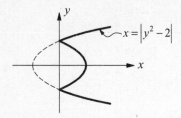

Reflect the portion of the graph of $x = y^2 - 2$ that lies to the left of the y-axis about the y-axis. Join the reflection with the portion of the graph of $x = y^2 - 2$ that lies to the right of the y-axis.

50. E

- The degree of the function is 5.
- The leading coefficient is negative.
- The polynomial function has three real roots.

(A)

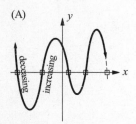

The degree of the function is 5, since there are 4 turning points.
The leading coefficient is negative since it is a 5th degree function that starts out decreasing.
The number of real roots is 5, since the graph shows 5 x-intercepts.

(B)

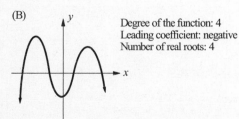

Degree of the function: 4
Leading coefficient: negative
Number of real roots: 4

(C)

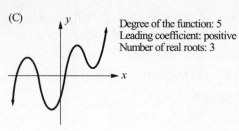

Degree of the function: 5
Leading coefficient: positive
Number of real roots: 3

(D)

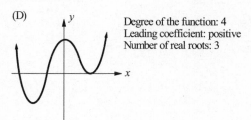

Degree of the function: 4
Leading coefficient: positive
Number of real roots: 3

(E)

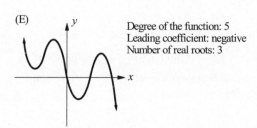

Degree of the function: 5
Leading coefficient: negative
Number of real roots: 3

Choice (E) is correct.

Scaled Score Conversion Table

SAT Subject Test in Mathematics Level 2

Raw Score	Scaled Score	Raw Score	Scaled Score	Raw Score	Scaled Score	Raw Score	Scaled Score
50	800	34	690	18	550	2	420
49	800	33	680	17	540	1	410
48	800	32	670	16	530	0	400
47	800	31	660	15	520	−1	390
46	800	30	650	14	510	−2	380
45	800	29	640	13	500	−3	380
44	790	28	630	12	500	−4	370
43	780	27	620	11	490	−5	360
42	770	26	620	10	480	−6	350
41	760	25	610	9	470	−7	340
40	750	24	600	8	470	−8	330
39	740	23	590	7	460	−9	320
38	730	22	580	6	450	−10	320
37	720	21	570	5	440	−11	310
36	710	20	560	4	430	−12	300
35	700	19	550	3	420		

Calculating Your Score

Step 1: Count the number of right answers: _____

Step 2: Count the number of wrong answers: _____

Step 3: Divide the number of wrong answers by 4: _____

Step 4: Subtract the result obtained in step 3 from the total in step 1: _____

Step 5: Round the number obtained in step 4 to the nearest whole number. This is your **raw test score**: _____

Step 6: Using the table above, find the scaled score that corresponds to your raw score. Remember, this is an **approximation** of your SAT Subject Test score: _____